~Timeles...

THE VERY BEST OF

R.K. NARAYAN

~ *Timeless Malgudi* ~

SELECTED FICTION AND NON-FICTION

RUPA

Published by
Rupa Publications India Pvt. Ltd 2014
7/16, Ansari Road, Daryaganj
New Delhi 110002

Sales centres:
Allahabad Bengaluru Chennai
Hyderabad Jaipur Kathmandu
Kolkata Mumbai

Swami and Friends was first published by Hamish Hamilton 1935
Talkative Man was first published by William Heinemann Ltd 1986
'An Astrologer's Day' and 'A Horse and Two Goats' were first published as part of
Malgudi Days by William Heinemann Ltd 1985
'Under the Banyan Tree' was first published as part of *Under the Banyan Tree and Other Stories* by William Heinemann Ltd 1985
The Guide was first published by Methuen & Co. 1958
'The Mispaired Anklet' was first published as part of *Gods, Demons, and Others* by William Heinemann Ltd 1964
My Days was first published by Viking Press 1974
'Misguided "Guide"' was first published as part of *A Writer's Nightmare* by Penguin Books India 1988
'The Problem of the Indian Writer' was first published as part of *A Story-teller's World* by Penguin Books India 1989
My Dateless Diary: An American Journey was first published by Indian Thought Publications 1964

ISBN: 978-81-291-3102-7

Fifth impression 2017

10 9 8 7 6 5

Printed at Tara Art Printers Pvt. Ltd., Noida

Contents

The Genius of R.K. Narayan

In a house in a quiet Mysore neighbourhood, distinctive for the fire of red hibiscus blossoming against its boundary walls, I spent an afternoon, three decades ago, interviewing R.K. Narayan for a long profile I would write about him for a Bombay magazine. I remembered that meeting when I was trying to distil the essence of his genius for this foreword. I suppose the reason I picked that one meeting from our long friendship and association was simple—it was then that I had the clearest personal insight into what underpinned his writing. Like most others familiar with his work I had read a number of theories about what made R.K. Narayan one of the greatest literary writers of our time (or any time for that matter), I was aware of some of his own views on the subject (not that he was particularly forthcoming on his craft), but I was hoping that on this occasion he would finally uncover for me, here in his hometown, that was clearly the place that had inspired his greatest fictional creation, Malgudi, how his fiction was made. I knew the 'what' of his genius, and it was this—it was the particularity of the world he had created. A hundred years from now, you will not mistake Malgudi, that little South Indian town with its railway station, its Mempi Forest, its Sarayu River, its Ellamman Street, its Nallappa's Grove, its Lawley Extension, its Krishna Dispensary, its bank, its little bazaar, the temple, Gaffur's taxi, and its myriad other details, for anywhere else. Its colours will not fade, the yellow of the plantains in the shops on Market Road will gleam as brightly as ever and, the jilebis in its sweetshop will never grow stale... And, these are, of course, the smallest part of its magic. Much more important are the dozens of immortal characters that Narayan created in book after book, the small men (and women) with big dreams whom V.S. Naipaul and John Updike and other great writers have marvelled at, the Margayyas, the Swamis, the Ramans, the Vasus, the Sampaths, the Rajus, the Rosies, the Daisys, who wandered the streets of Malgudi, scheming their schemes, living their lives, falling in and out of love, delighting us with their antics, providing us with all manner of insights into the human condition with the lightest of touches, each of them keeping the world of Malgudi forever alive, fresh and vital, even if the rupee in twenty-first century India is a fraction of its value in Narayan's little town and the anna no longer exists. That, in short, was the 'what' of R.K. Narayan. Now all I needed to know was the 'how'. How had he managed to pull it off? What was the secret of his writing? Being the exquisitely courteous man that he was, who would never let a guest or a friend leave empty-handed, he did try to give me something for my efforts, though it may not have been exactly what I was looking for. First, after offering me some superb home-brewed filter coffee, he showed me around the house that he'd had constructed to his specifications, especially the many-windowed study on the top floor from which he could look out upon the town which had provided much of the raw material for his stories, novels and reports (Narayan had been a newspaper and magazine reporter— this was one among the jobs he had tried out before settling down into his career as a writer of fiction). In the course of that afternoon he told me that he didn't care much for theories about how fiction was made, all that he tried to do was capture in his work the endless possibilities for drama and entertainment that were offered by his fellow human beings in the town and in the countryside every single day, the moment he set foot outside the house. He said he loved watching people, and the endless theatre of human existence was an unending source of material for his stories. He said that though he couldn't or rather preferred not to explain exactly how stories materialized or how novels began, ideas seeped into his mind from the people and situations he had observed in the streets of Mysore from the time he was a young man and that's how it all began. And that, so far as he was concerned, was all there was to be said about the 'how' of his method and 'craft'. Elsewhere, he says much the same thing, in the introduction to one of his story collections: 'All theories of writing are bogus. Every writer develops his own method or lack of method and a story comes into being for some unknown reason anyhow.'

So my advice to you, the reader of his book, is not to waste too much time analysing the writer's method or craft but to just enjoy the stories and essays for themselves. Writing doesn't get much better than R.K. Narayan at his best.

New Delhi   David Davidar
September 2013

Introduction

Rasipuram Krishnaswami Iyer Narayan Swami, or R.K. Narayan as every reader of Indian literature knows him as, was born on 10 October 1906. He spent his first fifteen years at his grandmother's house in Madras (now Chennai). His father, a schoolteacher, was posted in several small towns in Karnataka and his mother had her hands full with a number of younger children. In Madras he grew up under his maternal grandmother's benevolent but watchful eye and under the supervision of his uncle. In his autobiography, *My Days*, Narayan describes a somewhat lonely yet exciting formative years in Madras. His two companions were his pets, a monkey and a peacock, and he would spend a large part of his days looking out at the street with the two by his side. An early photograph, reproduced in his autobiography, shows a serious-faced little boy with large dark eyes looking almost piercingly at the photographer. Narayan's description of his childhood days in Madras, with his unusual companions and the sundry comings and goings of people in his grandmother's house, is a thoroughly enjoyable set of recollections which continues to delight readers of all ages.

When summer holidays came around, Narayan would go with his grandmother to his parents' house. The first such journey that he describes in detail was the one to Chennapatna, a small town somewhere between Bangalore and Mysore, where his father was working as the headmaster of a school. While initially reluctant to leave the blazing summer days of Madras, where he could run around to his heart's content with the tough city boys, a few days with his mother and siblings in Chennapatna would be enough for Narayan to not want to leave their company. However, when he was fifteen, his father was transferred to a school in Mysore and Narayan moved there. Narayan's father, of whom he was quite wary as a child given the headmaster's commanding persona, was now much mellowed. In Mysore he joined the school at which his father was principal, the Maharaja's Collegiate High School. (Narayan says about this experience: 'Soon I realized the advantage of studying in a school where one's father was the headmaster. One got more people seeking one's friendship. The teachers were on the whole more gentle—except one troublesome botany teacher…')

School, college, lectures and examinations were never things that Narayan either enjoyed or excelled at. Reading his memories of those days in his autobiography, one gets the sense of a boy who is gentle, dreamy and literary-minded. Of his views on education, he says, 'My natural aversion to academic education was further strengthened when I came across an essay by Rabindranath Tagore on education. It confirmed my own precocious conclusions on the subject. I liked to be free to read what I please and not be examined at all.'

After completing his graduation, Narayan contemplated various professions, including that of a college lecturer. He gave up that idea quickly on a friend's advice. He met a number of people on his father and uncle's direction, and had a short-lived stint as a schoolteacher, too. But his love for writing soon became clear to him and the first steps he had taken on this road during his college days finally propelled him to start writing his first novel, *Swami and Friends* (he called it *Swami the Tate*, and it was his publisher Hamish Hamilton who changed it to *Swami and Friends*).

In Narayan's own words: 'On a certain day in September, selected by my grandmother for its auspiciousness, I bought an exercise book and wrote the first line of a novel; as I sat in a room nibbling my pen and wondering what to write, Malgudi with its little railway station swam into view, all ready-made, with a character called Swaminathan running down the platform…'

Narayan also started working as a freelance writer for newspapers like *The Hindu* and *The Justice*. Meanwhile, the manuscript of *Swami and Friends* had been doing the rounds of various publishers in London. After it was rejected a number of times, and Narayan was beginning to despair, he received the news that it had been accepted by Hamish

Hamilton, the British book-publishing house. Graham Greene, the novelist with whom Narayan had struck up a deep friendship—which would last a lifetime—was instrumental in this. *Swami and Friends* was published in October 1935. In the meanwhile, Narayan had quit his reporting responsibilities for *The Justice* and had become a full-time writer. His next novel was *The Bachelor of Arts*, followed by *The Dark Room*. Short stories, magazine articles and other forms of writing also kept him busy.

A few years earlier, Narayan had met Rajam, then a fifteen-year-old girl, and had fallen in love with her. His marriage to Rajam, which had gone against the prevailing norm of arranged marriage and had ignored the supposed perils of mismatched horoscopes, was one of the happiest—and saddest—periods of his life. They were married for six years and had a daughter, Hema, before Rajam died of typhoid. After his wife's death, Narayan went through perhaps the bleakest period of his life. On one hand, he had to deal with the pain of losing his beloved; on the other, he had to shoulder the responsibility of bringing up his motherless daughter without letting his loss affect her life. He finally found some solace after coming in contact with a couple, the Raos, who acted as mediums and through whom he believed that he was able to communicate with Rajam once more. This finally helped him gain peace of mind and 'an understanding of life and death'.

The novel he wrote after this, *The English Teacher*, is considered by most Narayan aficionados as his best. It is almost entirely autobiographical and tells the story of an English teacher and his wife who dies of typhoid. Despite its dark and sad theme, the writing is unsentimental yet deeply moving.

More works flowed from his pen—*Mr Sampath: The Printer of Malgudi*, *The Financial Expert*, *Waiting for the Mahatma*, *The Painter of Signs*, *A Tiger for Malgudi*, *The Vendor of Sweets*, *The Man-eater of Malgudi*. In each of these, the town of Malgudi and its citizens appeared, growing and changing with the times. In 1956, Hema married her cousin Chandru and moved to Coimbatore. That year, the Rockefeller Foundation awarded a travel grant to Narayan and he left for the United States in October. The stories of his travels in the US were published in *My Dateless Diary*. In it he recounts travelling across the country on a vegetarian diet which usually consisted of rice and yoghurt, his despair at 'black' or 'white' coffee, his memorable encounters with writers, actors, academics, publishers and even, in one instant, with muggers (reproduced in this volume in the excerpts from *My Dateless Diary*) and being proclaimed as one of the world's three greatest living writers. As a travelogue, *My Dateless Diary* is a delight—it is charming and eccentric, and little details and impressions build up to create an account that is both humorous and thoughtful.

Narayan left for the US with the kernel of an idea for a novel 'about someone suffering sainthood', as he pithily puts it. The idea crystallized further and, over three months in Berkeley, he completed writing *The Guide*.

It is the story of Raju, a Railway guide, who becomes involved with Rosie. Rosie is the wife of an archaeologist and nurses an ambition to become a dancer. Raju seduces Rosie away from her husband, and even becomes her agent, but then lands up in jail. When he is set free, he finds himself in a village where he takes shelter near a temple. There, he is mistaken for a holy man. When the village is stricken by drought, the villagers look to him to undertake a fast so that it will rain again.

The Guide has been called Narayan's most brilliantly crafted novel. It is also his most popular work and has never been out of print. It has also been translated into various languages. Narayan won the Sahitya Akademi Award in 1958 for *The Guide*. The novel was adapted into a Hindi-language movie by Dev Anand and also became the subject of a stage production. Both these adaptations deviated wildly from the original work. Narayan writes about the making of the film, its subsequent promotion, and the absurdities and quirks of the movie world with his gentle, deadpan humour in the essay "The Misguided 'Guide' ".

Narayan continued to write essays and short stories between his novels. The short pieces he wrote for *The Hindu*, with subjects ranging from coffee to education to travel to neighbours, are a delight to read even today for their sharply described situations, analysis and portraits of men and women. He also wrote a number of pieces on the world of a writer, one of which, 'The Problem of the Indian Writer', is reproduced in this volume. The essay is a brilliant and concise meditation on what it means to be a writer in India—it ranges from the epics, from where much of the writing in this country originates, to finding inspiration in the modern world and writing about it in English, to the commercial prospects of an author in India—and still remains startlingly relevant. This is an essay which any reader who is interested in literature, and particularly about writing in India, will find edifying.

Narayan's short stories, by his own admission, were often born out of desperation to meet a newspaper deadline. However, he also relished the form for the freedom it gave him to range far and wide in search of material, as also for the scope they gave him, in his words, to present 'miniatures of human experience in all its opulence'. Some of the stories included in this volume are among the finest examples of the short story form to be found anywhere. 'A Horse and Two Goats' is a masterpiece of comic writing. Plucked out of the Karnataka countryside of Narayan's time, it would easily find a place in any anthology of great short fiction. Can anyone, who hasn't previously read 'An Astrologer's Day', not be swept away by the O'Henryesque twist to the tale? 'Under the Banyan Tree' could be a meditation on the magic that Narayan himself spun with his stories. If one were to add a coda to that story it would be that now that his lamp has gone out, all that we have to console ourselves with are anthologies such as this one. Fortunately though, Narayan's stories can be read and re-read and, of course, there are always new generations waiting to discover his genius.

Narayan was conscious of the influence of the Indian epics on Indian life. In his autobiography he describes how, in 1938, an uncle had advised him to read Kamban. At the time, with his third novel just published, the young Narayan had not heeded this suggestion. But three decades later, his interest in Kamban's *Ramayana* was piqued and he spent three years reading it completely. He then wrote a prose narrative based on Kamban. He also wrote a version of the *Mahabharata* and a collection of stories from the legends and epics called *Gods, Demons and Others*. In this, he retold stories from various classic sources—Kalidasa's *Abhijnana Shakuntalam*, the Tamil epic *Silappadikaram*, the *Shiva Purana*, the *Devi Bhagwatam* and episodes from the *Ramayana* and *Mahabharata* too. It is an excellent introduction to the vast ocean of Indian epics and legends, and of interest to both the scholar and the casual reader.

Narayan's work has been received variously by critics. Some, like Graham Greene, have compared him to Chekov, and Anita Desai has described his works as replete with 'compassionate realism'. But the greatest appreciation has come from his readers. Each one of his novels, short stories and essays have been read and enjoyed for decades.

In his introduction to *Memories of Malgudi*, a compilation of five novels by R.K. Narayan in a single volume, S. Krishnan, who edited this and several other volumes of Narayan's works, writes: 'In my view, he is quite simply our greatest fiction writer in the English language; humour and humanity, love for the oppressed and sympathy for the underdog, and a general overall kindness mark his literary persona.'

R.K. Narayan lived to the age of ninety-four. His dearly loved daughter passed away in 1994, and he spent the last years of his life reading the newspaper, going over his mail (and throwing away letters from strangers), taking short walks and visiting his granddaughter's house in the evenings to spend time with his great-granddaughter. He was planning a novel about a grandfather when he was admitted to hospital in May 2001 in Chennai. That novel, unfortunately, never got written when he passed away on 13 May 2001. Yet, his large and vibrant body of work remains. He will forever be spoken of as one of the greats of Indian literature.

SELECTED FICTION

Swami and Friends

(An Excerpt)

IN FATHER'S PRESENCE

DURING SUMMER Malgudi was one of the most detested towns in south India. Sometimes the heat went above a hundred and ten in the shade, and between twelve and three any day in summer the dusty blanched roads were deserted. Even donkeys and dogs, the most vagrant of animals, preferred to move to the edge of the street, where cat-walks and minor projections from buildings cast a sparse strip of shade, when the fierce sun tilted towards the west.

But there is this peculiarity about heat: it appears to affect only those that think of it. Swaminathan, Mani and Rajam would have been surprised if anybody had taken the trouble to prove to them that the Malgudi sun was unbearable. They found the noon and the afternoon the most fascinating part of the day. The same sun that beat down on the head of Mr Hentel, the mill manager, and drove him to Kodaikanal, or on the turban of Mr Krishnan, the Executive Engineer, and made him complain that his profession was one of the hardest, compelling him to wander in sun and storm, beat down on Swaminathan's curly head, Mani's tough matted hair, and Rajam's short wiry crop, and left them unmoved. The same sun that baked the earth so much that even Mr Retty, the most Indianized of the 'Europeans', who owned a rice mill in the deserted bungalow outside the town (he was, by the way, the mystery man of the place: nobody could say who he was or where he had come from; he swore at his boy and at his customers in perfect Tamil and always moved about in

3

shirt, shorts, and sandalled feet), screamed one day when he forgetfully took a step or two barefoot, was the same sun that made the three friends loath to remain under a roof.

They were sitting on a shore culvert, half a mile outside the municipal limits, on the Trunk Road. A streak of water ran under the culvert on a short stretch of sand, and mingled with the Sarayu farther down. There was no tree where they sat, and the sun struck their heads directly. On the sides of the road there were paddy fields; but now all that remained was scorched stubble, vast stretches of stubble, relieved here and there by clustering groves of mango or coconut. The Trunk Road was deserted but for an occasional country cart lumbering along.

'I wish you had done just what I had asked you to do and nothing more,' said Rajam to Mani.

Swaminathan complained: 'Yes, Rajam. I just showed him the coachman's son and was about to leave him, just as we had planned, when all of a sudden he tried to murder me...' He shot an angry glance at Mani.

Mani was forlorn. 'Boys, I admit that I am an idiot. I thought I could do it all by the plan that came to my head on the spot. If I had only held the top firmly, I could have decoyed him, and by now he would have been howling in a lonely shed.' There was regret in his tone.

Swaminathan said, nursing his nape: 'It is still paining here.' After the incident at Keelacheri, it took three hours of continuous argument for Mani to convince Swaminathan that the attack on him was only sham.

'You needn't have been so brutal to Swami,' said Rajam.

'Sirs,' Mani said, folding his hands, 'I shall stand on my head for ten minutes, if you want me to do it as a punishment. I only pretended to scratch Swami to show the coachman's boy that I was his enemy.'

A jingling was now heard. A closed mat-covered cart drawn by a white bullock was coming down the road. When it had come within a yard of the culvert, they rose, advanced, stood in a row, and shouted: 'Pull up the animal, will you?'

The cart-driver was a little village boy.

'Stop the cart, you fool,' cried Rajam.

'If he does not stop, we shall arrest him and confiscate his cart.' This was Swaminathan.

The cart-driver said: 'Boys, why do you stop me?'

'Don't talk,' Mani commanded, and with a serious face went round the cart and examined the wheels. He bent down and scrutinized the bottom of the cart: 'Hey, cart-man, get down.'

'Boys, I must go,' pleaded the driver.

'Whom do you address as "boys"?' asked Rajam menacingly. 'Don't you know who we are?'

'We are the Government Police out to catch humbugs like you,' added Swaminathan.

'I shall shoot you if you say a word,' said Rajam to the young driver. Though the driver was incredulous, he felt that there must be something in what they said.

Mani tapped a wheel and said: 'The culvert is weak, we can't let you go over it unless you show us the pass.'

The cart-driver jabbered: 'Please, sirs, let me go—I have to be there.'

'Shut up,' Rajam commanded.

Swaminathan examined the animal and said: 'Come here.'

The cart-driver was loath to get down. Mani dragged him from his seat and gave him a push towards Swaminathan.

Swaminathan scowled at him, and pointing at the sides of the animal, asked: 'Why have you not washed the animal, you blockhead?'

The villager replied timidly: 'I have washed the animal, sir.'

'But why is this here?' Swaminathan asked, pointing at a brown patch.

'Oh, that! The animal has had it since its birth, sir.'

'Birth? Are you trying to teach me?' Swaminathan shouted and raised his leg to kick the cart-driver.

They showed signs of relenting.

'Give the rascal a pass, and be done with him,' Rajam conceded graciously. Swaminathan took out a pencil stub and a grubby pocket-book that he always carried about him on principle. It was his habit to note down all sorts of things: the number of cycles that passed him, the number of people going barefoot, the number going with sandals or shoes on, and so forth.

He held the paper and pencil ready. Mani took hold of the rope of the bullock, pushed it back, and turned it the other way round. The cart-driver protested. But Mani said: 'Don't worry. It has got to stand here. This is the boundary.'

'I have to go this way, sir.'

'You can turn it round and go.'

'What is your name?' asked Rajam.

'Karuppan,' answered the boy.

Swaminathan took it down.

'Age?'

'I don't know, sir.'

'You don't know? Swami, write a hundred,' said Rajam.

'No sir, no sir, I am not a hundred.'

'Mind your business and hold your tongue. You are a hundred. I will kill you if you say no. What is your bullock's name?'

'I don't know, sir.'

'Swami, write "Karuppan" again.'

'Sir, that is my name, not the bullock's.'

They ignored this and Swaminathan wrote 'Karuppan' against the name of the bullock.

'Where are you going?'

'Sethur.'

Swaminathan wrote it down.

'How long will you stay there?'

'It is my place, sir.'

'If that is so, what brought you here?'

'Our headman sent ten bags of coconut to the railway shed.'

Swaminathan entered every word in his notebook. Then all three signed the page, tore it off, gave it to the cart-driver, and permitted him to start.

Much to Swaminathan's displeasure, his father's courts closed in the second week of May, and Father began to spend the afternoons at home. Swaminathan feared that it might interfere with his afternoon rambles with Rajam and Mani. And it did. On the very third day of his vacation, Father commanded Swaminathan, just as he was stepping out of the house: 'Swami, come here.'

Father was standing in the small courtyard, wearing a *dhoti* and a *banian*, the dress which, for its very homeliness, Swaminathan detested to see him in; it indicated that he did not intend going out in the near future.

'Where are you going?'

'Nowhere.'

'Where were you yesterday at this time?'

'Here.'

'You are lying. You were not here yesterday. And you are not going out now.'

'That is right,' Mother added, just appearing from somewhere. 'There is no limit to his loafing in the sun. He will die of sunstroke if he keeps on like this.'

Father would have gone on even without Mother's encouragement. But now her words spurred him to action. Swaminathan was asked to follow him to his 'room' in his father's dressing-room.

'How many days is it since you have touched your books?' Father asked as he blew off the fine layer of dust on Swaminathan's books, and cleared the web that an industrious spider was weaving between a corner of the table and the pile of books.

Swaminathan viewed this question as a gross breach of promise. 'Should I read even when I have no school?'

'Do you think you have passed the BA?' Father asked.

'I mean, Father, when the school is closed, when there is no examination, even then should I read?'

'What a question! You must read.'

'But, Father, you said before the examinations that I needn't read after they were over. Even Rajam does not read.' As he uttered the last sentence, he tried to believe it; he clearly remembered Rajam's complaining bitterly of a home tutor who came and pestered him for two hours a day thrice a week. Father was apparently deaf to Swaminathan's remarks. He stood over Swaminathan and set him to dust his books and clean his table. Swaminathan vigorously started blowing off the dust from the book covers. He caught the spider carefully, and took it to the window to throw it out. He held it outside the window and watched it for a while. It was swinging from a strand that gleamed in a hundred delicate tints.

'Look sharp! Do you want a whole day to throw out the spider?' Father asked. Swaminathan suddenly realized that he might have the spider as his pet and that it would be a criminal waste to throw it out. He secretly slipped it into his pocket and, after shaking an empty hand outside the window, returned to his duty at the desk.

'Look at the way you have kept your English text! Are you not ashamed of yourself?'

Swaminathan picked up the oily red-bound *Fourth Reader*, opened it, and banged together the covers, in order to shake off the dust, then rubbed the oily covers violently with his palm.

'Get a piece of cloth, boy. That is not the way to clean things. Get a piece of cloth, Swami,' Father said, half kindly and half impatiently.

Swaminathan looked about and complained, 'I can't find any here, Father.'

'Run and see.'

This was a welcome suggestion. Swaminathan hurried out. He first went to his grandmother.

'Granny, get me a piece of cloth, quick.'

'Where am I to go for a piece of cloth?'

'Where am I to go?' he asked peevishly and added quite irrelevantly, 'If one has got to read even during holidays, I don't see why holidays are given at all.'

'What is the matter?'

This was his opportunity to earn some sympathy. He almost wept as he said: 'I don't know what Rajam and Mani will think, waiting for me there, if I keep on fooling here. Granny, if Father cannot find any work to do, why shouldn't he go and sleep?'

Father shouted across the hall: 'Did you find the cloth?'

Swaminathan answered: 'Granny hasn't got it. I shall see if Mother has.' His mother was sitting in the back corridor on a mat, with the baby sleeping on her lap. Swaminathan glared at her. Her advice to her husband a few minutes ago rankled in his heart. 'You are a fine lady, Mother,' he said in an undertone. 'Why don't you leave us poor folk alone?'

'What?' she asked, unconscious of the sarcasm, and having forgotten what she had said to her husband a few minutes ago.

'You needn't have gone and carried tales against me. I don't know what I have done to you.' He would have enjoyed prolonging this talk, but Father was waiting for the duster.

'Can you give me a piece of cloth?' he asked, coming to business.

'What cloth?'

'What cloth! How should I know? It seems I have got to tidy up those—those books of mine. A fine way of spending the holidays!'

'I can't get any now.'

'H'm. You can't, can you?' He looked about. There was a piece of cloth under the baby. In a flash, he stooped, rolled the baby over, pulled out the cloth, and was off. He held his mother responsible for all his troubles, and disturbing the baby and snatching its cloth gave him great relief.

With fierce satisfaction he tilted the table and tipped all the things on it over the floor, and then picked them up one by one, and arranged them on the table. Father watched him: 'Is this how you arrange things? You have kept all the light things at the bottom and the heavy ones on top. Take out those note-books. Keep the Atlas at the bottom.' Mother came in with the baby in her arms and complained to Father, 'Look at that boy, he has taken the baby's cloth. Is there nobody to control him in this house? I wonder how long his school is going to be kept closed.' Swaminathan continued his work with concentrated interest. Father was pleased to ignore Mother's complaint; he merely pinched the sleeping baby's cheeks, at which Mother was annoyed and left the room.

Half an hour later Swaminathan sat in his father's room in a chair, with a slate in his hand and pencil ready. Father held the Arithmetic book open and dictated: 'Rama has ten mangoes with which he wants to earn fifteen annas. Krishna wants only four mangoes. How much will Krishna have to pay?'

Swaminathan gazed and gazed at this sum, and every time he read it, it seemed to acquire a new meaning. He had the feeling of having stepped into a fearful maze…

His mouth began to water at the thought of mangoes. He wondered what made Rama fix fifteen annas for ten mangoes. What kind of a man was Rama? Probably he was like Sankar. Somehow one couldn't help feeling that he must have been like Sankar, with his ten mangoes and his iron determination to get fifteen annas. If Rama was like Sankar, Krishna must have been like the Pea. Here Swaminathan felt an unaccountable sympathy for Krishna.

'Have you done the sum?' Father asked, looking over the newspaper he was reading.

'Father, will you tell me if the mangoes were ripe?'

Father regarded him for a while and smothering a smile remarked: 'Do the sum first. I will tell you whether the fruits were ripe or not, afterwards.'

Swaminathan felt utterly helpless. If only Father would tell him whether Rama was trying to sell ripe fruits or unripe ones! Of what avail would it be to tell him afterwards? He felt strongly that the answer to this question contained the key to the whole problem. It would be scandalous to expect fifteen annas for ten unripe mangoes. But even if he did, it wouldn't be unlike Rama, whom Swaminathan was steadily beginning to hate and invest with the darkest qualities.

'Father, I cannot do the sum,' Swaminathan said, pushing away the slate.

'What is the matter with you? You can't solve a simple problem in Simple Proportion?'

'We are not taught this kind of thing in our school.'

'Get the slate here. I will make you give the answer now.' Swaminathan waited with interest for the miracle to happen. Father studied the sum for a second and asked: 'What is the price of ten mangoes?'

Swaminathan looked over the sum to find out which part of the sum contained an answer to this question. 'I don't know.'

'You seem to be an extraordinary idiot. Now read the sum. Come on. How much does Rama expect for ten mangoes?'

'Fifteen annas of course,' Swaminathan thought, but how could that be its price, just price? It was very well for Rama to expect it in his avarice. But was it the right price? And then there was the obscure point whether the mangoes were ripe or not. If they were ripe, fifteen annas might not be an improbable price. If only he could get more light on this point!

'How much does Rama want for his mangoes?'

'Fifteen annas,' replied Swaminathan without conviction.

'Very good. How many mangoes does Krishna want?'

'Four.'

'What is the price of four?'

Father seemed to delight in torturing him. How could he know? How could he know what that fool Krishna would pay?

'Look here, boy. I have half a mind to thrash you. What have you in your head? Ten mangoes cost fifteen annas. What is the price of one? Come on. If you don't say it—' His hand took Swaminathan's ear and gently twisted it. Swaminathan could not open his mouth because he could not decide whether the solution lay in the realm of addition, subtraction, multiplication, or division. The longer he hesitated, the more violent the twist was becoming. In the end when Father was waiting with a scowl for an answer, he received only a squeal from his son. 'I am not going to leave you till you tell me how much a single mango costs at fifteen annas for ten.' What was the matter with Father? Swaminathan kept blinking. Where was the urgency to know its price? Anyway, if Father wanted to know so badly, instead of harassing him, let him go to the market and find it out. The whole brood of Ramas and Krishnas, with their endless transactions with odd quantities of mangoes and fractions of money, was getting disgusting.

Father admitted defeat by declaring: 'One mango costs fifteen over ten annas. Simplify it.'

Here he was being led to the most hideous regions of Arithmetic, Fractions. 'Give me the slate, Father. I will find it out.' He worked and found at the end of fifteen minutes: 'The price of one mango is three over two annas.' He expected to be contradicted any moment. But Father said: 'Very good, simplify it further.' It was plain sailing after that. Swaminathan announced at the end of half an hour's agony: 'Krishna must pay six annas,' and burst into tears.

At five o'clock when he was ready to start for the club, Swaminathan's father felt sorry for having worried his son all afternoon. 'Would you like to come with me to the club, boy?' he asked when he saw Swaminathan sulking behind a pillar with a woebegone face. Swaminathan answered by disappearing for a minute and reappearing dressed in his coat and cap. Father surveyed him from head to foot and remarked: 'Why can't you be a little more tidy?' Swaminathan writhed awkwardly.

'Lakshmi,' Father called, and said to Mother when she came: 'there must be a clean dress for the boy in the box. Give him something clean.'

'Please don't worry about it now. He is all right. Who is to open the box? The keys are somewhere... I have just mixed milk for the baby—' said Mother.

'What has happened to all his dresses?'

'What dresses? You haven't bought a square inch of cloth since last summer.'

'What do you mean? What has happened to all the pieces of twill I bought a few months ago?' he demanded vaguely, making a mental note at the same time to take the boy to the tailor on Wednesday evening. Swaminathan was relieved to find Mother reluctant to get him a fresh dress, since he had an obscure dread that his father would leave him behind and go away if he went in to change. A car hooted in front of the house. Father snatched his tennis racket from a table and rushed out, followed by Swaminathan. A gentleman, wearing a blazer that appealed to Swaminathan, sat at the wheel, and said 'Good evening,' with a grin. Swaminathan was at first afraid that this person might refuse to take him in the car. But his fears were dispelled by the gentleman's saying amiably: 'Hello, Srinivasan, are you bringing your boy to the club? Right O!' Swaminathan sat in the back seat while his father and his friend occupied the front.

The car whizzed along. Swaminathan was elated and wished that some of his friends could see him then. The car slid into a gate and came to a stop amidst half a dozen other cars.

He watched his father playing tennis, and came to the conclusion that he was the best player in all the three courts that were laid side by side. Swaminathan found that whenever his father hit the ball, his opponents were unable to receive it and so let it go and strike the screen. He also found that the picker's life was one of grave risks.

Swaminathan fell into a pleasant state of mind. The very fact that he was allowed to be present there and watch the game gave him a sense of importance. He would have something to say to his friends tomorrow. He slowly moved and stood near the screen behind his father. Before stationing himself there, he wondered for a moment if the little fellow in khaki dress might not object. But the little fellow was busy picking up balls and throwing them at the players. Swaminathan stayed there for about ten minutes. His father's actions were clearer to watch from behind, and the twang of his racket when hitting the ball was very pleasing to the ear.

For a change Swaminathan stood looking at the boy in khaki dress. As he gazed, his expression changed. He blinked fast as if he disbelieved his eyes. It was the coachman's son, only slightly transformed by the khaki dress! Now the boy had turned and seen him. He grinned maliciously and hastily took out of his pocket a penknife, and held it up. Swaminathan was seized with cold fear. He moved away fast, unobtrusively, to his former place, which was at a safe distance from his enemy.

After the set when his father walked towards the building, Swaminathan took care to walk a little in front of him and not behind, as he feared that he might get a stab any minute in his back.

'Swami, don't go in front. You are getting between my legs.' Swaminathan obeyed with a reluctant heart. He kept shooting glances sideways and behind. He stooped and picked up a stone, a sharp stone, and held it ready for use if any emergency should arise. The distance from the tennis court to the building was about a dozen yards, but to Swaminathan it seemed to be a mile and a half.

He felt safe when he sat in a chair beside his father in the card-room. A thick cloud of smoke floated in the air. Father was shuffling and throwing cards with great zest. This was the safest place on earth. There was Father and any number of his friends, and let the coachman's son try a hand if he liked. A little later Swaminathan looked out of the window and felt disturbed at the sight of the stars. It would be darker still by the time the card game was finished and Father rose to go home.

An hour later Father rose from the table. Swaminathan was in a highly nervous state when he got down the last steps of the building. There were unknown dangers lurking in the darkness around. He was no doubt secure between Father and his friend. That thought was encouraging. But Swaminathan felt at the same time that it would have been better if all the persons in the card-room had escorted him to the car. He needed all the guarding he could get, and some more. Probably by this time the boy had gone out and brought a huge gang of assassins and was waiting for him. He could not walk in front as, in addition to getting between his father's legs, he had no idea which way they had to go for the car. Following his father was out of the question, as he might not reach the car at all. He walked in a peculiar side-step which enabled him to see before him and behind him simultaneously. The distance was interminable. He decided to explain the danger to Father and seek his protection.

'Father.'

'Well, boy?'

Swaminathan suddenly decided that his father had better not know anything about the coachman's son, however serious the situation might be.

'What do you want, boy?' Father asked again.

'Father, are we going home now?'

'Yes.'

'Walking?'

'No. The car is there, near the gate.'

When they came to the car, Swaminathan got in first and occupied the centre of the back-seat. He was still in suspense. Father's friend was taking time to start the car. Swaminathan was sitting all alone in the back-seat, very far behind Father and his friend. Even now, the coachman's son and his gang could easily pull him out and finish him.

The car started. When its engine rumbled, it sounded to Swaminathan's ears like the voice of a saviour. The car was outside the gate now and picked up speed. Swaminathan lifted a corner of his *dhoti* and mopped his brow.

Talkative Man

THEY CALL me Talkative Man. Some affectionately shorten it to TM:
I have earned this title, I suppose, because I cannot contain myself. My
impulse to share an experience with others is irresistible, even if they
sneer at my back. I don't care. I'd choke if I didn't talk, perhaps like
Sage Narada of our epics, who for all his brilliance and accomplishments
carried a curse on his back that unless he spread a gossip a day, his skull
would burst. I only try to interest my listener or listeners, especially
that friend Varma who owns the Boardless Hotel. (He is considerate,
keeps a chair for me inverted in a corner so as to prevent others from
occupying it, although from the business point of view I am not worth
more than a cup of coffee for him, whenever I stop by.)

My chair was generally set facing a calendar portrait of that
impossible demon Mahishasura with serpents entwining his neck and
arms, holy ash splashed on his forehead and eyeballs bulging out
through enormous side-whiskers, holding aloft a scimitar, ready to
strike. I never liked that picture...too disturbing. It was a seven-year-
old calendar, ripe to be discarded, but Varma would not hear of it.
He would boast, 'I have never thrown away any calendar for thirty
years. They adorn my walls at home, sometimes four on a nail, one
behind another. All our gods are there. How can anyone discard god?'

It was no use arguing with that man Varma; he was self-made,
rising from a menial job to his present stature as the proprietor of the
Boardless, which fact proved, according to him, that he knew his mind
and could never be wrong. I never tried to correct him, but listened,
even appreciatively, to his spasmodic reminiscences. Fortunately he
was not much of a talker, but a born listener, an ideal target for a
monologist: even while counting cash, he listened, without missing a
word, as I sat beside his desk and narrated my story.

The story that enchanted Varma was the one about Dr Rann, which I told him off and on spread over several weeks.

Dr Rann was actually, as I discovered later, Rangan, a hardy Indian name which he had trimmed and tailored to sound foreign; the double N at the end was a stroke of pure genius. One would take him to be a German, Rumanian or Hungarian—anything but what he was, a pure Indian from a southernmost village named Maniyur, of the usual pattern: tiled homesteads and huts clustering around a gold-crested temple that towered over an expanse of rice fields and coconut groves; similar to a hundred others, so commonplace that it escapes the notice of map-makers and chroniclers.

From this soil arose Rann of double N. He had blonde hair, a touch of greenish-blue in his eyes, and borderline complexion—unusual for an Indian of these parts. My private view on his ethnic origin might sound naughty, but is quite an historic possibility. A company of British, French or Portuguese soldiers must have camped at Maniyur or in its vicinity in the days when they were fighting for colonial supremacy and, in the intervals of fighting, relaxed by philandering among the local population.

I met him for the first time at the Town Hall reading room. Those were the days when I was struggling to establish myself as a journalist. They used to call me Universal Correspondent since I had no authority to represent any particular publication. Still, I was busy from morning till night, moving about on my bicycle or on my neighbour Sambu's scooter. I was to be seen here and there, at municipal meetings, magistrates' court, the prize distribution at Albert Mission, with a reporter's notebook in hand and a fountain pen peeping out of my shirt pocket. I reported all kinds of activities, covering several kilometres a day on my vehicle, and ended up at the railway station to post my despatch in the mail van with a late fee—a lot of unwarranted rush, as no news-editor sat fidgeting for my copy at the other end; but I enjoyed my self-appointed role, and felt pleased even if a few lines appeared in print as a space-filler somewhere.

I did not have to depend on journalistic work for my survival. I belonged to one of those Kabir Street families which flourished on the labours of an earlier generation. We were about twenty unrelated families in Kabir Street, each having inherited a huge rambling house stretching from the street to the river at the back. All that one did was to lounge on the *pyol*, watch the street, and wait for the harvest from our village lands and cash from the tenants. We were a vanishing race, however, about twenty families in Kabir Street and an equal number in Ellamman Street, two spots where village landlords had settled and built houses nearly a century back in order to seek the comforts of urban life and to educate their children at Albert Mission. Their descendants, so comfortably placed, were mainly occupied in eating, breeding, celebrating festivals, spending the afternoons in a prolonged siesta on the *pyol*, and playing cards all evening. The women rarely came out, being most of the time in the kitchen or in the safe-room scrutinizing their collection of diamonds and silks.

This sort of existence did not appeal to me. I liked to be active, had dreams of becoming a journalist, I can't explain why. I rarely stayed at home; luckily for me, I was a bachelor. (Another exception in our society was my neighbour Sambu, who, after his mother's death, spent more and more of his time reading: his father, though a stranger to the world of print, had acquired a fine library against a loan to a scholar in distress, and he bequeathed it to his successor.)

I noticed a beggar-woman one day, at the Market Gate, with Siamese twins, and persuaded my friend Jayaraj, photographer and framer of pictures at the Market Arch, to take a photograph of the woman, wrote a report on it and mailed it to the first paper which caught my attention at the Town Hall reading room; that was my starting point as a journalist. Thereafter I got into the habit of visiting the Town Hall library regularly to see if my report appeared in print.

The library was known as Lawley Memorial Library and Reading Room, established on a bequest left by Sir Frederick Lawley (whose portrait hung from a nail high up near the ventilator) half a century ago. An assortment of old newspapers and magazines was piled up on a long table in the middle of the hall, mostly donated by well-wishers in the neighbourhood. Habitual visitors to the reading room sat around the table on benches, poring over newspaper sheets, not noticing or minding the dates on them. An old man sat at the entrance in a position of vantage and kept an eye on his public. He had been in service from time immemorial. He opened the doors precisely at nine in the morning and strictly closed them at five in the evening, shooing off the habitués, who sometimes stepped in the opening and stayed on. 'Fortunately,' said the old man, 'the Committee won't sanction candles or lanterns, otherwise those loungers would not leave till midnight.' He was intolerant and suspicious of most people, but tolerated me and, I could say, even liked me. There was a spare seat, a wooden stool at his side, which he always offered me. He admired my activities and listened to my city reports, and hoped I'd find some donors to subscribe for current newspapers. I managed to get some money from Varma himself, though he was resistant to all approaches for money, that enabled us to get two morning papers from Madras.

Today when I entered the Reading Room, I found my usual seat occupied, and the librarian looked embarrassed. A man dressed in full suit was sitting on my stool. He looked so important that the librarian, as I could see, was nervous and deferential, which he showed by sitting forward and not leaning back with his legs stretched under the table as was his custom. He looked relieved at the sight of me, and cried, 'Here is a man waiting for you.' The other made a slight movement, acknowledging the introduction. I threw a brief glance at him and decided he was an oddity—dressed as he was in a blue suit, tie, and shining shoes, and holding a felt hat in hand. He sat without uttering a word. Somehow, I resented his presence and suppressed an impulse to say, 'Why do you sit there dumb? Say something and above all quit my seat. I am not used to standing here.' The newspaper addicts at the long table were watching us, so unused to seeing anyone in a blue suit and hat in the Town Hall. The old librarian was fidgeting, unable to attend to his routine work.

I fixed my look rather severely at the stranger and asked, 'You wish to talk to me?'

'Yes,' he said.

'Then come out,' I said. 'We must not disturb the readers.' I felt triumphant when he rose to his feet and followed me to the veranda.

I surveyed the prospect before me with authority and declared to my companion, 'Not an inch of space for us to sit,' and then glanced at him from head to foot, and realized that the fellow was short— though while seated he looked imposing. 'Not an inch,' I declared again, 'everybody is everywhere.' Vagrants were stretched out on the lawn, fast asleep; idlers sat in groups cracking peanuts and popping them in. The cement benches scattered here and there were all taken.

'Let us step down and see,' he said, looking about, trying to conceal his disgust at the spectacle of Malgudi citizenry. 'How is it so many are asleep at this hour?'

'They must have spent a busy night,' I said.

I began to enjoy his discomfiture and said, 'Why don't we go over and sit in that shade?' indicating the southern corner where a spreading banyan tree stood with its aerial roots streaming down. He threw a glance in that direction and shuddered at the sight of more loungers in addition to a couple of donkeys standing still like statues, and mongrels curled up in the dust. He looked outraged at my suggestion. I added, 'The grass is soft there,' asking myself, What, did this man expect Spencer's Furnishing Department to provide him cushioned seats?

He simply said, 'I am not used to sitting down. Lost the habit years ago.'

'How long ago?' I asked, trying to draw him out. Hoping he would become reminiscent. He ignored my question and asked suddenly, 'Is there a bar or a restaurant where we may possibly find a quiet corner?'

I really had no idea still why he sought me, out of the hundred odd thousand populating our town. The librarian must have given him a golden account of me. Why was that old man so fond of me? I suspected that he might be a match-maker and have his eyes on me as eligible for his granddaughter, me a bachelor with not a care in the world, owning property in Kabir Street.

'No bar or a good enough restaurant,' I said and added, 'nor do we have an airport or night club except Kismet in New Extension, not very good I hear. If you are interested I could give you a long list of things we don't have—no bars, sir, we have only toddy shops, which serve liquor in mud pots, which one has to take out.'

'Not interested, thank you. I am a TT. I only order orange juice at a bar and seek a quiet corner for a chat.'

'Nor are apples and oranges known here. We only come across mango, guava, gooseberry, all cheap fruits,' I said, getting into a devilish mood and resenting more and more this man's presumptuous presence in our town. I was exaggerating its shortcomings, avoiding mention of Pasha's Fruit Stall at the northern end of the market, which displayed on its racks every kind of fruit. He was said to get his apples directly from Kulu valley, grapes from Hyderabad, dried fruits from Arabia, and so on. He won prizes every year for the best display of fruits at the market.

'When did you arrive?' I asked Rann when we had managed to find a vacant space on the fountain parapet. Two men had just moved away, and I grabbed their seats as if jumping out of a queue. He had no choice but to stoop down, blow off the dust, spread his kerchief, and sit beside me on the parapet. After all these preambles I now left it to him to begin a conversation. He remained silent waiting for me to question him. After a few minutes, I remarked on the weather and went on to a lot of political titbits to prove that I wasn't taken in particularly by his blue suit.

'What did the old man tell you about me?' I asked.

'That you were the one person who could help me.'

'What sort of help? I had no notion that I was so important.'

'Don't say so, one can never judge oneself. You are a journalist, active and familiar with this town, and certainly would know what's what.'

That won me over completely, and I asked, 'Where are you from?'

'Timbuctoo, let us say.'

'Oh, don't joke.'

'No joke. It is a real place on the world map.'

'Oh!' I said. 'Never expected any real person to come out of it. You are the first one.'

He became serious and said, 'A lovely place on the west coast of Africa. A promising, developing town—motor cars in the streets, skyscrapers coming up—Americans are pouring in a lot of money there.'

'May I know what took you there and what has brought you here?'

'I was on a United Nations project.'

I didn't ask what. Project is a self-contained phrase and may or may not be capable of elaboration. I come across the word in newspapers and among academicians, engineers and adventurers. One might hear the word and keep quiet, not probing further. Sometimes a project might involve nothing more than swatting flies and sending reports to the headquarters.

He volunteered an explanation as if catching the trend of my thoughts. 'I have to send a report to my headquarters out of the voluminous data I have collected. I am also writing a book on a vital theme. I learnt that this is a quiet town, where I may collate my material in peace. Here I have been the last three days, practically living in the little waiting room of your railway station. Oh! the bed-bugs there! I sit up all night for fear of them. Tell me, who is the railway minister now, and help me to draft a letter to him.'

His presumptuousness annoyed me. Ignoring his question I hallooed to the peanut vendor hovering about with a bamboo tray on his head. When he came up I engaged myself in a game of haggling, disputing his measure and quality, before buying a handful of nuts which I kept on the parapet beside me. My friend looked rather shocked. I explained, 'Full of protein, you know, packed and hermetically sealed by nature, not the minutest microbe can sneak in: you may pick the nut off the road dust, crack it open, and eat it without fear of infection. Don't you consider the arrangement splendid?'

I demonstrated my observation by hitting a nut on the cement surface to crack it open, and held it out to him. He shrank from it, mumbling an excuse.

The next duty he imposed on me was to bring him out of the railway waiting room. The station master was distraught. He was a diminutive person whose job was to flag in and out two passenger trains at wide intervals, the non-stop express, and the goods wagons. After each performance he re-rolled the flags, tucked them under his arm, and turned into his office to make entries in a buff register while the

Morse keys tapped away unattended. After the passengers left, he put an iron lock on the platform gate and retired to his 'quarters', a small cottage fenced off with discarded railway sleepers, besides a Gul Mohur tree in whose shade his children, quite a number, swarmed, playing in the mud. He was a contented man, one of the thousands apparently forgotten by the Railway Board in far-off Delhi. He still had two years' service before retirement, and then he would go back to his village a hundred miles away. It was a life free from worries or hurry until this stylish passenger alighted from Delhi. His blue suit and manner overwhelmed the little man, as he stepped out of a first-class compartment majestically.

The old porter thought, with some pride, Someone from London, and hoped for a good tip. The train moved. The porter tried to lift the big suitcase. The visitor said, 'Waiting room,' at which the porter looked embarrassed.

The diminutive station master noticed the scene and came running after completing his duties in his little office.

'You are in charge?' inquired the visitor.

'Yes, sir, I'm the station master,' replied the man with a touch of pride but restraining himself from adding, I've still two years to go and then will retire honourably, back to my village where we have our ancestral land, not much, four acres and a house.

'Where is the waiting room?'

'Over there, sir, but please wait, I'll get it ready for you.'

He himself took charge of the suitcase from the porter, although he was only a few inches taller than what was really more like a wardrobe trunk, and hauled it along to the station veranda.

'Don't drag it, I'll carry it,' implored the visitor.

'Never mind, sir,' said the station master and would not let go his grip till he reached the veranda. The porter was gone to fetch the keys of the waiting room and also a broom, duster, mop and a bucket. Opening the door, the station master begged, 'Don't come in yet.' With the porter's help he opened a window, dusted and swept the room, and got it ready for occupation. He kept saying, 'I've requisitioned for carpet and furniture at headquarters.'

After a couple of days, he realized that the grand visitor had no intention of leaving. Dr Rann went out in the morning and came back only at night. It was against the rules to let anyone occupy the waiting room for more than two nights, but the station master was afraid to say so to the present occupant. Next time I visited the railway station with my letter for posting, the station master said, 'The Railways Act is very clear as to rules for occupancy of waiting rooms, but there is this man who wants to stay permanently. I fear I'll get into trouble—for thirty years I've served without a single adverse note in my service register—if the DTS ever stops for inspection, it'll be the end.'

'How can he know how long the occupant has been—'

'Entries in the register.'

'Don't make the entry.'

'For thirty years I have lived without a remark in my service records.'

'I'll ask him to buy a ticket for the next station, while waiting for the train. He can buy a ticket for Koppal, which will cost after all two rupees,' I said. But, he looked miserable at the prospect of a doom after thirty years of unblemished service.

'Don't worry about it,' I said finally. 'Keep him for another day or two till I find him a place. I'm sure your DTS won't come in the near future. Even if he does, mention my name, and he will say OK.'

I had the journalist's self-assurance although I did not have any paper or news editor to call my own. (The station master, I noticed, was too timid to ask my full name, knowing me only as a journalist.) He was busy fingering the telegraph keys.

'7 Down will be at the outer signal in a few minutes.'

He got up and directed the porter to run up to the yard and release the signal. The train arrived, and a group of villagers returning from the weekly market fair at Koppal got off with their baskets, bags, bundles and children. I ran up to the mail van and handed in my despatch for the day, with the late fee. The mail sorter said, 'Why do you waste money on the late fee, when you could post normally at the HO?'

'You may be right,' I replied, 'but I have to wait till the last minute for news. Anything might turn up at the last minute.'

He stamped the envelope and the engine whistled and moved, while the station master stood flourishing the green flag. The porter went up to lock the signal lever.

I chose this moment to take out a five-rupee note and present it to the station master, with, 'Just a goodwill token for the festival.' I could not specify a festival, but there was bound to be one every day in the Hindu calendar. 'We have 366 festivals for 365 days,' said a cynic once. The station master was used to receiving such goodwill tokens from businessmen, who did not want their parcels to be held up in the goods yard and loaded on a later train. The station master looked pleased as he pocketed my five-rupee note.

I whispered, indicating the waiting room, 'The one in there is no ordinary soul—he is from Timbuctoo.'

The station master was duly impressed with the manner in which I delivered this news. He asked, 'Where is Timbuctoo?'

I did not know myself, so I said: 'One of those African countries, you know...interesting place.'

Between the bugs and the station master, Rann felt uncomfortable continuing as a resident of the waiting room. And for me the daily visit to the railway station for mailing my despatch was becoming irksome. The moment he flagged off the 7 Up, the station master would turn his attention to me; luckily, he would not immediately be free, as he always had something to write on those hideous buff-coloured forms, or had to give a couple of taps to the telegraph key in his office, all this activity taking less than five minutes. When he dashed into his office for this brief interregnum, I could dash out and escape, but when he found me trying to slip away, he gripped my arm and led me into his office. I fully knew his purpose—to talk about his waiting-room occupant.

'Sir, you must think of my position—you must do something about that man there—he can't make this his home.'

'Why do you tell me?'

'Whom else am I to tell?'

'How can I say? I'm not his keeper. Why don't you speak to him yourself?'

'I don't know how to speak to such gentlemen.'

'A pity! I don't know how to speak to such gentlemen myself. I have not been taught.'

He wailed, 'I don't know how to approach him. He goes out, and when he comes back, he shuts himself in and bolts the door. Once Muni knocked on the door and was reprimanded severely. When he comes out he moves so fast, I can't speak to him at all.'

'That's how they live in foreign countries—they always move fast and won't tolerate any disturbance except by previous appointment.'

'Oh, I didn't know that,' he said seriously.

Another day he wailed, 'That gentleman was angry this morning. He said he is going to report to the Railway Board about the upkeep of the station—you think I care? I have served for thirty years—I can ask for retirement any moment if I like. What does he think? Am I his father-in-law to look after him?'

'Definitely not,' I said and he looked pleased at my concurrence.

'He is grumbling about bugs and mosquitoes as if the railways were cultivating them! The notions some people have about railways!'

Rann would buttonhole me in the Town Hall, where he knew my hours of visit. He also browsed among the musty ancient volumes in the back room, having gained favour with the librarian.

'I say, my friends—the bugs are eating me up every night. Do something. That funny man at the station says that it is not his business to keep the waiting room free of bugs and mosquitoes.'

'May be that is the Railway Board's policy to discourage the occupants from staying too long.'

'Should I write to the Railway Board?'

'No use, the bugs being a part of our railway service—they are service bugs actually.'

'Oh, I didn't realize,' he said, taking it literally.

'Anyway, why should you stay on there?'

It was the wrong question. 'Where else can I go?'

I shook my head, trying to evade any responsibility he might thrust on me. But there was no escape. He said, 'I can leave the railway station only when you find me another place.'

I ignored this proposal but could not suppress my curiosity. 'How long do you have to be here?'

'I don't know,' he said, 'till my work is completed. I have to make a field study, collate and organize my material and write. I have found some rare reference volumes in the stack room of the Town Hall library—some early nineteenth-century planters' experiences and their problems, which give me priceless data for my study.'

At my next visit to the station, the master cornered me again: 'Impossible situation. This is the third week, your friend must go. He can't make the waiting room his father-in-law's house.'

'Why not?' I bantered.

'I have told you a hundred times, rules don't permit more than eight hours' stay between trains, may be extended by a couple of hours at the discretion of the station master. Not more. I'll lose my job at this rate!'

'Why don't you throw him out? What have I to do with him?'

'Don't go on in this strain, sir. How can I treat roughly a big man like that?'

'Rules are rules and he may not be so big, after all.'

'I have never seen anyone dressed like him!' the station master said reflectively. 'I feel afraid to talk to him. I asked Muni to go up and tell him, but when Muni peeped in, that man turned round and asked, "What do you want?" and Muni withdrew in confusion. Please help me get him out of here somehow.'

I thought it over and said, 'Keep him for a week or ten days on a ticket to the next station each day and I promise to pack him off or find him a room.'

The station master looked doleful and began, 'Thirty years' service—'

I held out twenty rupees and said, 'You will buy him a ticket for Kumbum every morning and punch it for ten days and you will say he arrived by 7 UP or something, waiting to catch the 17 Down or whatever it is.'

This proved effective. Whether he pocketed the money or bought the ticket each day was not my business to probe. That gave Rann ten days' extension.

I utilized the time granted to search for a room. It was proving an impossible task; Rann could not specify what he wanted. I took him around all over the town—east, west, north and south. I had no confidence to have him on the pillion of Sambu's scooter, so I thought it best to engage an autorickshaw. One had to make an advance booking for it—it was gaining such popularity among the citizens. One morning I set aside all my other business and went to Nalli's Hardware, owned by Gopichand, an astute businessman who had migrated from Sind during the partition. He said, 'Take the auto at the stand if you find it. I never can say where they may be found until they return at night to give me the day's collection.'

I drew myself up and asked haughtily, 'Why should I come to you if I can find it at the stand?' My tone was indignant. I had served him in my own way—helped him to print his handbills when he started his autorickshaw business, brought him customers for his hardware, and also enlisted subscribers for a crazy financial scheme. He remembered my help and at once relaxed, 'Anything for you, my friend. You are my well-wisher,' and summoned his boy and said, 'Go at once and find Muniswamy and come with the vehicle.'

It was an idle hour for hardware business and he seated me on an aluminium stool and discussed politics. When we exhausted politics, I watched the crowds milling about the market, leaving Gopichand to read a newspaper reclining on a bolster amidst his hardy environ of nails and rods and chains and clamps.

The boy came back to say, 'Muniswamy is away, can't be found.'

Gopichand proclaimed grandly, 'Tomorrow morning the vehicle shall be at your door. Very sorry to disappoint you today.' As a compensation he drove the boy out to the next stall to fetch a sweet drink for me which came in an opaque unwashed glass. I declined at first, but had to pretend to drink in order to please him.

Next morning the autorickshaw was at my door.

'Ah, you have also started using an auto!' commented my immediate neighbour Ramu, who had grown so fat and immobile that he could do nothing more than sit on the *pyol* leaning on a pillar morning all night enjoying the spectacle of arrivals and departures in Kabir

Street. I looked on him more as a sort of vegetation or a geological specimen than as a human being. He loved to play rummy, provided the company assembled around him.

Now he remarked from his seat that an autorickshaw ride was heating to the blood and also disjointed the bones. The autorickshaw driver Kari was upset at this remark and retorted haughtily: 'People are jealous and create such rumours. Simpson Company at Madras have built the body and they know what is good for our bones.'

And he stepped out and approached Ramu to explain his point with vigour. I didn't like this development and summoned him back to his seat, hurriedly shut and locked the door of my house, and got into the rickshaw.

'Railway station,' I commanded.

He started the auto and over its rattle said, 'Did you hear what that fatty said, as if—'

I didn't encourage him to go on. 'Don't you pay any attention to such things. They are all an old-fashioned, ignorant lot in our street.'

'People are better informed in Lawley Extension. More enlightened men there.'

'Naturally,' I said, which agreement pleased him, and by the time we reached the station he was quite at peace with the world. I left the auto in the shade of the giant rain-tree outside the station, went up and found Rann half asleep in a chair in the waiting room. He stirred himself and explained: 'Not a wink of sleep—what with bugs and mosquitoes and the rattling goods wagons all night.'

'Get ready, we'll inspect the town. I'll wait outside.'

While I waited, the station master sidled up to me and whispered, 'DTS is coming...'

'You have already said that several times.'

He lowered his voice and asked, 'Does he drink?'

'How should I know?'

'He was wild last night, threatened to kick Muni for some small fault of his—'

'Never mind,' I said indifferently.

'Please take him away before bad things begin to happen.'

Rann was wearing olive-green shorts with his shirt tucked in at the waist, and crowned with a solar topee as if going out hunting in a jungle or on a commando mission. Actually, as we proceeded through the crowds in the Market Road he looked as if watching wildlife, with eyes wide open in wonder, and over the noise of the vehicle, he kept saying, 'Never been in this kind of vehicle—a bonerattler really...' (I prayed to god that Kari would not hear) and kept asking, 'Where are you taking me?'

I felt irritated and ignored his question.

First stop was at Abu Lane, which was off the East Chitra Road. We pulled up in front of an old building. He cried, 'Seems like a downtown area—not suitable.'

'What's your downtown? Anyway we are not placing you here—stay in the auto...I'll be back.'

He sat back sullenly while a small crowd of downtowners, old and young, stood around staring at the autorickshaw decorated with a pouncing tiger painted on its sides, and at the fantastic passenger. I dashed up a wooden stair in the veranda to a little office of a young real-estate agent, and picked up from his desk a list of available houses in the town, returned, and ordered Kari, 'First drive to North-end.'

'North-end? Where?'

'Across Nallappa's Grove, other side of the river.'

'Oh, there! No houses there,' said Kari.

'Twenty North-end, come on,' I said with authority.

'Cremation ground there...no houses.'

I flourished the list before his eyes. 'That chap there who gave me this list knows the city better than you. Just drive on, as I say.'

Rann seemed to be affected by the term cremation and began to fidget. 'Let us try other places...'

'Don't be scared. Hey Kari, don't talk unnecessarily...go on.'

One of the men watching obliged us with the statement, 'The cremation ground was shifted further off.'

'But the corpses are carried that way, the only way to cross the river—even two days ago—' Kari began.

But I said, 'Shut up, don't talk.'

'I don't want to live on that side of the river,' said Rann.

'Why are you sentimental?' I asked.

It was getting stuffy sitting in that back-seat and getting nowhere, with time running out. Rann began to narrate something about his days when he had to carry on his field studies with dead bodies strewn around. 'One gets used to such things…' he concluded grandly while the crowd stood gaping at us. I said determinedly, 'Driver, North-end. Are you going or not going? We have not set out this morning to parade ourselves in this street wasting our time…Rann, come out.'

He edged his way out and both of us stood in the street unused to so much publicity.

'Follow me,' I said. 'We'll find some other means of going.'

'Now where are we going?' he asked.

'Follow me, don't go on asking questions like a six-year-old urchin.'

He was cowed by my manner, and followed me meekly, with the locals forming a little procession behind us. I really had no idea what my next step was going to be. I had a general notion to go to the Market Place and complain to Gopichand about his driver or seek the help of Jayaraj to get a vehicle. Perhaps a *jutka*, but I was not sure if Rann could crawl into it and sit cross-legged. I was so grim that no one dared talk to me while I strode down the road without any clear notion of where I was going. The autorickshaw followed at the tail end of the procession. He honked his horn and cleared a way through the crowd and drew up alongside.

'Who pays the meter charges?' Kari asked.

I glared at him and said, 'Your boss Gopichand. I'm going on foot so that he will know what sort of a service he is running in this city with you as his driver. And with this distinguished person, whose feet have never touched the street!'

There was a murmur of approval from the assembly moving with us.

Someone came forward to confront Kari and say, 'You fellows deserve to be…to make a foreign gentleman trudge like this…' That settled it. Kari felt humbled and contrite.

'I never said anything to upset those masters. They themselves got out of their seats.'

And the busybody said, 'Forget and forgive, sirs. Get into your seats.' I took this chance and accepted his advice and pushed Rann into his seat, sat down, and said grandly, 'North-end first.'

An hour later we reached North-end over a broken causeway at Nallappa's Crossing. I had the satisfaction of noting water splashing off the wheels on the green uniform. Rann looked disconcerted but said nothing, bearing it all with fortitude. We arrived at North-end: a few thatched huts and, beyond them, an abandoned factory with all the windows and doors stolen, leaving gaping holes in the wall. Away from the factory four cottages built of asbestos sheets with corrugated roof, meant for the factory staff, stood in various stages of decay, and all passage blocked with anthills and wild vegetation.

I was a little shocked that the real-estate agent should have this first on his list. The young agent must have taken someone's word on trust and placed it on his list. Not a soul anywhere. We didn't even get down. Dr Rann smiled wanly. I said, 'These things happen, you know. Now Kari, turn round. The next on our list is...'

Kari looked quite battered by the strain of driving his rickshaw. Our eardrums were shattered, so were our joints. The man from Timbuctoo began to droop and looked bedraggled in his olive-green safari, which had now lost its original starched neat gloss, and revealed damp patches at the armpits and at the shoulders; the jacket was unbuttoned, exposing a grey vest underneath. If our expedition had gone on further, I'm afraid he would have stripped himself completely. This was the second day of our search, with no time left for tiffin or lunch. Yet I saw no end to our quest. We had our last trial at New Extension, a bungalow bearing the number 102/C. The auto stopped at the gate. The house looked fresh and promising. Rann surveyed it through the gate railings and declared, 'It'll be a nuisance to maintain the garden—and what should I do with a big house?' He shook his head without even waiting to inspect it. A caretaker came running, opened the gate and said, 'I've the keys.'

Rann was unmoved: 'I don't want a big house.'

'Not a small house, nor a medium-sized one, not on the east or west, north or south, neither downtown nor uptown,' I said singsong, carried away by the rhythm of the composition. I tried to sound light-hearted but felt bitter, and hated the whole business of house-hunting.

We got into the carriage. On the way back, I saw the Kismet, and stopped.

'Come in, I want to celebrate the non-conclusion of our expedition with ice-cream and coffee. Normally I'd have preferred the Boardless, but it is miles away at the other end—and I am not sure of being able to bear up that long.'

Rann brightened up. We refreshed ourselves. I ordered coffee and snacks to be sent out for Kari too, who had borne the brunt of our house-hunting and was waiting patiently outside. When the bill was brought Rann's fingers fumbled about his safari pockets. But I held up a warning sign grandly and paid down, although it was four times what it would have cost me at the Boardless. I belonged to the Kabir Street aristocracy, which was well known for its lofty, patronizing hospitality, cost what it may.

The moment we reached the railway station, the station master came up to tell me, while Rann had gone in, 'Message has just come that the DTS arrives at 1700 hours tomorrow for the day's inspection. Your friend must positively vacate right now. I have to tidy up.' There was no choice. As soon as Rann appeared, I asked, 'How many pieces have you, your baggage, I mean?'

'Not many. Why?'

'Pack them up at once. You have no time to lose. If the DTS arrives anytime now, you will have to live in the open. Pack up and be ready and come out in thirty minutes. That's all the time you have.'

'Outrageous. Where is that funny man the station master? Where are you taking me?'

'Don't become difficult or questioning, unless you want your baggage thrown out. The DTS has authority to throw out things you know.'

The station master stayed out of sight, but I was sure he was listening. I said to Rann finally, 'I'll leave now, but send the rickshaw back for you and your bags... I'm too tired to answer more questions. You have no choice—unless you want to take the next train to Madras.'

'Oh, no, that can't be done...'

When he arrived at my door with his heavy suitcase and an elegant roll of sleeping bag and other odds and ends, the whole of Kabir Street was agog. People stood at their doors to watch the new arrival.

Malgudi climate has something in it which irons out outlandish habits. It was not long before the blue Oxford suit was gone—perhaps embalmed in moth-balls; and the doctor began to appear in shirtsleeves and grey trousers, almost unrecognizable. In due course even that seemed odd and out of fashion in a street where everyone was seen in a *dhoti* from the waist down edged with a red border over a bare body, or at most in a half-sleeve shirt on occasions. For a few weeks Rann used to come out only in his three-piece suit puffing and panting in the heat. At home he would never emerge from the privacy of his room except in pyjamas and a striped dressing gown tasseled at the waist. Luckily I had inherited a vast house, no stinting for space as I have already mentioned. So vast and uninhabited, you'd be in order even if you wore no clothes when you emerged from your room; but here was this man, who never opened his door without being clad in his robe, his feet encased in slippers and a heavy towel around his neck.

We were not familiar with this costume. On the first day, the old sweeper who had been coming to clean and dust since the days of my parents gave one startled look at the gowned apparition emerging from the front room, dropped her broom, and fled to the backyard, where I was drawing water from the well, and said, her eyes wide open, 'A strange man in that room!' And the stranger was equally startled, and retreated like a tortoise into its shell, shutting the door behind him. He could not shut himself in indefinitely, however; he had to visit the toilet in the backyard.

I had to tell him that I could not change that century-old architecture in any way. He was aghast at first that he would have to travel all the way from his front room through two courtyards and corridors to wash and perform his ablutions at the well. But I gradually trained him, repeating every time, 'Where there is a will…' The latrine was a later addition, with a septic tank which I had installed after coming into possession of the property. On the very first day I had to explain to him a great deal, rather bluntly:

'You will have to accept this as it is. I cannot change anything—I can't bother myself with all that activity even if I find the time, money and the men.'

Following it, I gave him a tour of inspection of the house. When he saw the flush-out latrine he said:

'This is impossible. I have no practice—I need a European type—'

'In that case you have come to the wrong place. Our town has not caught up with modern sanitary arrangements, even this is considered a revolutionary concept. The Modern Sanitaryware man on Market Road is going bankrupt—sitting amidst his unsold porcelain things. Our ancestors bathed and washed and cleansed themselves at the well and the river. With the river running down our doorstep, they didn't have to make special arrangements, did not let themselves be obsessed with washing all the time, which is what Western civilization has taught us. Considering that the river flows almost all the year round, although thinning down a bit in summer—' I waxed eloquent and left him no choice.

'What do I do with the bathrobe?'

'Oh, don't worry about too many details. Things will sort themselves out. I'll drive a peg into the wall, where you can hang down your robe.'

'What does that word Timbuctoo sound like?' I began an article. 'It's a fairy-tale or cock-and-bull setting. Sometimes a word of disparagement or...' I went on for about a hundred words in the same strain, and finally came down to the statement, 'Hereafter we must pay more respect to that phrase. For I realize today that Timbuctoo is very real, as real as our Malgudi. I have actually shaken hands with a man from Timbuctoo. You will be right if you guess that I poked his side with my finger to make sure that he was real... He has come on a vital project on behalf of the UN and it's an honour for Malgudi that he should choose to work here. From his description of the place, Timbuctoo is a paradise on earth, and you feel like migrating, abandoning our good old Motherland.' And then I composed a word picture of Rann in his three-piece suit.

Every journalist has his moment of glory or promising glory—the brink of some great event to come, a foretaste of great events. A knock on my door, and my neighbour stood there outside, the fat man who rarely stirred from his seat on his *pyol*. This massive man held out a telegram.

'This came when you were away… I signed the receipt.'

While I tore it open, he waited to be told of its contents. I looked at him, murmuring a word of thanks, and wishing mentally that he would take his massive self off. Oh, big one—be off! I said mentally. I had much to think and dream over the message in the telegram, which was from my editor: 'News item interesting—but useless without a photograph of the Timbuctoo Man. Get one soonest.' For the first time in my life I was receiving encouragement. Normally whatever I mailed would be lost sight of, like flotsam on the current of Sarayu in flood. Or if it was printed, it would be so mutilated and presented in such minute type that you would have to search for it with a magnifying glass; and of course, no payment would be expected for it, not that I needed any, thanks to the foresight of my forefathers, who did not believe in spending but only in hoarding up endlessly. Here was the telegram in my hand, and this enormous man would not leave so that I might dream on it.

I turned to go in and he said, 'Hope all's well? Good news?'

'Oh yes, excellent news—from my news editor who wants something written up—routine stuff.' I sounded casual and tried to turn in, even as the fat man was saying, 'I'm very nervous when a telegram arrives. Otherwise I'd have opened it to see if it was urgent, and then of course, I'd have gone in search of you.' The picture of this paunchy man with multiple folds shuffling along Market Road barebodied in search of me was too ridiculous, and I burst out laughing, and shut the door, murmuring, 'Very kind of you.'

I gloated over the message secretly—not yet decided how far I could share the feeling of journalistic triumph with others. I went about my day feeling that I was on the brink of a mighty career. I don't aspire to become a so-called creative writer, I kept saying to myself, but only a journalist who performs a greater service to society, after all, than a dreamy-eyed poet or a storyteller. The journalist has to be in the thick of it whatever the situation—he acts as the eye for humanity.

Sitting in my corner at the Boardless lost in thought, my coffee was getting cold, which was noticed by Varma in spite of his concentration on the cash flow in the till. He suddenly ordered, 'TM's coffee is getting cold. Boy, take it away and bring hot.' I woke from my reverie to explain:

'A telegram from my editor, important assignment—but it depends very much on a photograph…'

'Whose?' he asked.

'I'll tell you everything soon.' I left it at that. Didn't want to make it public yet. I brooded over it the rest of the day and decided on action—since it was urgent and could be a turning point in my career—I must be ready to go anywhere if ordered, even if it meant locking up my home in Kabir Street. But I had misgivings about Rann, doubts about his reaction to a photo. Some instinct told me that it would not be so simple. And my instinct proved reliable when I faced him with the request. He was in his room. When I sounded him out, he became wary, and asked: 'Why?'

'Just for the fun of it… You have lived in many countries and must have interesting photographs.'

He brushed aside the suggestion with a wave of his hand, and resumed the study of the papers on his desk. Remarkable man. Though I had given him an unfurnished room, he had furnished it with a desk and chair and a canvas cot. I hadn't entered his room till now— he always locked it when leaving for his bath. He had been getting about evidently.

'How did you manage to secure a desk?'

'On hire. I found a shop on Market Road…for the four pieces they will be charging fifteen rupees…not bad, less than a dollar and a half, that's all very cheap…'

Rather disconcerting. He was entrenching himself while I had thought of giving him only a temporary shelter. I asked in a roundabout manner:

'How much advance for the whole period?'

He was evasive, 'Well not much really by world standards. He'll collect the hire charges from time to time, and no timelimit.'

He was too clever for me. I left it at that, looked around the walls and said, 'No photographs?'

'What sort of photograph?' He shook his head. 'I don't like photos of any sort.'

'I thought you might have an interesting collection, having lived in so many parts of the world...' I sensed this man would not give me his photograph. Today he was wearing a Japanese kimono and looked grim and busy.

'I must get these reports off—already overdue—all this amount of travelling is unsettling and interferes with one's schedule.'

I rather resented his continuing to be seated while I stood. I was consumed with curiosity to know what the report was about; there was a pile of typed and handwritten sheets. Where were the reports going? But I let the queries alone. My immediate need was for a photograph of this man. Some instinct told me not to mention it now.

I consulted Jayaraj later. 'I want a photograph of the man...'

'Put him before my camera and you will have it.'

'But he seems to shy away from the camera—I do not know why. Otherwise I could invite him to have a group photo with me as a mark of friendship.'

'I'd charge twenty-five for photographing two figures...'

Following this I got into a pointless debate which in no way concerned the present problem. 'So does it mean that if you take a group photo of fifty school children you will count the heads and charge pro rata?'

'Naturally' he answered. 'How else? I have to survive. If you find another photographer, you are welcome to go to him. Can't get rolls, either 35 or 120, no developer, no printing paper—hopeless situation. I think our government is trying to suppress photographers, and they draft their import rules accordingly. The little supply I have is thanks to that helpful breed called smugglers, who come regularly to that coastal village at Kumbum, their country craft loaded with things—where I go once a month to buy materials. The bus fare is five rupees each way, and I have to recover it in the charges to my customers. The Councillor came for a frame of a wedding group. I told him point blank that he was welcome to bring anything to frame, but no photo business please. Nowadays I am concentrating more and more on framing pictures and the painting of signboards—but even there...' He went on haranguing an imaginary audience about the conditions; frames that were flimsy, cheap wood, dyed and passed off as gilt frames by the suppliers, which once again was due to government policy. He was obsessed with the wiles of a hostile government out to do him in. I always allowed plenty of time for his speech, while sitting comfortably on the bench which jutted out of his shop at the Market Entrance. The authorities did their best to remove the bench, as it obstructed the public passage, but could do nothing about it, and Jayaraj always boasted that he would go to the Supreme Court if necessary to keep his long bench where he chose. His fundamental right could not be questioned.

He talked on squatting on the floor, his hands busy nailing and cutting frames; in a recess at the back wall he had his photographic department, that mysterious darkness where he professed to have treasures of photographic equipment through the grace of his friendly smuggler. After allowing him as long a speech as he desired, I said:

'Be a good chap. My whole career depends on your help now. I'll manage to bring that man this way, and you must manage to snap him, front or side, without his knowledge, and enlarge it. We want only a bust.'

'Done,' he said readily. 'My camera is the old type, on a tripod, but the best ever made, I can't take a snap with it, but I'll get the Japanese one from the Councillor who got it from the smuggler recently, which I can hold in my palm, and work wonders with the telephoto lens and superfast film.'

He got into the spirit of adventure and stood up at the entrance of his dark room and said, 'I can stand here and click when you step into that arch. But tell me the precise date and hour when you propose to bring him. I'll do anything for a friend who remains undiscouraged by what I may say.'

'Of course, I know that—otherwise wouldn't I try the Star Studio?'

'That wretched fellow! Don't go near him. He is a photographer of propped-up corpses—no good for live subjects.'

He approached his task with a lot of seriousness. He brooded over the logistics. He held a sort of dress rehearsal next morning with me understudying for Rann. In this season sunlight fell aslant at a particular spot under the Market Arch for about twenty minutes, but as the sun rose higher there was a shade...

'I must catch him in full light while it is available—otherwise I may have to use a flash, which is likely to put him off. Five minutes, that's all. You must see that he faces the market and stands still for a moment. I'll see to it that no one crosses in at that time. I'll post my boy to keep people away, only for a few minutes and no one will mind it either, not a busy hour... It'll be up to you to see that he doesn't pass through without stopping. Perhaps you should hold him and point at something. Don't worry that you may also be in the picture—I'll mask you and blow up the other.'

He leapt down, marked the spot for me under the arch, directed me to look straight ahead, hopped into his shop, concealed himself in the dark room, and surveyed through the viewfinder. I'd never expected he would plunge so heartily into the scene.

'You should be a film director,' I said.

I fell into an anxious state. The rehearsal was very successful but the star would have to cooperate without knowing what was going on. And he could be manoeuvred only once, there could not be a retake. I was pressed for time—the newspaper might lose interest if the photograph was delayed. Jayaraj could borrow the smuggled Japanese camera only for a day from the Councillor. I'd have to catch hold of Rann and manipulate him through. It was nerve-racking. In order to think I had to retire, to what used to be known in our family as a meditation room, a sort of cubicle in the second court, away from the general traffic routes of the family where you could retreat. It was dark and musty with a lingering smell of stale incense, a couple of pictures of gods faintly visible in the sooty wall. There I retired so that Rann might not intrude. A blue glass pane among the tiles let in a faint sky light, enough for my purpose. I sat down on a wooden plank, cross-legged, and concentrated on my problem, with a scribbling pad on my lap. I jotted down a script for the scene ahead.

Evening today: 1. Meet Rann and describe the Swami's Cottage Industries at the market as worth a visit. Talk him into it. (*Earlier* prepare Sam to be ready with a souvenir for Rann.) Explain to Rann that Sam is one who respects international personalities, and always invites them to honour him with a visit, and that he has collected and treasured letters of appreciation from outstanding men. Rann must spare a little time for my sake. *10.10 a.m.* Leave Kabir Street and walk down. *10.25 a.m.* Market Arch. Stop and push him gently towards the foundation tablet now covered with grime. Encourage him to scrutinize the inscription. *10.30 a.m.* Leave Arch.

Rann fell into the trap readily. I knocked on his door and saw him lounging in my canvas chair, my heirloom, and wool-gathering. He was probably feeling dull. So it was a propitious moment for me to make the proposal.

'Can you spare half an hour for me tomorrow morning?'

'Well, of course, what for?'

'You have been here and not known the peculiar treasures of this town.'

'I'm so preoccupied with my work...'

'I know, I know, but still you must look around. You will find it worthwhile... I want to take you to meet a friend of mine in the market.'

'Market! It'll be crowded.'

'Not always. I'll take you at a time when it is quiet. I want you to see a handicrafts shop—a very small one, managed by a chap we call Sam—absolutely a genius, dedicated. He makes lacquerware and sandalwood stuff which are famous all over the world. So many awards at Leipzig and other international fairs. He has distributors in Africa, Europe, the US and everywhere. He is well known all over the world; mainly foreigners come in search of him and place orders.

He is less known here as usual. No visitor from a foreign land ever misses him. Their first question will always be, 'Where's *Sam's Crafts*? Ten o'clock tomorrow morning we will walk up; spend half an hour at his workshop and then you will be free. He will feel honoured by a visit from an international figure.'

The scheme worked according to timetable. At the Market Arch I paused, he also paused. I stepped aside. I pointed at the fading tablet on a pillar facing us and as he stood gazing at it, I was aware of the slight stirring of a phantom at the threshold of Jayaraj's dark chamber. I kept talking.

'It's mud-covered, but if you are keen we may scrape the mud off and see the date of the foundation stone... He stood gazing at it and said, 'Thanks, don't bother about it,' and we moved on to Sam's.

I had gone as usual to post my news at the mail van when my friend the station master came to see me, all excited, saying, 'There is a large woman who came by 7 Down, staying at the waiting room and won't leave, just like the other fellow, that London man whom you took away—perhaps you should take away this woman too.'

'None of my business, whoever she may be,' I said.

'Not my business either,' he said. 'The waiting room is not my ancestral property to be given to every—'

Before he could complete the sentence, the subject of his complaint was approaching—a six-foot woman (as it seemed at first sight), dark-complexioned, cropped head, and in jeans and a T-shirt with bulging breasts, the first of her kind in the Malgudi area. She strode towards us, and I knew there was no escape.

'You must be the journalist?' she asked menacingly having observed me at the mail van. She took out of her handbag a press cutting of 'Timbuctoo Man', with the photograph of Rann I had managed to get.

She flourished the press cutting and said, 'You wrote this?'

'Yes madam,' I said meekly.

'No one can fool me,' she said.

The diminutive station master tried to shrink out of sight, simpered and stayed in the background. I felt rather intimidated by the woman's manner, but still had the hardihood to retort, 'What do you mean by it?'

'I mean,' she said, undaunted, 'if you know where this so-called doctor is, you will lead me to him.'

'Why?'

'For the good reason that I am his wife—perhaps the only one wedded to him in front of the holy fire at a temple.'

I took time to assimilate the idea.

'Of his possibly several wives I was the only one regularly married and the first. You look rather stunned sir, why?'

'Oh no,' I said clumsily. I had no other explanation. The whole picture of Rann was now assuming a different quality if this lady was to be believed. The station master looked embarrassed but, held by curiosity, hovered about with the rolled flags under his arm, and behind him stood the porter. We were the only ones on the railway platform. She eyed them for some time without a word and then asked, 'Station master, is your work for the day over?'

'Practically—9 Up is not due until 2000 hours.'

'What's 2000 hours? Now the bother of addition and subtraction,' she muttered. 'Why don't you railway people use a.m.-p.m. as normal civilized beings do?'

'Yes madam,' he said sheepishly.

'Is that your only porter?' The porter, on being noticed by the queen, came a few paces forward.

'I've served here for thirty years, madam,' he said. The queen accepted his statement without displaying any special interest, whereupon he withdrew a few paces back, but within hearing distance. She swept her arms about and said, 'Normally, they'd have a couple of cement benches on any railway platform, but here nothing. Come on, let us go into the waiting room anyway, there at least are a couple of chairs. Come! Come!' she said beckoning me authoritatively. Sheepishly I followed her. She had a commanding manner.

The station master followed discreetly at a distance. She carried two chairs out of the waiting room. 'No, no,' I persisted, 'let me—'

But she would not pay any attention to my gallant offer and said, 'You have seen him, tell me all about him.'

'I cannot say much… Ours was a brief meeting. I was interested because—' She did not let me complete the sentence: 'It is more important for me to know where he is rather than anything else.'

She looked so fixedly at me that I said, 'Not in my pocket,' and tried to laugh it off. 'We met for less than fifteen minutes at our Town Hall library where he had come for a reference work and did not like to be interrupted.'

'So studious indeed! How marvellous! Good to know that he is still bookish.' And she laughed somewhat cynically. Then she became serious and said, 'All that I want to know is where is he at the moment. If you will only give me a hint I'll give you any reward.'

I felt slightly upset and said righteously, 'I'm in no need of a reward. I can survive without it.' The station master who was following our dialogue from a respectable distance, added, 'He is rich, madam, comes from a big Kabir Street family really.'

She said, 'Station master, perhaps you would like to attend to other things?'

The station master shrank out of sight, and the porter too melted away. I got up saying, 'I must go now, you must excuse me. The only novelty about him was his mentioning Timbuctoo, and as a journalist I thought it had news value. After that I lost sight of him, never asked him where he was going—that's all. He was inquiring about some long-distance buses… That's all madam, all that I can say is that if he is staying in this place, he cannot remain unnoticed.' I had given full rein to my imagination. 'I'd suggest you look for him at Madras or a place like that instead of wasting your time here.' And I rose, carried my chair in and said, 'Goodnight.' I felt uncomfortable in her presence with a constant dread lest I should betray myself. And so I hurried away, glancing back over my shoulder to make sure she was not following me. She stuck to her chair without a word and watched me go.

Rann was in his kimono when he opened the door, on my knocking repeatedly, with a scowl on his face. I resented his attitude: in my own house he was a visitor to whom I'd offered asylum for no clear reason. It had just been an impulse to help him, nothing more, and to rescue him from bed-bugs flourishing in the railway station waiting room. Yet he behaved as if I were a hotel steward violating the privacy of a guest.

'Why don't you hang a "Don't disturb" board on your door? I thought you might have brought a souvenir from one or the other of the hotels in your travels—'

He was taken aback. 'Why do you say that?'

'I see that you are busy—' I said cynically. He wasn't. I could see that he had been lounging on the canvas easy chair (my heirloom) which I had let him have out of idiotic kindness. Yet this man dared to shut the door and look too busy to open it. There were no papers on his table, nor a book at his side in the canvas chair or anywhere. He must have been lounging and staring at the ceiling and wool-gathering, and he chose to scowl at me—me, his saviour from bed-bugs. Soon my anger was mitigated as I anticipated the pleasure of shocking him with news at which I knew his flamboyance and foreign style would be punctured. I simply announced, from the door, like the opening lines of a play, 'A lady to see you,' and turned round, shutting the door behind me (a piece of deliberate good manners). I went down to the backyard and shut myself in the bathroom and stayed there, although I had heard him open his door and follow me. I took my own time.

When I opened the bathroom door, he stood there, his face full of questions, and he seemed to have become a little paler and shrunk a few inches into his Japanese kimono. I had not needed a wash, but I had splashed water over my head for no better reason than to taunt him. 'Oh!' I cried with feigned surprise. Then I raced along the back courtyard to my room, while he followed me. My clothes and things were widely scattered in various rooms in different blocks of that house, and I never found at any time what I wanted, towel in one room, kerchief in another, trousers at another corner, and so forth. Now I was dripping, water running over my eyes, and wet all over— very annoying. I cried, 'Where is the damned towel?' At which Rann vanished for a minute and fetched a fresh towel from his room. I felt pleased with my show of authority, murmured a thanks indistinctly, and wiped my face and head. We were standing in the passage.

'I'll return it washed tomorrow—' I said.

'Oh, that's all right,' he said. 'No hurry.'

'So soft and strong,' I said admiringly and stretched it and held it to the light from the courtyard. I noticed an embroidered corner and spelt out 'Neville'.

'What's that?' I asked.

'Hotel in Rhodesia—it's a souvenir.' Perhaps he had stolen it.

'How long were you there?'

'Oh, quite a few times in connection with the project—'

'But they say, it's difficult for coloured people—'

'Oh, it's all exaggerated. Don't you believe it. For me, no problem, the UN passport can't stop you anywhere.'

I felt inclined to provoke further elaborations on the subject, while I knew he was dying to ask questions about the lady but feeling rather awkward about reviving the subject. I felt a sudden compassion for him—his bewilderment and awkwardness as he shrank into his fancy kimono. I asked suddenly, 'You want to ask about that lady?'

'Yes, yes,' he said meekly with a sigh, 'I don't understand it at all. Who is she?'

'The station master says that he saw a photograph in her hand, looking like your good self.'

'Ah!' he cried involuntarily.

'It matches the picture in *The Telegraph*.'

'How did my photo get in anywhere?'

'Newspapers have their sources, you know.'

He asked, 'What sort of a person is she?'

'Well, a long time ago I gave up staring at women and studying their worth, so I'm not able to provide a good description. Anyway, I'll dress and come to your room, please wait there.'

He was waiting impatiently in his room. I had taken my own time to look for my clothes, to groom myself before my mirror, the ornate oval in a gilded frame with a vine pattern carved on it, perhaps a wedding present for my grandmother: it was full of spots and blank areas. Now fresh from an unnecessary bath and dressed in my kurta and a laced *dhoti* and a neatly folded upper cloth over my shoulder, I felt ready to face the emperors of the earth. I strode into his room, where he had had the good sense to leave the door open. I had a glimpse of him fidgeting impatiently in his chair. The moment he saw me he rose and offered me the seat, and lowered himself into it only after I had sat elsewhere. Now I looked as if ready to go on with our conversation and give him a hearing.

'I told you about a lady at the railway station where I had gone to post my evening despatch.'

I knew that Rann was dying to have a description of the lady as he sat squirming and fidgeting.

'Was she tall?' he asked, trying to draw me out.

'Could be,' I replied.

'Medium height?'

'She did not seem short,' I said. 'I could see her only from a distance.'

'How far away were you?' he asked stupidly.

I felt irritated. 'I forgot to take a measuring tape with me,' I said, and tried to laugh it off. He looked miserable and I had to ask: 'Why are you bothered?'

He said, 'Because—I don't know. You are right. Dozens come and go at the railway station, do I care?'

'Bravely said,' I remarked. 'Let us go to the Boardless. You will feel better.'

He shrank from the idea. He had, apparently, a fear of being waylaid by the woman. I persuaded him, but before coming out, he spent much time to decide how to dress for the visit. I advised, 'The Boardless is a special place, where you could go in your underwear or in royal robes, it's all the same to the crowd there. No one will question or notice.' Still, he took his time to decide and came out in a pink slack shirt and grey flannel trousers.

We walked up. I took him to my usual corner, facing the Mahishasura calendar, had another chair put up. The habitués turned round to study him for a moment and then resumed their coffee and talk. I ordered *dosai* and coffee, but he couldn't enjoy it; he seemed overwhelmed and self-conscious. Varma, the proprietor, said 'Hallo' to him formally and looked gratified that the Boardless should be attaining an international touch with this man's visit. I briefly explained, 'He is a scholar, come on business,' avoiding Timbuctoo because of its phoney sound. I thought I should do something to integrate this stranger in our society and cure him of his kimono and carpet-slipper style and alienation, and so had persuaded him to walk along. Of course, it had not been an easy passage though, people stared at us—it was inevitable.

The lady's haunting presence at the railway station somehow drove Rann closer to me. He seemed to depend on me in some obscure manner for any information I might spring on him. He looked on me, I suppose, as a possible harbinger of some good news such as that the lady had left suddenly by some train or that she had thrown herself under the midnight goods train. So he watched my movements eagerly with almost a questioning look to say, 'Any good news? How good is the goods train? Anything under it?' Formerly, he had always shut himself in his room and bolted the door. These days he kept a door open so that he might not lose glimpse of me; while I moved about he watched me surreptitiously from his chair, which was an excellent position for spying. My forefathers must have used that same strategic position to keep an eye on the household, particularly the army of servants, so that no one could slip out unnoticed. Rann found this advantageous. As I passed in and out he greeted me with casual ease. 'Good day to you, TM. Starting on your interesting rounds for the day?' Sometimes he just smiled and nodded, without obviously questioning, feeling perhaps: 'If he has anything—he is bound to tell me—not the sort to keep mum—'

On the whole, he seemed to have limbered up, and was slightly more relaxed. It suited me, too. I took advantage of his leniency and the half-open door policy to step into his room informally for a chit-chat now and then. I'd walk in and make straight for the easy chair without any preamble.

I lounged in his canvas chair comfortably. He sat in his hired chair uneasily, pretended to be looking through some papers on his desk, put them away, and got up and paced the narrow room up and down like a bear in the cage. After a pause and silence for fifteen minutes I just pronounced:

'You seem very agitated, why?'

'Oh, no. I am sorting out some problems in the paper I'm writing.'

'Very well then, let me leave you in peace...'

'No, no, stay,' he said. It seemed to me that he wanted to say something but was reluctant to begin or rather unable to find an opening line.

'I do not mind relaxing and lounging here all day, but you will have to do something about it, about the lady in question,' I said.

'What do I care? Hundreds of persons come and go at a railway station.'

'Not everyone carries your photo asking questions—'

'What the hell!' he cried, red in the face. I enjoyed the annoyance he displayed and added, 'Also calls herself your wife.'

'Nonsense!' he cried, and paced up and down. I had never found him in such a mood or using intemperate language. The thought of this woman seemed to loosen the bolts of his mental framework.

'What's he to Hecuba or Hecuba to him?' I asked light-mindedly.

'Does she call herself Hecuba? I know no one of that name.'

I had to explain to him that I was quoting Shakespeare.

'Ah, Shakespeare. I had almost forgotten. Long time ago, of course. Would you believe it? Once I sat down and read the Oxford edition from the title page to the last.'

'Yet, thou varlet weakeneth at the mention of a perfidious female!'

'I say, this is maddening! Please do something and send her away.'

'Why? This is a free town for anyone to come and go or stay. How can I arrogate to myself any right to expel anyone! I don't think I'll see her again...'

'What's she like?' he inquired suddenly. I couldn't continue in a mood of levity—if she was really his wife. So I just said, 'Well, an impressive personality—slightly dark, but a commanding personality, rather large build, I should say. Perhaps exaggerated by the blue jeans and T-shirt and bobbed hair. The station master was quite cowed by her manner and opened the waiting room promptly when asked...'

'Though he made such a fuss when I wanted it! That funny character. Did she mention her husband to him also?'

'I don't know,' I said, 'but he was the first to be shown your photograph.'

'Outrageous!' he cried. 'You have done me a disservice!'

'On the contrary I was doing you a service without being asked. Do you know the number of men who curry my favour to get their names in print?'

'You could have at least consulted me!'

'It'd be against the journalists' code. Freedom of the press and all that. Even the PM cannot say "Yes" or "No" to a journalist when he is out to make his copy,' I said grandly.

'Photograph! How did the photo get in?'

'I can't say—you have been in so many places, anyone might have snapped you.'

After about an hour's rambling talk he begged, 'Don't betray me. You have been hospitable right from the beginning, just help me now by leaving me alone and without mentioning me to that person, whoever she may be, in jeans and T-shirt. Is she Indian? I'll explain everything when the time comes. Not now. Don't ask questions.'

'After all,' I said, pitying his plight, 'she is not going to live permanently in the waiting room. She will have to leave some time. Don't be seen too much for some time,' I said encouragingly.

'I need a lot of mental peace at least till I complete my work. That's why the shelter or asylum you have given is doubly valuable. I must have no sort of distraction till I complete the writing of my book. Anyone who helps me to work in peace will be my benefactor. To me nothing is more important than the book. It's going to be a sensation when it comes out. It will shake up the philosophers of today, the outlook will have to change. It's in this respect that I value your hospitality and shelter. When I publish I'll acknowledge your help surely.'

'Ah ha, my name too will be in print. Excellent! While my profession is to get a lot of people's names in print, that is the first time it will be happening to me. Great! Do you know my name? You have never gone beyond calling me TM or UC as those people at the Boardless do—why not we adjourn to the Boardless for refreshments, after all you have visited it only once. I'm hungry.'

He resisted the suggestion.

'Are you afraid to come out?' I asked and left it at that.

'Why should I be afraid? The world's full of evil things. I have seen all sorts of things, everywhere in this world. I'm not afraid of anything. Any airline hostess or a waitress in a restaurant might turn round and blackmail you if you were foolish enough to have said, "How do you do?" in a friendly tone. These are situations which develop unasked. I won't be disturbed too much by these things.'

'So, a man of experience! Come out with me and if you are accosted, draw yourself up and say, "Begone phantom wretch! I know you not."'

'You are very Shakespearean today,' he commented. I was happy to see him thawing. 'I've also as I told you read Shakespeare with genuine pleasure,' he added.

I decided to protect him from wifely intrusions.

How she found her way to Kabir Street must forever remain unexplained. There she stood on my threshold one afternoon. The neighbours viewing her from their *pyols* must have been startled; her dress and deportment were so unusual in our setting. She was attired like a Punjabi woman, *kurta* or *salwar kameez* or whatever they call it, which seemed to exaggerate her physical stature, which was already immense. She was a large woman by any standard.

In our street where women were used to glittering silk sarees, gold and diamonds, she looked like a visitor from another planet. She wore around her neck white beads in a string; like a gypsy, and had around her shoulder a pink muslin wrap—the total effect was startling, really. No wonder the spruce tailor's dummy called Rann quailed at the very thought of her. I was happy that the fellow had gone out, and I only prayed that he would not blunder in and stumble on her. I seated her with her back to the window opening onto the veranda as you came up the steps so as to prevent her catching sight of Rann if he happened to come.

I didn't know where he was nowadays. I thought he went out to do research, but later learnt from our gossip sources what he was actually doing. I'll come to that later.

Now the big lady was settled squarely in the hall. I had placed her strategically so that she could have a view of the second courtyard and the crows perched on the roof-tiles and the drumstick tree looming beyond, and not notice Rann if he should appear on the other side of the window.

'I'm sorry, I've nothing to offer...this house is just a shell, I go out to eat—not a soul anywhere.'

I refrained from questioning how she had managed to come. I guessed the station master must have given her directions.

She said, 'I don't expect anything from you except help to get at that man.'

I remained silent, not knowing what to say, dreading that she might turn her head at the sound of footsteps. She was there to investigate thoroughly.

'That station master is helpful...good man. But for him I'd have taken the next train back instead of continuing in this wretched place—Oh, the bugs in the waiting room!'

'Yes, yes, others also run away on account of it...' realizing how similar Rann's experience was. That seemed to be their only common bond. (Bug-bond was the phrase that kept drumming in my head.)

'I gave him five rupees and he has been so helpful—even got a spray pump and eliminated the bugs almost fifty per cent! Now it is tolerable. He has also arranged to send me food from his house,' she said.

Why is that fool of a station master so helpful, I wondered. Must warn him.

'He must be having special regard for you. Usually he applies the rules and won't let anyone occupy the waiting room for more than a few hours.'

'Yes, he mentioned something, but five rupees goes a long way; first thing in the morning after 7 Up or 6 Down or whatever it is passes, I slip the five-rupee note before he can mention the rules and his unblemished service record in the railways. Also a couple of rupees to the porter, who sweeps and cleans the room and does not let anyone approach it—and so there I am. No one except yourself has set eyes on the so-called Rann for years. You must help me get at him…a strange character. Sometimes I have felt like wringing his neck but on the whole I'm very very fond of him, although I am not sure what I'll do if I set eyes on him. Anyway, first show him to me and then I will decide.' She tightened and bit her lips—her expression was so forbidding that I shuddered at the picture of slippery Rann in her grip.

'How did you get his photograph? He was always shying away from photographs. Even our wedding photograph he tried to destroy but I saved it. I have it with me in my box at the station.'

'Why so?'

'Because he was a crook and wanted to remain invisible, that's all.' She said this without hesitation. I didn't explain how I got the photograph because I feared she might call me a crook too, being so uninhibited and loose-tongued. She suddenly went on, 'Now tell me all about him. Though I loathe him, I like to hear about him.'

I didn't see why I should oblige her with information and so just said, 'I too met him only at the Town Hall where I had gone to look at a paper. I stopped by because he was rather strange-looking in his three-piece suit and all.'

She laughed at the mention of his suit. 'Oh, three-piece suit. Three-piece suit! What a gentleman! Once he was one hundred per cent Madrasi—only *dhoti* and *khaddar* half-arm shirt.'

'One could easily take him for a London banker now.'

'Three-piece suit indeed! What shade?'

'Blue—all blue or near blue,' I said, getting into the spirit.

'Tell me about him, I'm dying to hear all about him…ages since I saw him, years and years, what does he look like? Has he grown stout? Your photograph doesn't say much.'

'Newspapers won't print more than a bust or the head as on a coin or postage stamp, and that seems to have brought you down.'

'If you had published a full photograph, that might have brought quite a crowd to your railway station, enough to drive the station master crazy.'

'Must have been a popular man,' I said.

'A regular lady-killer, sir; the only one who could survive was myself. I've been to the capitals of the world hunting for him with the help of the Interpol and met only the poor wrecks he left behind when he vanished. What does he look like these days? Has he put on weight?'

I realized presently that like the Jesting Pilate, she would not wait for an answer. If I remained silent, still she would go on—

'He was quite attractive in those days. Does he have a moustache?'

'Yes, a thin line—reminds one of—reminds one Adolphe Menjou, a film actor in the thirties—'

'Must be greying, surely...or does he colour? I wouldn't put it past him.'

I remained quiet, letting her talk on. It looked as though I'd have to surrender my title of Talkative Man and take a second place in the world of talkers. My constant fear was that the fellow might arrive. I was apprehensive as to how they would react to each other, also about my position as his keeper. The lady would unhesitatingly call me a liar and might even assault me, which would create an unprecedented sensation in Kabir Street. She looked as if she might make a move. She must have heard rumours of my hospitality toward Rann—again from the station master.

On an idea, I got up with an excuse to go out: 'I'll be back in ten minutes, suddenly remembered something...' I went down the steps to the fourth house in the same row, Sambu's. As usual, he was reading in his small study.

'Look, when Rann comes back to return your scooter, keep him here, lock him away if necessary till I sound the all-clear. Tell him someone is waiting for him—he'll understand.'

After that I hurried down to the corner shop and bought a dozen bananas, a packet of biscuits, and a couple of soft drinks, went home, and set them on a plate before the lady.

'Ah, you are a thought reader. Very welcome.'

She must have been starving. She ate three plantains, half a packet of biscuits and washed it all down with a soft drink that claimed to be pure orange juice. Revived, she remarked, 'Husband-hunting is a fatiguing business.'

'Are you sure we are referring to the same person?' I asked.

'No doubt about it. The photograph is unmistakable: he might make himself into Adolphe Menjou or whoever, or grow a beard or a horn on his head, but he can never change. Eyes and nose betray a man unmistakably. They cannot change or cheat. I have done nothing but gaze on his wonderful countenance for months and years out of count, and I know.'

She paused and wept a little. I tried to look away, and did not know what would be the right statement to make in this situation. It was awkward. I did the best I could under the circumstances, looking away through the window—hoping and hoping that the man would not come back suddenly, bypassing Sambu or because the bookworm Sambu should forget to hold him, as was likely with bookworms. I contemplated this possibility while glancing at her mopping her tears with a minute handkerchief which she had to fish out of her bag each time, and wondered if it would be appropriate to lend her the 'Neville' towel Rann had given me. Suppose she was settled here for the day?—since my parlour was as good as the waiting room for her. In a voice thickened with nose-blowing, she said, 'If I had the slightest clue that he would act like this... At Madras, I was reading at St Evans in Egmore, and lived with my parents in one of those sidelanes nearby. My father had a furniture and carpentry shop and this man you call Rann would often come in on a bicycle; he was a delivery boy for a circulating library, delivering and collecting magazines, mostly film journals, charging a daily fee. He was also a student at Loyola College, supplementing his income through his job, which he seemed to enjoy, as it suited his wandering temperament. The library had a few journals of a serious kind in addition to film magazines, which appealed to my youthful taste in those days. He enjoyed his job because he could read all sorts of things, some of the serious journals too like the *National Geographic*. Occasionally he would recommend a special article in a journal to improve my mind. He reserved his visit to us as the last on his rounds—bringing us the cheap magazines we liked as well as the serious ones which he would recommend to us. In addition to delivering magazines his boss would send him to get racks and stools and benches for his shop from my father's workshop, which was a small shed in the backyard, though he employed many hands and turned out a lot of furniture for the shops around. A stone bench under a mango tree in our compound was very convenient for us. We sat close to each other, while he read out of a journal something that he felt I should know and understand. You know how it is when two young persons sit close to each other and discuss intellectual matters in soft whispers! Inevitable, inevitable...'

At this moment I noticed Sambu coming up my veranda steps. I excused myself for a moment and went outside. Sambu whispered: 'That chap is come—about an half-hour ago—and is restless. What shall I do?'

'Kick him up a ladder to that loft in your hall and remove the ladder. He had better stay out of view for a long time. There is someone in there waiting to dismember him; I'll tell you the story later. She shows no sign of moving, but I'll do something about it soon. Please wait, and tell the idiot not to peep in at the window.'

Sambu, an ever-obliging neighbour, threw a brief glance at the window and withdrew.

I had to explain to the lady, 'I'm afraid I've a meeting to report. My friend is waiting. I suggest that you go back to the railway station. I'll meet you in your room later when I come to post a letter in the mail van—after that I'll be free. You must also want to eat and rest. I'll definitely see you?'

She narrated her life story further, after ordering a couple of chairs to be placed under a tree on the railway station platform. She ordered the station master about and commanded the porter unreservedly until they supplied all her needs. I had posted my despatch dutifully—a court case and a municipal meeting, in the 7 Up to Madras. The platform was deserted; only the station mongrel lay curled up on the signalling platform. The lady had rested and looked refreshed and had now changed to a cotton saree, which made her look larger than she seemed in the morning. A mild breeze was blowing from the mountains, some birds were chirping in the tree.

'The waiting room must have been a dungeon at one time where prisoners were cooped up. I'd not want even my worst enemy to come in there. This tree is my shelter all through the day. I watch the travellers come and go and would willingly sleep under it during the night, but for my sex—still the world is not an easy or safe place for us.'

I resisted the impulse to blurt out, Who would dare to come near you? As if reading my thoughts she said, 'I always carry a little pistol—of course licensed, because I'm an officer in the Home Guards at Delhi, though I have never had to shoot even a fly. I took a rifle-training course the police once organized at Madras, and I know which is the right end of a gun.' And she laughed. She seemed to be in a benign mood now, having probably got it off her chest in the morning. 'There is no train till 2100 hours, to use the master's language—I think it is the 11 Up, a lumbering goods train which is so noisy that you can't sleep till it has passed the outer signal. You see, I'm picking up the railway language quite successfully.'

After a few more pleasantries of this kind, she paused to look at the station master and the porter, standing respectfully a short distance away, and said, 'That'll be all for the present, master. Tell your wife not to go to any trouble tonight. All I'll need is a glass of buttermilk if she can manage it.'

'Definitely, madam,' said the master and withdrew, followed by his porter. 'I'll be away to do some marketing, madam, not more than an hour.'

'Away till 1730 hours?' she asked with a laugh.

'Very much earlier,' he said. 'Muni will be here and will attend to any important messages...he's experienced.' At which the porter looked pleased.

'I don't wish to bore you,' she said to me, 'but I have to tell you. In addition to our meetings in the evening at my home, he used to waylay me on my way to or from school and take me on his bicycle. I began to miss my classes happily, and spend the time with him at a coffee house or ice-cream parlour. He was very liberal in entertaining me. I was charmed with his talk on all sorts of subjects. Our discussions on the cement bench under our mango tree became infrequent since we were together in other places. We went to the museum, where he would take me through, explaining all sorts of things. I liked his voice and felt thrilled to be told about the eleventh-century bronzes or in another corner about the nomads or forest tribes and their cowrie-shell ornaments, and so on. And of the stuffed animals, their habits and character, whatever he said would just charm me. I couldn't decide how much of what he explained was genuine—but it held me, his voice lulled my senses. The museum was the nearest rendezvous for us, and I could go back home from there unnoticed, but sometimes we took the bus to the beach and enjoyed the ozone in the air, the surf and sand: he held my arms and dragged me knee-deep into the waves. A thrilling experience—made me forget my home and parents. Of course, a matinee at the Elphinstone on Mount Road occasionally. At Egmore, I had felt hemmed in, the horizon was restricted—but now this boy was opening my eyes to the wide world. I was not yet eighteen, but I possessed all the craftiness needed to save my skin. When my father demanded to know why I was late, I would always say that I had had a special class or was on an excursion with the teachers or doing joint study with a friend in some difficult subjects. My father, battling all day with carpenters to execute his constantly overdue orders, would not probe further. Fortunately, I was passing my exams and that was what he was particular about. But my mother, who had possessed sounder instincts, took me aside while I was leaving for school and said, "I can hear your evening school bell quite clearly, remember. If you are not here within ten minutes of the bell, I'll tell your father. You know what he will do if he is upset. He will chip the skin off your back with his tools."

'The next few days I came home punctually at the end of the school, avoiding the young man's company. When he cycled up and brought us magazines, my mother told him, "We don't have time for magazines. You may stop."

'"Why? Why?" he asked. And I could hear my mother's answer, "That's so, that's all, go…"

'He hesitated, "Perhaps uncle may want to read."

'"Uncle! He is not your, uncle! Begone!" she shouted, while my father kept himself deliberately in the shed, away from the scene. Listening to it all, I felt a sudden pity for the fellow and for all the kindness he had shown me, and I dashed out to say. "Why should you be so rough?" At which my mother slapped my face and I ran in crying.

'I became a virtual prisoner in the house—allowed only to get to my school and back under strict surveillance, escorted by Thayi, our old servant maid. My mother seemed a terrible woman in those days. I stopped talking to her, answered her questions in monosyllables, and whenever I thought of the boy, my heart bled for him. Leaning on his bicycle bar, he was bewildered by all the rudeness he was encountering in the world. I missed the warmth of his company and his enlightening talk, and above all the timid pecking on the neck and hugs when no one was looking.

'Though we were apart, we still found a way to communicate. Little notes or bits of paper passed between us through the agency of the woman chaperoning me. At the circulating library she dropped my note on his desk and brought back an answer. Thus I saved my head from being sawn off. To that extent, I respected, or rather we respected my parents' command. My final examination was due in a few months. I was not going to do anything that might disrupt my studies. So I acted the model child at home, and my parents looked very happy and pleased, and plied me with their kindness and trust. I concentrated on my studies and did well in my examinations in March. Although I felt desperate sometimes for his company we kept up our show till the May of that year when the results were announced.

'Occasionally we did meet when my parents were away. My mother's family lived at Avadi, fifty miles away. My father would escort her in the morning and they would come back by the evening train, which would leave me free for a full day. They would always warn: "Don't leave the house, take care of everything. Take care." The old servant would be told to stay to guard me from intruders (which was my mother's indirect way of indicating the young man). But I bribed the old lady to guard the house and that left us free to visit the circulating library. This would be our happiest moment. He would lock up his little office and take me out. We would go out to the farthest place possible, most times Elliot's Beach in Adyar, which was another planet as far as Egmore citizens were concerned. Elliot's Beach has one or two shacks where sea-bathers could dress—ideal retreats for lovers. All afternoon we stayed in a shack: they were happy hours. We were recklessly happy. I took care not to go beyond a certain limit in caresses, cuddling and fondling—though within that limit, we attained supreme happiness. We discussed plans for our future—many alternatives. We stayed in the shack watching fishermen go out to sea on their *catamarans*. Sometimes they would peep into the shack, smile and leave us alone. Sometimes they would demand a rupee or so for cigarettes—and then leave us alone. Thus the hours passed—while we stayed in the pleasure of each other's company listening to the waves splashing on the shore, blue sea and blue sky and birds diving in and the breeze. All of it made him say: "Let us go on and on here, why should we go back? Let us stay here till we die."

'But we had to scramble to our feet when the six o'clock chimes were heard from the San Thome cathedral. My father's train was due at seven at the Egmore Station and he would be home in fifteen minutes walking down the railway track. The old lady showed me the utmost sympathy and cooperation, seemed to get a vicarious thrill out of my romance. If my father threw a searching look around and asked the old woman: "Is everything all right?" she would answer, "Yes, of course, the child went on reading the whole day. Oh! how much she reads!"

"'Book? What book?" my father would ask suspiciously, on the alert to find out if it was from the circulating library.

"'I want to prepare for a correspondence course in accounting and borrowed a book from Shanta," I said.

'He was relieved and happy and commended my studious habits, but also warned me against overdoing it, "because you have just worked hard for your Matriculation Exam."

'This kind of deceitful existence did not suit us. I felt rather dirty and polluted. When the results came and I was successful, I made up my mind. The next time my parents left for Avadi, my lover brought an old car, borrowed from one of his well-wishers, to the carpentry shop and took me away. He gave the old woman, my chaperone, ten rupees, and before we drove away told her: "You must bless us." I bundled up a change of clothes, while the old woman shed tears at the parting. In a voice shaking with emotion, she placed her hands on my shoulder and said, "May god bless you with many children!" the only blessed state that she could ever imagine.

'He stopped at a flowerseller's on the way, bought two garlands of jasmine and chrysanthemum, and drove straight without a word to a temple on the outskirts of the city: he seemed to have been busy earlier preparing for our wedding. A priest had lit oil lamps all around the image of some god. He presided over the exchange of garlands, asked us to prostrate before the god, lit a heap of camphor, got a couple of his friends to witness, in addition to god, distributed fruits to the gathering, lit a little flame which we circled, and sounded a bell. He then gave the bridegroom a yellow thread, and told him to tie it round my neck, charged us fifty rupees for his service, issued a rubber-stamped receipt, and we were man and wife.'

The lady's volubility overwhelmed me. I felt like the wedding guest whom the Ancient Mariner held in a spell of narrative, preventing his entry into the reception whence the noise of festivities was coming. He wailed that it was late and he should go in, but the Ancient Mariner held him with his eyes, ignoring his appeal and just said, 'With my crossbow I shot the Albatross' and continued his hypnotic narration while the wedding guest beat his chest. I didn't go so far, but went on punctuating her speech with 'I think it's time for me...college socials to attend and report...'

She brushed off my protestations and hints and continued her narration as if only her tongue functioned, not her ears. She was quite carried away by her memories.

'We found an outhouse, a cozy one with a kitchen and bed-sitting room in Poonamalle High Road, and lived there happily, as happily as we could. Both of us worked. He continued in his library, which was now bigger, and he held a senior position with a lot of responsibilities. I was a receptionist at a travel agency. Both of us left at nine every day after breakfast and with a one-item simple lunch to pack and carry. I got up at 5 a.m. and cooked the food for the day. We returned at different times in the late evening and most days, being too tired to do anything else, ate some cold leftovers and went to bed.

'Occasionally I visited the carpentry to see my parents who had become friendly, perhaps taking a realistic view that they had acquired a son-in-law without spending money on dowry, feasts or celebrations.'

When she found me fidgeting and trying to get up, she waved me back to my chair and said, 'Spare me some more time please, I'll finish as briefly as I can, though it's a long story. We may not meet again. While I can hold you, I'm anxious you should know the full story—I've not given up hopes you'll see him again, and you must have the full picture of your hero.'

'Oh no, not my hero and I'll not,' I protested.

'Please don't interrupt,' commanded the Ancient Mariner. 'If you don't keep interrupting, I'll finish my story quickly...otherwise you may make me forget and I've to go back and forth. Already, I think I missed an important episode. It's a vital link. Have I told you what happened on the day of my wedding and my father found me missing when he came home from Avadi?

'When he found me missing, the man seems to have lost his head completely. The old woman Thayi defended herself by explaining, "A car came into our gate suddenly: Roja (my name at home) was standing at the door, two young men seized and pulled her into the car and drove away... I don't know anything more... I ran down crying but the car was gone." After that my father went to the Egmore Police Station and gave a written complaint that I was missing and that he suspected kidnapping. Inspector Natesh was a family friend. Many were the table legs and rickety stools that my father had mended for him. He seems to have said with gusto:

"Leave this to me. I'll recover your lost daughter. These are days when young persons try to imitate the cinema stories."

'He spread his net wide and surprised us at a remote place called Fisherman's Hut, beyond Adyar, where we were hiding but living a beautiful existence. Two policemen came in a jeep with Inspector Natesh. We were just enjoying our lunch on the seashore, trying to live all the romantic poetry one has read in one's life. It was awkward when Natesh seized my husband's wrist and put the fetters on. However, he said to me, "Don't cry—you are all right."

'We drove back—a long, silent drive back to the city. First halt at the penitentiary, where the young man was dropped and handed over to a sergeant at the office, and then I was taken home and handed over to my parents—the worst kind of homecoming for anyone.

'The young man was charged with abducting and kidnapping a minor under eighteen years of age. A lawyer who was a customer of the circulating library and known to my husband came into the picture at this stage and said: "This is nonsense. I'll get the young fellow out, first on bail." Three days later the young man went back to his library as if nothing had happened. After that the case came up, off and on at the Presidency Magistrate's court, adjourned again and again. I went through hell, and so did my husband. The validity of our marriage was questioned, and I had to bear the hostility of my mother and relatives. I felt outlawed and miserable. In addition to all this misery, my father's lawyer coerced me to sign a document to say that I had been abducted and forced into a marriage. Said the legal luminary, "She is a minor and it cannot be a valid marriage." They bullied and browbeat me to sign a document charging him with abduction.

'This was the most painful part of the whole drama and I could never forgive myself for doing it. Signing a long story based on the old lady's report. How I had been snatched up from our house when I stepped out to get a couple of bananas from the shop across the street. How suddenly a car pulled up, the door opened and I was bodily dragged into the back-seat, and the car sped away. The rest of the story was that I was first taken somewhere and kept a prisoner, locked up and watched, and also tortured until I agreed to go through the exchange of garlands at the temple. My parents and their lawyer stood over me to sign the document, the old woman was asked to put her thumb impression as a witness to the kidnapping part of the story. At first I threw away the pen and wept and went without food, but my parents were firm. They kept saying: "No girl will be safe in this country unless we act. Young scamps like him must be taught a lesson." All my pleading was to no avail. Finally they broke my spirit, but assured me: "Nothing will happen to that scamp. Our lawyer will recommend clemency. All this is just to give him a fright, that's all."

"'Why?" I asked, "What has he done? He is my husband."

"'Husband! Husband!" they laughed, "Don't keep saying it. You'll be ruining your future! Some rascal—don't mention it outside."

'Then the lawyer added, "That sort of marriage is not valid my dear child…you are under eighteen."

'At every session of the hearing, the boy had to stand in the box and face the cross-examination. Being on bail, he could go back to his room or to work after attending court. His lawyer was, however, determined to save him. He got busy investigating and going into old records, located the Government Maternity Hospital where I was born and took extracts from the old registers to prove the hour and date of my birth. He proved that we were married at 3.30 in the afternoon of 18 May 1978, and my birth date and hour according to the hospital register was 11.30 a.m. and so it confirmed that at the time of my marriage I was eighteen years and three hours old, I had become a major with full power to decide my own course of life, and at the time of the so-called abduction, I was thirty minutes past eighteen years. Our lawyer demolished the prosecution's time scheme in a series of cross-examinations. I don't want to go into those details now as I may take time. To be brief, the court declared us properly married husband and wife.

'After the case I joined my husband and we established our home as I have already explained. In the course of time, forgotten were the police case and all the earlier bitterness and the feud. My parents once again doted on me. But the son-in-law could not accept the compromise. He refused to visit them or meet them—one point on which he would never yield, although he never interfered with my visiting my parents. He not only refused to visit them, but kept aloof and silent when they happened to come to see us at Poonamalle Road, always bringing some food or delicacy—but he never touched it in spite of my pleadings. I noticed a new development in him—he had become rather firm and hardened in his outlook. He brooded a great deal and seemed to have undergone a change of personality. It was not the trial and prosecution but my sworn statement read out at court that seemed to have shattered his faith. I could never forget the expression on his face when the lawyer read it out and I had to confirm it in public. Our wedded life had now acquired the dull routine of a fifty-year-old couple. I put it down to physical fatigue on his part, and did my best to cheer him and draw him out but only with partial success.'

I kept murmuring that I had to attend a function, but the Delhi woman continued. I almost expected her to say, 'With my crossbow I shot the albatross.' Instead of that she simply said, 'He didn't come home one evening—that was the end.' Her voice shook a little, and again she fumbled in her handbag for the tiny handkerchief. It was not a moment when I could leave. She could not stop her narration. Even if I left she would still be talking to the stars, which had come out, with the pale lantern of the railway station throwing an eerie illumination around. The goods train had arrived and lumbered along, but still she went on.

At some point when she paused for breath I resolutely got up murmuring, 'I'll have to go to a wedding reception, having missed the college socials.' She concluded, 'A man from our travel agency noticed him at the airport at the Kuwait Air counter. Through our associates at Kuwait I tried to get information about him, but they could not trace him. god only knows what he calls himself now. I seem to have lost him forever.'

The lady left the next day for Delhi. The station master became maudlin at the parting—a man who was used to seeing off hundreds of passengers each day in either direction, in a cold businesslike manner, had tears in his eyes when the engine pulled up.

'Great woman! She was welcome to stay any length of time—even if the inspector came, I'd have managed without disturbing her.'

His wife and children were there to bid her farewell. First time I noticed what a lot of children he had produced under his little roof. I suspected that the Delhi woman must have distributed liberally gifts and tips—not overlooking Muni.

When the engine whistled the lady took out of her handbag her card, and gave it to me remarking, 'Most important—I almost forgot it in this mela of leave-taking—although I suspect the masterji held up the train for full ten minutes.'

I accepted her card and promised, 'If I get the slightest clue I'll reach you by every means of communication possible.'

I found Rann moping and felt sorry for his lonely alienated existence. I declared with extra cheer, 'Time to be up and celebrate.'

'What?' he asked without much enthusiasm, thinking that it was a bit of a joke.

I said, 'The lady has left for Delhi by the 7 UP.'

'Are you serious?' he asked.

'Absolutely. Just an hour ago. My hands are still warm with all the handshakes. We all broke down at the parting.'

'Oh, where, where is she gone?'

'I've told you, Delhi. Not to the next station but far-off Delhi.'

He nearly jumped out of the easy chair. I said, 'Let us go out for a walk after a visit to the Boardless.'

'Where?' he asked without moving.

'To the river.'

'You have it at your backyard.'

'This is no good now; much better at Nallappa's Grove, beyond Ellamman Street.'

He hesitated at first. I talked him out of his reluctance. Finally he agreed. 'How should I dress?' he asked.

'Better tie a *dhoti* around your waist and wear a half-sleeve shirt.'

He had bought these recently at the Khadi Stores, made in handspun material.

'If you wear khadi, they'll respect you, take you for a nationalist, a follower of Mahatma Gandhi.'

'He was a great man,' he exclaimed irrelevantly.

'That's all right. Get ready, let us go.'

'I'm not used to a *dhoti*. I can't walk. It keeps slipping down to my ankles, can't make it stay around the waist.'

'All right, come in any dress you like… I'll wait outside.'

I sat on the *pyol* and waited for him. He had the sense to appear in a shirt and grey trousers, but still, when we went down Market Road, people looked at me, as if questioning, 'What is this oddity always keeping you company?'

'I feel uneasy when they stare at me.'

'No harm, better get used to it. I don't know what it is like in Timbuctoo, but here we don't mind staring, actually encourage it. It gives people a lot of pleasure. Why not let them please themselves that way? It costs nothing.'

He wouldn't say anything but fixed his gaze on the far-off horizon, looking at no one in particular.

I said, 'No one will mind if you stare at them in return. You miss a great deal by not staring. It's a real pleasure and an education, really.' He said nothing but took it as a sort of perverse quipping on my part, probably saying to himself, Cranky journalist. We reached Ellamman Street which dissipated into sand, beyond which the river curved away gently. People were sitting around in groups, students, children, old men, ancient colleagues and pensioners, young men hotly arguing, and of course also a peanut vendor going round crying his ware. On the main steps, people were washing clothes and bathing in the river, or reciting their evening prayers sitting cross-legged. I found a secluded spot near Nallappa's Grove where bullock carts and cattle were crossing. I selected a boulder for a seat so that Rann could be perched comfortably, while I sat down on the sand. The hum of Market Road reached us, but softly, over the chatter of birds settling down for the night in the trees. I realized that he was responding to the quality of the hour—the soft evening light with the rays of the setting sun touching the top branches of trees, the relaxed happy atmosphere with children running about and playing in the sand. He said all of a sudden, 'Have you noticed the kinship that seems to exist between sand and children? It's a feature that I have noticed all over the world—in every part of the globe, in any continent.'

I was happy to note his sudden eloquence. 'It's one of the things that unites mankind and establishes the sameness. Sand and children and this…' he said, all of a sudden stooping and pulling out a bunch of some tiny obscure vegetation from the ground. A plant that was hardly noticeable under any circumstance…a pale tuft of leaves and a stalk with little white flowers. His eyes acquired a new gleam—unseen normally. 'This is the future occupant of our planet,' he said in a tone of quiet conviction: 'This is a weed spreading under various aliases in every part of the earth—known in some places as Congress weed, don't know which congress is meant, Mirza Thorn, Chief's Tuft, Voodoo Bloom, the Blighter and so on. Whatever the name, it's an invader, may have originated out of the dust of some other planet left by a crashing meteor. I see it everywhere; it's a nearly indestructible pest. Its empire is insidiously growing—I have surveyed its extent and sent a memorandum to headquarters.'

I refrained from asking, Which headquarters? Like the word 'project' it's a tabloid word which needs no elucidation. He went on as if inspired: 'No one has found a weedicide capable of destroying it. They seem to go down at the first spraying, we tried it in Uganda, but a second generation come up immune to it… I have calculated through computers that, at the rate of its growth, the entire earth will be covered with it as the sole vegetation by about AD 3000. It'll have left no room for any other plant life; and man will starve to death as no other growth will be possible and this has no food value—on the contrary, it is a poison. You will notice that cattle don't touch it. In addition to other disservices, it sucks and evaporates all the ground water. We should call it the demon grass. My notes on this are voluminous—and the book, when it comes, will be a sensation.'

'What's your field of study?' I could not help asking. I suspected he was egging me on to do so, why not oblige him? I was feeling kindly toward him. I was softening. His outlandish style of living and dressing was fascinating. Why should I grudge him a little attention, a fellow who was giving me so much entertainment?

He seemed pleased at my query. 'Call it futurology—a general term which involves various studies. We have to make a proper assessment of all our resources and dangers; human as well as material. All kinds of things will have to go into it. We must get a scientific view and anticipate the conditions and state of life in AD 3000. To know whether we shall, as the human species, survive or not.'

I could not help bursting into a laugh. 'Personally, I wouldn't bother—what, ten centuries hence, none of us, even the most long-lived, will not be involved...so...'

'How do you know?' he asked. 'Present developments in biology and medicine may prolong life endlessly.'

'You crave for immortality. I don't care.'

'Whether you crave for it or not, that's not the question. We are moving in that direction willy-nilly, and it's important to assess how much of present civilization is going to survive...taking into consideration various conditions and symptoms.'

'You remind me of our psychology professor who used the words "tensions", "symptoms", and "trends" at least once every nine seconds, when I was a student.'

He didn't like my frivolous attitude and suddenly became silent.

The reason why I wanted to puncture this pompous fellow was this: the old man at the town hall library had a granddaughter who brought him a flask of coffee and some tiffin in a brass container at about three in the afternoon most days. The old man, who came after an early meal to the library before 10 a.m., faded progressively in his chair until the tiffin came, and if any of the readers at the library asked a question at that time, he barked out his reply and looked fierce. 'My fate has not decreed me a better life than sitting here guarding dusty volumes. Don't add to my troubles. If you don't see the book, it's not there, that's all... Go, go take your seat; don't stand here and block the air, please.' This would be his mood on the days when the girl came late, but generally she was punctual. At the sight of her, his face would relax. He would welcome her with a broad smile, and say, 'Baby, come, come! What have you brought me today?' The sight of her brought him endless joy. He would get up from the chair and say: 'You sit here, child—I'll come back.' He carried the little plastic handbag with the flask and tiffin packet to a back room, beyond which was a washroom with a tap. While he was gone the girl occupied his seat, and listened to the water running in the washroom and then stopping and, after an interval, running a second time, and she would know that he washed his hands before touching the tiffin and washed again after eating, and she would get up and vacate the seat for him as he returned, timing it all perfectly. As expected by her, he would reappear wiping his lips with a checked towel and beaming with contentment.

'Was it all right?'

'Yes, of course, can't be otherwise…'

'Grandmother got sugar from the neighbour. We had run out.'

'Tell her, I'll buy some this evening on my way home.' The girl was about seventeen years old. He called her 'baby' and derived a special joy in thinking of her, watching her come and go, and talking to her. She was at Albert Mission in the BA class. Tall, and though not a beauty, radiated the charm of her years.

Rann came into the library one afternoon when the girl was occupying the chair. Just then I was rummaging in the old newspaper sheets on the central table, searching for some information, what it was I forget now. I was at the newspaper end of the hall and he didn't notice me, but I could see him as he approached the table and halted his steps, with all his faculties alert and tense like a feline coming upon its unsuspecting prey.

Ah! he seemed to say, I didn't know that the Town Hall library possessed this treasure! Is that old fellow gone and my good fortune has put you in his place? He greeted the girl with an effusive, ceremonious bow, and put on an act—of the most winsome manner. I wanted to cry out, Keep away, you— I don't know what to call you! She is young enough to be your daughter. You are a lecherous demon and wouldn't mind even if it were a granddaughter! Keep off!

The girl said something and both of them laughed. I wished the old man would come back from his lunch, back to his seat. But he was in the habit of reclining on an easy chair and shutting his eyes for fifteen minutes. It was generally a calm hour at the library and he left the girl to take care of things for a while, which seemed to be a god-sent chance for Rann. I felt it was time to apply the brake. I folded the newspaper, put it away, got up, and approached the table. The girl cried from the table, 'Uncle, here is an interesting gentleman from Timbuctoo. I didn't know there was such a place! Where is it?'

'Ask him,' I said, not ready to be involved in a geographical problem.

Rann rose to the occasion. He took a few steps to the table and demanded, 'Get a piece of paper. I'll show you.' On the blank sheet, with a stylish slim gold pen, he drew a map. When he said, 'You see this is where we are. Timbuctoo is—' the girl brought her face close to his. I'm sure he was casting a spell at that moment, for it seemed to me that the girl was relishing the smell of the after-shave lotion and hair-cream, which, I suspected, made him irresistible to women. He knew it and turned it on fully. With his palm resting on the map, he manoeuvred and agitated his forefinger and middle finger as if playing on a musical instrument, to indicate places, volubly explaining historical, topographical, economic matters of Timbuctoo in detail; he looked up from time to time to ask, in a sort of intimate whisper, Now do you understand? I feared that he was going too far, rather too close to her, when the old man reappeared with the plastic bag in hand, the very picture of contentment, and threw a kindly look at the visitor. He was not overwhelmed by the other's personality as on the first day since Rann was no longer in a three-piece suit but had adapted himself to a normal Malgudi executive costume, cotton pants and shirt-sleeves. The girl rose to give up her seat to her grandfather, who lowered himself in the chair saying, 'Long time since we met, how have you been, sir?'

'Thanks,' Rann said with a bow. I noted how accomplished an act he was putting on. He was versatile—one moment to impress the girl and patronize her and take her under his wing—so solicitous, kindly in tone—the world of the fairytales, the next moment the international scholar academician adopting his manner to impress the old man—on whose goodwill he would have to depend in order to get closer to the girl.

And there were other reports I was getting about Rann from here and there that I did not like at all. At the Boardless, Gundu Rao, a horticulturist (in municipal service and responsible for maintaining the nominal park around the Town Hall, the struggling lawns at the Central Police Station and the Collector's Office, and for seeing that the fountain sprayed up and rose to the occasion on national festivities such as Gandhiji's birthday and Independence Day), approached my table to whisper: 'Want to tell you something...'

Varma who was watching us said, 'What secret?'

Rao simpered and replied, 'Nothing important.'

Varma having to listen to so much all day left us alone. When I had finished the coffee, I found the horticulturist waiting in the street, leaning on his bicycle. He said, 'That man in your house. Who's he?'

'Why?' I asked, resenting his method of inquiry.

'You see...you know the Protestant Cemetery far out on Mempi Road?'

'Yes, though I have had nothing to do with it.'

'I have been asked to trim the hedges and some of the border plants. The Collector called me and told me to take it up—I don't know why this interest in the cemetery, not my business, really, but I must obey orders.'

'Naturally, but you were trying to say something else?'

'Ah, yes, about that man who is living with you. I notice him often there, sitting on a far-off bench in a corner—always with a girl at his side. I know who she is, but I won't tell you. That place is at least five miles out—it's my fate to cycle that distance everyday—such a strain really—but if I don't go the old gardener who lives in a shed won't do a thing and the Collector will come down on us, though I can't understand what the Collector has to do with the cemetery!'

'All right, tell me more about that man.'

'Well, I wondered why they had come so far and how; but then

I noticed a scooter parked at the gate—and he rides down with the girl sitting at his back—as they do nowadays. Not my business really, when a man and a woman sit close to each other, I generally stay away—it makes me uncomfortable—'

And then Nafaraj, manager of the Royal Theatre, met me at the magistrates' court veranda and said, 'You don't come to my theatre at all, why? I have improved the seating and upholstered the sofas, with foam rubber cushions and nylon covers—why don't you drop in some time and write a few words about our improvements? We are showing a picture with a karate expert acting in it. Full house, every show, I tell you. Your guest reserved two sofas in the balcony a couple of days ago. He appreciated the new designs and furnishing—coming from one who has seen the world—'

And Jayaraj, the photographer at the Market Arch, who is really the main reservoir of local gossip (with several tributaries pouring in about people and their doings), where I generally stop to know what's happening everywhere, said, 'Your guest is very active nowadays. He used to hire a cycle from Kennedy, but that poor fellow has lost the regular customer. You know why? Because Sambu seems to have surrendered his Vespa scooter to him freely. You know why the scooter for the gentleman?'

'Because he has a pillion rider?'

'You know who it is?'

'Yes, yes, I guess.'

'And so that's that! He is very attentive to the girl,' he added with a leer. He was in his element with gossip of this stature in hand. 'You know what his routine is? At 10.30 he is ready behind the Town Hall compound, as 10.35 the girl materializes on the pillion of Sambu's Vespa, 10.45 Kismet Ice-Cream Stall at New Extension, 10.58 at the level-crossing so that she may walk up to the Albert Mission College gate as if she had come walking all the way. After the college she is met again at the level-crossing—and where they go after that is their business, don't ask me.'

Others also mentioned the subject—each in his own way. The old man at the library, during one of my morning visits, said, 'I see very little of Baby nowadays. She used to bring my tiffin, but I walk home for my tiffin nowadays, leaving the watch to some known person in the reading room. Obliging fellows really—some of the old library users. I even take a few minutes' nap after tiffin and come back. But Baby never comes home before eight nowadays—final year for her and special classes and joint studies every day, I suppose. Nice to think she will be a graduate soon. Then what? Up to her parents to decide. But you know my son-in-law is not a clear-headed fellow—too much of a rustic and farmer and his wife, my daughter, has developed almost like her husband although I had visions of marrying her to a city man in Madras or Calcutta, but this fellow was rich and was studying at Madras and I thought he would pass a civil service exam, but the fellow settled in their village when his father passed away—and now his mind is full of cowdung and its disposal, and a gobar gas plant which utilizes it. He and his wife can talk of nothing else—but gas, gas, gas, which lights their stoves and lights everything. Baby, when she goes to her parents for a holiday, cannot stand that life though I insist upon her spending at least ten days with her parents—I brought her away when she was ten so that she could have her education. After she finishes her college, what? That's the question that bothers me day and night. I'd like her to become an officer somewhere—but not too far away. Also I want her to marry and be happy—and again stay not too far away from me. I'm so accustomed to her presence—my wife too says we should not live too far away from her. Anyway let us see what god proposes.'

At this point an old reader approached us to ask, 'The tenth page of the *Mail* is missing.'

'What's special in it?'

'Crosswords,' the man said.

The old man replied, 'I suspected so.' He took it out of his drawer and gave it with the warning, 'Copy it down, don't mark on the paper.'

I bottled up my uneasiness at these reports. I had no clear notion what I could do about the situation or why. It was not my business, I said to myself, but then I began to have suspicions about Rann's background. Before tackling him, I wanted to arm myself with facts. I had no other recourse but to act as a spy. These days he went out after breakfast and kept away till lunch, came in and went out again. I realized that his movements were based on Girija's timetable. When he left in the afternoon I could count on his absence all evening till eight o'clock or longer. I opened his room with a duplicate key. When I stepped in I felt like a burglar in my own home. I felt excited and hard-pressed for time. I quickly examined his briefcase and a portfolio of letters—quite a handful. Envelopes addressed to different names—only two to Rann—and the address was always Poste Restante in different towns and countries. Like our gods, he seemed to have a thousand names—Ashok, Naren, D'Cruz, John, Adam, Shankar, Sridhar, Singh and Iqbal and what not. The letters were all from women: imploring, appealing, and accusing and attacking in a forthright manner; some of them were intensely passionate, from Mary, Rita, Nancy, Manju, Kamala, and so on. One or two had been addressed to Dubai or Kuwait, and forwarded from place to place. And there were some from Roja herself, who somehow managed to reach him. There was a common feature in every letter: the cry of desertion. A few blackmail attempts, some threats to inform the police and set Interpol on his track. You would have needed a world map to mark his movements as deduced from the postmarks and the various postage stamps—quite an album could be made with stamps from his envelopes. No wonder he had so many pursuing him, but unable to get at him. 'You are heartless—a monster, don't you have a feeling for the child you pampered, who is crying for you night and day? How can he understand the perfidy of your action in melting into the night without even a farewell kiss?' Another letter said, 'Come back, that's enough for me. I'll forget the money.' In another, 'You need not come—if you appear at my door, I'll throw you out. Only return the share due to me—at least 20,000 pesos and you may go to the devil. If you ignore this, I'll write an anonymous letter to the Interpol.' This last made me wonder if he was a drug trafficker too. He had a way of slipping away from address to address: it puzzled me why he left any postal addresses at all, and was not afraid of being discovered while collecting mail. He must have had a pathological desire to collect letters and preserve them. This was rather puzzling. Why would any man treasure such correspondence?—enough to damn him and send him to prison. Extraordinary man! I admired on one side his versatile experience, indifference and hardihood. What was the great driving force in his life? I picked up a fat bound book, which seemed to be a journal written from time to time. I was nervous about going through it. If I sat reading it, I might not notice the time passing and he might come back. And so I hurriedly gave it a glance, opening a page here and there. Why this man perpetuated his misdeeds in chronicles was beyond my understanding. On one leaf he noted, 'No use hanging on here. S is proving impossible. No woman supposes that a man has any better business than cuddling and love talk.' Another entry said, 'My project is all important to me. I am prepared to abandon everything and run away if it is interrupted. Again and again I seem to fall into the same trap like a brainless rat. It is difficult at this stage to make others see the importance of my book—which has to go side by side with the project even if it is only an offshoot. The world will be shaken when the book is out. The highest award in the world may not be beyond my dream.' He noted on another sheet, 'Your Majesty, King Gustav and Queen, Members of the Nobel Committee—I'm receiving this award, I feel you are honouring my country. India and Sweden have much in common culturally.' I heard the hall clock chime five, and quickly put all the letters and diary back in their original place in the drawer, shut the drawer, locked it as before and quickly and quietly withdrew, leaving no thumb impression on anything.

'What do you think of that girl?' I asked him innocently one day.
'Which girl?' he asked.
'Girija—the librarian's granddaughter, whom he calls Baby.'
'I don't know,' he said, 'I don't know her very well—though I see her here and there—especially at her school whenever I go there to see one of the professors. Now that you ask, she is quite smart, and will go far with proper training. But this place is no good for her.

She must get out of this backwood, if you don't mind my saying it.'

I was rather irked. 'But you seem to prefer this to a lot of other places in the world.'

'My job is different—but for a young mind starting in life, a more modern, urban, cultural feedback will help. My private view is, don't quote me, from what I have seen, she shouldn't grow up with her grandfather. A hostel would be preferable—where she can compare and compete with her age group. Anyway after her final exam in March, she should decide her future.'

'Marriage?'

'Oh, no, not necessarily, though I would not rule it out. A girl can be married and still pursue intellectual and social values. But the important thing is she should get out of this—'

'Backwood.' I completed his sentence. He only smiled. Impossible to fathom his mind's workings.

The old librarian said, 'Girija is lucky. That man has agreed to coach her through. He seems to be an expert in certain subjects. What do you think of it?"

I hesitated. It was a complex situation. I did not know how far the old man was aware of the situation. In his zeal to see his granddaughter well placed he might welcome Rann's proposal. I couldn't understand anything until I could speak to Girija, but it had become impossible to get at her, though formerly I always enjoyed a little banter with her at the library. Now I remained silent while the old man waited for my comment. One or two at the reading-room table paused, looked up and turned in our direction expectantly. I said to the old man to put the eavesdroppers off the track, 'It's getting unusually warm these days—' and left, at which the inquisitive souls at the long table looked disappointed and resumed their reading.

I returned to the library at closing time with the definite objective of talking to the old man when others would not be there. The old man was closing the windows, pushing the chairs back into position, and giving a final look around before locking the door.

'What brings you here at this hour?' he asked.

'I was passing this way and I thought I might as well stop by. I'll walk with you.'

He tucked his old umbrella under his arm, its bamboo handle dark yellow with the age-old contact with his fingers, and strode off. I pushed my bicycle along. He lived nearby—fifteen minutes away—at old Palm Grove, in a small house with its broad cement platforms overlooking the street. All the way down he was talking of Girija and her future, which seemed to be very bright. I dropped the idea of warning him about Rann. I felt I'd be making myself unpopular if I spoke against Rann.

He invited me in. I leaned the bicycle against a lamp post and sat down on the *pyol*. He excused himself and went in for a wash, and came back drying himself with a towel and bade me come in, and settled down in the easy chair. He had hung up his upper cloth on a nail and the shirt over it, his bare body covered with the towel.

'Only two of us in this house—and Baby, you see that's her room. You may peep in if you like.' To please him, I went in and dutifully peeped. She had a small table on which were heaped her books and papers, and clothes, on a little stand, again in a heap. On the wall she had pasted up some portraits of film stars and one or two gods also; on the latter she had stuck flowers. A small window opened on the next house; there was only a small bulb throwing a dim light. 'She always studies in the hall, sitting on the floor with her books spread about,' complained the old gentleman. 'Not a soul in the house to disturb her. When she is reading I tiptoe around, and her grandmother doesn't dare raise her voice. Our only interest is to see her pass with distinction, and she must get a Government of India scholarship too.'

Meanwhile his wife who had gone to a neighbour's came back. He introduced me to her as the host of the distinguished foreigner, and added, 'He is a Kabir Street man. They are not ordinary men there.' He gave a grand account of my ancestors.

The venerable lady added her own knowledge of my family members, traced various relationships, and also claimed kinship with one of my aunts, whom I had never heard of. She said: 'You are really fortunate to have a guest of such distinction. Good guests really bring us honour. There was a time when I used to cook and feed with my own hands any number of men and women, not here but in our original home at Gokulam. Well, we had to move here—that was god's will. My daughter was not married at that time—Girija was born in this house when we lost that house—'

'Why do you tire the gentleman with that old tale?'

None the less she continued: 'My husband was the registrar of the District Court—'

'Don't be absurd. I was only a sheristedar, not the registrar. I've corrected you a hundred times.'

'What if! You had so much money coming in every day and so many visitors—no one would come bare-handed. We had no need to go to the market for anything: vegetables and fruits or rice—'

'Friendly people all round in those days,' he explained.

I understood what this meant: a court sheristedar had favours to dispense in the shape of judgement copies, court-orders and so on, and he favoured court-birds in his own way.

The old man did not feel comfortable and tried to change the topic. 'Only after I retired did I take up the library work—convenient, being close to this house. When I hesitated, the judge who started the reading room, whose portrait is on the wall beside Sir Frederick Lawley's, compelled me to accept it, as a sort of social service. On the opening occasion—it was a grand function—he also referred to me in his speech.'

I suspected the judge accepted bribes chanelled through the sheristedar. 'I must have been in high school at that time,' I added.

The lady said, apropos nothing, 'Dr Rann came here a couple of days ago. Girija brought him. He is such a simple man—absolutely without conceit—considering his status. He has held such great posts in so many countries—knows so much! I could have listened to him all night! His conversation is so absorbing, but my husband felt sleepy—I insisted the distinguished visitor have food here, and he enjoyed it, though our fare was simple and we couldn't give him porcelain dishes or a spoon. He ate with his fingers! Only thing, he could not sit on the floor like us.'

When I got back home, I saw the light in Rann's room. I had an impulse to go and demand an explanation as to what game he was trying to play, to warn him to keep off, and not to add one more desperate correspondent to his files. But I felt doubts about my own understanding of the situation. I might be misreading the whole scene. After all, he must have seen enough women, and Girija might mean no more to him than a niece of whom he was growing fond and whom he would like to see develop academically so that she might have a worthy career. The old couple seemed to have developed a worshipful attitude to Rann. They might misunderstand if I said anything contrary to their views; it might seem as if I had evil motives or was envious of the girl's good luck. They might turn round and say, None of your business...we know. And I could not very well reveal Rann's private affairs. If he walked out of my house it might give rise to public talk, and perhaps compromise the girl and cause an innocent family embarrassment and scandal. I might be misreading the whole situation. After all, a child whom I had been seeing for years, since her Albert-Mission-Nursery-School-uniform days, but now too tall for her age, dressed in perfectly starched and pressed cotton saree and looking quite smart, this wouldn't mean that she was an adult woman capable of devious and dubious adventure. She might well still be a child at heart, like most womanly-looking girls. But if so why the Protestant Church rendezvous? That didn't seem so innocent. If he was only helping her studies and general knowledge, it was not necessary to go so far... Lying in bed I kept sifting and analysing and finding justifications and overcoming doubts and suspicions about Girija and Rann, till I fell asleep well past midnight.

Our Lotus Club was twenty-five years old, and we decided to celebrate its silver jubilee with a grand public lecture at the Town Hall by Dr Rann of the United Nations, on a brand new subject, 'futurology'. Rann somehow accepted the proposal when I mentioned it. He said, 'Normally I have an aversion to public speaking. I am a writer, not a speaker. However, you have been good to me, and I can't say no to you. I must oblige you.' This was on the day following our evening on the river sand when he had expounded to me his theory of the cosmic extinction of all life through the Giant Weed.

The Lotus Club was desperately in need of a show to boost its prestige, but more than prestige, the Lotus Club had sufficient funds to spend on an occasional burst of activity, and a rich man, decades before, had left an endowment and special fund for the silver jubilee. The President, who had been rusting, readily agreed. He was proud to have an international personality to deliver the jubilee lecture and on a subject that was so mysterious: 'futurology'. 'Everyone knows what astrology, physiology and zoology are, but no one knows about "futurology". I am agog to hear this lecture.'

He wanted me to print a brochure entitled 'Lotus Twenty-five Years of Public Service' and distribute it in the hall, also several thousand handbills announcing the meeting, and five hundred special invitations printed on decorated cards to be mailed to India's President, Prime Minister, the editors of national newspapers, every VIP of the land. Nothing could appeal to me more than this activity.

At the Truth Printing Works, the printer Nataraj cleared a corner of the press for me. I sat there in the morning writing up the pages of the jubilee brochure, arranging the invitations and notices; hot from my desk, the matter was passed to the printer. Nataraj had set aside his routine work and devoted all his energy and time to this task. I felt happy and fulfilled, being so active, and was already worried at the back of my mind as to how I would stand the dull days ahead when all this activity should cease.

The President of the Lotus Club was one Mr Ganesh Rao, a pensioner now but at one time a judge of the Supreme Court at Delhi. My day started with a visit to his bungalow at Lawley Extension. A gracious elder of the community who looked like Lloyd George or Einstein with white locks falling on his nape, he was a prized possession of our town—the citizens remarked with awe and gratitude that after decades of distinguished service at Delhi, Kashmir, and even at some international courts, he should have chosen to return to the town of his origin.

Gaffur the taxi driver, whose Ambassador always occupied a position of vantage beside the Fountain Wall on the Market Road—except at train time when it could be seen under the Gul Mohar tree at the railway station—was the man I was desperately searching for before the big meeting. I had to go round town distributing invitations and notices and on various other errands in connection with the meeting. I had so much to do that I felt the need for a transport quicker than my bicycle or Sambu's scooter, if available.

Gaffur was not to be seen. I had to go in search of him here and there. No one was able to guide me. I was pressed for time; the day of the jubilee was drawing near. As ever, Jayaraj came to my rescue. He said, 'He lives in Idgah—one of those houses. I'll find out and leave word on my way home tonight.'

Gaffur's Ambassador was at my door the next morning. He left the car at the street corner and came to my room while I was shaving before my ancient mirror. 'Madhu, you want me?' he asked, being one of the boyhood associates who called me Madhu instead of TM. My face was still full of soap. I spoke to him looking from the mirror.

'Gaffur! Where have you been all these days? You have become scarce—and I want you so badly for the next week.'

'Madhu, your tenant is the one who keeps me busy. I have to be at his call every morning. I don't call for him here, he doesn't want it that way, but he hails me at the fountain almost at the same hour each day at about ten-thirty, and then he leaves me at five o'clock, after I have returned that girl.'

'Which girl? Where do you take her?'

'I think they are going to marry—the way they are talking in the back-seat and planning, he is taking her to America...though it is none of my business, I can't help listening.'

'Oh, god!' I cried, involuntarily blowing off the soap on my lips.

'Why do you worry, Madhu? Is it that you want to marry her yourself?'

'Oh, god!' I cried a second time. 'I've known her since she was a baby, and she is like a daughter to me.'

'So what?' he said. 'You must be happy that she found a nice man for a husband. Otherwise you'd have to spend so much money to get her a husband. After all, in your community, unlike ours, girls are free to go out without a veil and talk to men—and so what is wrong?'

'He is old enough to be her granduncle.'

'I won't agree with you. He is very sweet, looks like a European… Good man, pays down by the meter without a word, a gentleman. If there were more like him, I could buy a Rolls Royce or a Mercedes Benz.'

I left it at that. I learnt a great deal from Gaffur that morning. I had also noticed the past two days that Rann was packing up; and had settled with the furniture company to cart their pieces away after the Jubilee meeting. The plot was revealed by Gaffur: after the meeting at the Town Hall he was to pick up Rann's suitcases from my house, meet Rann at the Town Hall, then drive away to Peak House on Mempi Hills the same night, with the girl, who would be waiting some place. From Peak House they would descend on the other side of the mountain to Mempi Town, and then leave by bus to god knows where. I was shocked by the smooth manner in which Rann was manoeuvring to elope with the girl.

Gaffur's report was invaluable. I had to base my future action on it, but I realized I was facing a delicate situation. I had to avoid upsetting anyone on any side. The old librarian must be protected from shock or a stroke, Girija from a public scandal and an eventual desertion in some far-off place and all the frustration and tragedy that befell every woman captivated by Rann's charms. My mind wandered over morbid details as to how far the girl had admitted him; when it was all over, one must somehow take her to Dr Lazarus, the lady doctor at the Government Hospital, to get her examined for a possible abortion, a lesser evil than being burdened with a fatherless child. While the other women in Rann's life were perhaps hardy and sophisticated, capable of withstanding the tragedy, this girl was innocent, her mind in a nascent state, unless already complicated and corrupted by association with Rann. It was not a good sign that she was lying to her simple-minded grandfather. I doubted if she cared for her studies at all nowadays; Rann might have promised any degree she chose from any university on earth. I could well imagine his boastful assurance, 'Oh, you leave it to me—I'll speak to Turnbull, president of…when we get to the United States.' His voice rang in my ears with this sort of assurance, and the picture came before me of this girl looking up at him adoringly. I luxuriated in a passing vision of slapping this girl for her stupidity. And shutting her up in a room and kicking out Rann, but on the other hand Rann had to be kept in good humour. If he was upset and backed out and vanished, I'd be hounded out of Malgudi by its worthy citizens for being fooled with all that trumpeting about the Town Hall lecture. Sitting in the meditation room after Gaffur left, I brooded and brooded and came to the conclusion not to speak about anything till the meeting was over. I would pretend not to notice Rann's packing up either.

It was an inspiration. I moved out of the meditation room and rummaged in my desk till I picked up the pocket diary in which I remembered placing the address card of the lady from Delhi. At first it eluded my search—all kinds of other cards, addresses and slips of paper fell out from between the leaves. I almost despaired, then gave a final shake and her yellow card fell out—'Commandant Sarasa, Home Guards Women's Auxiliary, Delhi', with her address, telephone, and telex numbers. I hurried to the post office and sent off a telegram.

COME IMMEDIATELY. YOUR HUSBAND FOUND. COME BEFORE HE IS LOST AGAIN. YOUR ONLY FINAL CHANCE TO ROPE HIM. STAY RAILWAY WAITING ROOM. I'VE FIXED IT. TAKE CARE NOT TO BE SEEN IN TOWN. WILL MEET AND EXPLAIN FURTHER PROCEDURE.

The strategy was perfect.

I had to soften the station master again with a five-rupee note, and he promised to entertain the lady royally in the waiting room as before. I expected her to arrive on the eve of the jubilee meeting at the Town Hall, when Rann would be preoccupied with both his romantic plans and his preparations for the lecture, now of course facilitated by having Gaffur's taxi at his disposal. I was in suspense while I waited for the train from Madras, but it did not bring the lady in.

The second train, from Trichy, also disappointed me. No sign of her. However, she arrived late that night by road from Trichy, where she had flown from Delhi. Her car was parked in the station compound. She woke up the station master and got the waiting room opened.

Having been busy the whole day with a hundred things to do before the meeting, I found time to go to the station master's house only at midnight and was relieved to learn that the lady had arrived. I didn't want to spend any more time at the station. I gave him another token of esteem in cash, as well as a sealed envelope addressed to the Commandant to be delivered to her without fail in the morning. I also gave him a VIP invitation card to attend the Lotus Club meeting, which pleased him tremendously.

My letter, which I had composed under great strain, gave the lady precise instruction as to what she should do next.

The extraordinary publicity generated by the Lotus Club brought in a big crowd. On the day of the meeting, the Town Hall auditorium was packed. The organizers were plucky enough to have organized a Deputy Minister to preside, which meant that the local officials could not stay away. The police and security arrangements were spectacular. The Deputy Minister was in charge of Town Planning, Cattle Welfare, Child Welfare, Family Planning, Cooperation and Environment, Ecology and other portfolios too numerous even for him to remember. In Delhi he had six different buildings for his offices and files.

The President of the Lotus Club had written a letter to him requesting him to grace the occasion, and he had readily agreed. Being the most ubiquitous minister one could think of, every day the newspapers carried reports of his movements. Malgudi had been rather left out of his official circuits, but now it was coming on the official map, much to the satisfaction of the townsfolk.

When the meeting began, the foot-lights came on. The minister was seated at the centre of the stage in a high-back gilded chair; Rann was seated on his right in a not so high and less gilded chair; and three other chairs were occupied by the President of the Lotus (ex-judge of the Supreme Court) and two other factotums. I was given a seat at right angles to this main row as became the press and also because I was really the creator of the entire function. Behind the minister sat his secretary and behind him a uniformed orderly in a high-rise glittering lace-edged turban.

The hall was packed, as I noted from my position of vantage; students, lawyers, businessmen and a motley crowd of men and women, mostly wives of government officials. A lot of noisy children ran around chasing each other. The organizers were kept busy trying to catch and immobilize them, but the little devils were elusive and ran behind and between the chairs. The distinguished men seated on the dais looked away and tried not to notice, but the ex-judge beckoned to an executive and whispered, 'Can nothing be done to quieten these children?'

Whereupon the man went up to the women and said, 'Please control your children.'

A woman retorted haughtily: 'Tell their mothers, not me.'

'Where are the mothers?' No answer came. The man was helpless and felt foolish and lost. He caught hold of a boy and whispered to him: 'They are distributing sweets over there,' pointing outside, and the boy turned round and ran out gleefully, followed by all the other children. 'Children from the neighbourhood, not ours,' explained someone.

The ex-judge rapped on the table with a paperweight, took a gulp of water from the glass, and began, 'We are honoured by the presence of the Honourable Minister.' He elaborated the minister's role in building up a first-rate nation. This presentation took twenty-five minutes. He devoted two minutes to Rann the main speaker today, about whom he did not have much to say, and hurried on to call upon the Hon'ble Minister to speak. The minister, a seasoned orator, clutched the microphone expertly, drew it to his lips, and began:

'My respected elders, the noble mothers of the land, and the distinguished brethren here, we have in our midst a distinguished scholar who has come from afar and has dedicated his life to...' He fumbled for the right word and paused for a second to look at a piece of paper. 'Futurology,' he went on. 'You may ask what is futurology. The speaker of this evening is going to tell us about it. I should leave it to him to explain his subject. I'll only confine myself to what Jawaharlal Nehru said once—' He somehow twisted the context of futurism, and whatever meaning it might have, to an anecdote centring around Jawaharlal. And then he explained Mahatma Gandhi's philosophy. 'In those days,' he reminisced, 'I was a *batcha*, but serving our motherland in some capacity, however humble, was my only aim in life, inspired by our leaders and encouraged by them. I was always in the presence of Mahatmaji wherever he camped, and of course Jawaharlal was always with him and so were many of our distinguished patriots and leaders. Though I was a *batcha* Mahatmaji and Nehruji encouraged me to be with them, and if I count for anything today, I owe it to their affection and if I have served our motherland in any capacity, it's through their grace.' He managed to add a mention of Lord Mountbatten also as one of his gurus, and then he came back to Mahatmaji and explained how two days before his death, Gandhiji had said to him, 'My inner voice tells me that my end is near,' and how he, the future Deputy Minister, broke down on hearing this and implored him not to say such things, whereupon Gandhiji said, 'Yesterday at the prayer meeting at Birla's house; were you present? Didn't you notice a group at the gate? I could infer what they were saying...'

At this point I noticed a couple of old men nodding in their seats, lulled to sleep by the minister's voice. I looked at our well-groomed Rann in the full regalia of his Oxford blue three-piece suit—he, too, was bored with the minister's rambling talk. He kept gazing at the typed sheets as if wondering if he would have a chance at all to lecture. The minister had gone on for an hour without a scrap of written material, sentences spewing out without interruption. Those who were familiar with his speeches would have understood that as a routine he narrated the Mahatma Gandhi episode at the conclusion. But most of the assembly was unaware of this and now despaired whether they were fated to listen to this man until midnight.

From out of the student group was heard a voice saying, 'We want to hear the speaker of this evening.' Undaunted by this request, accustomed as he was to hecklers in parliament, the minister retorted cheerfully, 'You are right. I'm also anxious to hear our friend on the subject of—' He had to refer again to the piece of paper. 'But let me finish what I was saying. You'll find it relevant to the subject today.' And he went on to talk about the importance of rural handicrafts. After fifteen minutes, while his hecklers looked resigned to their fate, he sat down. Then he whispered to Rann at his side: 'I'd like to read your speech in the papers tomorrow, I'm sure. Now I've another meeting at Bagal, people will be waiting. Have to finish and drive to Trichy airport—must be back in Delhi tonight. So you will excuse me...' When he half inclined his head, his aide stood up and took charge of the minister's garland, bestowed earlier by the ex-judge, and they left abruptly.

Rann came to the microphone after a formal introduction and abruptly began: 'As you are all aware how near disaster we are—'

'No, not yet,' said a heckler in the audience. 'Not heard the worst yet. Do go on.'

Unperturbed, Rann read on, holding up a warning finger all through. 'Man was born free and everywhere he is in chains, Rousseau said.'

'No, Voltaire,' said the heckler.

'One or the other, it doesn't matter. It's time we noticed our chains, invisible though they may be, these chains are going to drag us down to perdition unless we identify them in good time, and those chains and fetters which are imperceptible now will overwhelm—'

'That's all right; we'll call the blacksmith to file them off. Now go on with your story.'

From another group a man shouted, 'Throw this wag out. He is disturbing the meeting. Don't mind sir, please go on.' At this point a scuffle ensued, and the heckler was dragged out of the hall by a couple of strong men. They came back and said generously to Rann: 'Please go on sir, don't mind the disturbance; that fellow disturbs any and every meeting.'

Rann resumed his reading. He had the theatricality of a Seventh-day Adventist. His voice rose and fell as in a sort of declamation. He hissed and snorted, sighed and screamed according to the theme of the drama he was developing. The theme was the collapse of this planet about AD 3000. When he described, holding aloft a specimen, how the tuft of a grass-like vegetation, an obstinate weed, was going to overrun the earth, people watched without response. But then he went on to say: 'This looks insignificant, like the genie within a bottle. Take out the cork and you will see the dimension to which it can grow,' and described its tough, persistent growth, told about how by AD 2500 half the surface of the globe would be covered up.

'It's a cannibal, in certain places along the Amazon it is actually called the Cannibal Herb, which nomenclature was at first mistaken to mean food for the cannibals, but actually means that it fattens itself on other plants. Where it appears no other plant can grow. It swallows every scrap of vegetation near at hand, root, stalk and leaf, it quenches its thirst by sapping up groundwater however deep the water-table may be. I have in my collection a specimen—a wire-like root three hundred feet long when it was pulled out. Under a microscope at the root-terminal were seen sacs to suck up water. Ultimately no water will be left underground, in rivers or in the sea, when billions of such sacs are drawing up water and evaporating them at the surface.

'Scientists, biologists, biochemists are secretly working on formulations that would eliminate this weed. Secretly because they do not want to create a scare. But the weed develops resistance to any chemical or bacteria and in a second generation that particular culture has no effect. Actually any weedicide acts as nutrition for it. Does this not remind us of the demon in our stories whose drop of blood shed on the ground gave rise to a hundred other demons?'

He went on and on thus and then he came to a further menace: 'Are you aware that for one citizen there are eight rats in our country, which means that only one-eighth of the food produced is available for legitimate consumption—'

'What is legitimate consumption?' shouted a voice from the back of the hall. 'Have rats no right to eat? They also are creatures of this earth like any of us.'

The chuckers realized that the interrupter they had thrown out was back in the hall somewhere, though he could not be spotted.

Someone else cried, 'Don't mind him, doctor, go on…a crackpot has smuggled himself in.'

'I'm no crackpot but also a scholar. I'm a Ph.D.'

The chuckers stood up to locate the speaker. There was a slight disturbance. Some of those in the audience who felt bored edged their way towards the door. Rann stood puzzled. I whispered to him, 'Why do you pay attention to these things, go on, go on.'

He continued, 'There are dozens of such problems facing us today,' and then elaborated for the next forty-five minutes all the things that menaced human survival. Ghastly predictions. His voice reached a screaming pitch when he declared, 'The rats will destroy our food stock and the weed will devour everything, including the rats, and grow to gigantic heights although rising in our present observation only at the rate of a tenth of a millimetre per decade, but it will ultimately rise to gigantic heights sticking out of our planet skyward, so that an observer from another planet will notice giant weeds covering the surface of the globe like bristles, having used all the water. If the observer peered closer with his infra-red giant telescope, he would find millions and billions of skeletons of humans and animals strewn about providing bone-meal for this monstrous and dreadful vegetation…'

At this point a scream was heard, 'Ah, what is to happen to our grandchildren?'

'The lady has fainted. Get a doctor someone.'

People were crowding round a woman who had fallen down from her chair. They were splashing water on her face and fanning her.

'Give her air, don't crowd.'

Someone was saying soothingly, when she revived, 'After all, madam, it'll only be in AD 3000. Not now.'

'What if?' she retorted.

Another woman was saying, 'We don't want to perish in this manner—our children must be saved.'

At the sound of the word 'children' the fainted lady who had just revived let out a wail and screamed again, 'Oh, the children! Take them away somewhere to safety.' Many other women began to moan in sympathy and tried to rush out of the hall clutching their children, while the children themselves resisted and howled playfully. 'Come away, this place is cursed—not safe. Oh, come away.' Several men tried to calm the women down, saying, 'Be calm, it will happen only one thousand years later, no danger immediately.'

'Who are you to say so? What authority have you to say so? It may happen today.'

People were on their feet and the assembly was in complete disarray. The ex-judge, who had escorted the Deputy Minister, strayed out and ultimately disappeared. So did the police. Various spirited young men lifted and smashed the folding chairs. People rushed to the exit in confusion.

'Cobra! A cobra is crawling under the chair! Take care!' a mischievous urchin shouted.

'Where? Where?' People hoisted themselves on benches and chairs. The smashed chairs were collected, heaped up outside and set on fire. Someone switched off the hall lights in the pandemonium, though somehow the stage lights were still on. A gang of toughs approached the dais, armed with the legs and remnants of the splintered chairs and shouted, 'Down with—'

While Rann continued to sit stupidly watching the show as if gratified with the preview of the cataclysm he forecast, I tugged him up by his collar, crying, 'Come out, you fool, before they kill you.'

'Why? Why?' he asked. I dragged him out to the back of the stage, pushed open a door, propelled him into the darkness at the rear of the Town Hall, and led him out to an open space.

Two men approached saying, 'This way doctor, your car is there.' They hustled him in the dark. Presently I heard the door of a car bang and then move off. That was all, the final glimpse I had of the man called Rann. Never saw him again.

A postcard arrived a few days later from the Commandant: 'This is just a thank-you note. My well-wishers brought Rann to the car in which I was waiting. I am sure he is going to be happy hereafter. I won't let him out of sight again. He asks you please to freight his baggage to our address.'

Gaffur had parked his Ambassador on the drive, a little away from the main entrance to the Town Hall. In half darkness, waiting patiently for his distinguished customer. After the hall emptied, the turbulent crowd had left, and the lights were switched off, I started homeward. As I came down the drive I noticed Gaffur's taxi. 'What are you doing here?'

'You know—he asked me to wait here, I don't know, a long drive ahead to Peak House—I've all his baggage in the boot. Picked it up at your house this evening on his order.'

'You are hoping for your Rolls Royce still?' I asked suppressing a laugh.

'Why not?' he asked. 'At the rate he is giving me business, I think he'll even want me to drive him to Bombay and Delhi—'

'He's already left for Delhi,' I said, and then I told him the story. 'You can't blame him. After all, he's gone back to his wife, who has a right, holds an authorized certificate for his role as a husband.'

'But what about the girl who is waiting?'

'Where?'

'She has packed up and is waiting at the school veranda. They were supposed to go to Peak House and—'

'Let us go and take her home.'

The girl came out running and crying, 'Ah! The meeting over? How I wished I were there to listen to you and watch your triumph in public—' She blurted out: 'Oh, darling, how happy you must be... now we are free—' and checked herself.

Gaffur hurriedly got down from the car and ran to meet her halfway to explain the changed situation. When she saw me, she broke down hysterically. 'I don't believe you people. You are all against him. He was so good, oh, he was kind and generous and loving. You don't understand him, nobody understands him. Take me to him, wherever he may be, let me know the truth from his own lips. Please, please, I beg you.' She went on ranting and lamenting.

I realized that she had a totally different picture of Rann. She worshipped him as a god who could do no wrong. Her face was disfigured with tears and her words, mostly panegyrics of her god, gushed forth in a torrent. I was shocked, never having thought their

relationship had grown so deep. I was appalled at the extent to which
the affair had grown, and couldn't help picturing it as a spread of the
weed Rann was bothered about. No use talking to her about Rann—it
would make no impression on her, would not pass through the barrier
she had built against the outside world.

We let her go on. Gaffur being my friend, did not mind wasting
time with us. He too had known her since childhood and was
bewildered by the transformation he saw. It took us time to persuade
her to come to the car. Gaffur carried her trunk. She was so dead
exhausted that with a little push we got her into the car and with
a further push leaned her back against the seat cushions. She was
apathetic and did not care where we went. When we took the turn
into Palm Grove Street, she just said, 'Don't wake up my grandfather.
I'll find my way in.'

I hesitated for a moment—it was midnight—but it would have
been futile to argue with her. We put her down noiselessly in front
of her door with her trunk and sped away with the least noise. We
had nothing to say to each other and remained silent till we came
to Kabir Street. Stopping at my house, Gaffur said gruffly (he was
choking with emotion and was unusually shaken), 'What shall I do
with his baggage?'

'I'll keep it and send it on later.'

'Who pays the meter charge?'

'I'll fix it with the Lotus Club tomorrow.'

He drove off gloomily, remarking, 'She used to be such a sweet
creature!'

I found no time to visit the Town Hall library for a week. When I
resumed my news-hunting and reporting, I dropped in at the library
quietly one morning, and the old man said, 'Oh, you. I wanted to
see you badly. Where have you been? Do you know Baby has not
been well? That outing with her classmates seems to have upset her
somehow, eating all sorts of things…young people…she came back
sooner than I expected. I called Dr Krishna and he has given her
some medicine.'

'Oh, she'll be all right,' I said with a forced cheer.

'We must fulfil our vow at our family temple in the village, and then she will be all right. There has been a lapse on our part,' he said.

'Quite, surely, go ahead,' I said, suppressing the advice, 'Also propitiate Dr Lazarus, that will also help.'

I rather missed him. Without Rann the front room seemed barren. I felt lonely and bored. I kept the room vacant, hoping for another Rann to turn up, or, who could say, Rann himself might return to complete his masterpiece, or to resume the mission of minding the librarian's granddaughter's higher education. Even that question, though it had upset me at first, didn't seem quite so objectionable now. I had perhaps misread the situation. Their relationship might have been purely platonic. I laughed to myself at this (im)possibility. For platonic purposes one did not have to take a trip to Peak House in Gaffur's taxi. Platonic love did not call for secret, long journeys! Let me not gloss over it, I said to myself. Let me speak the truth unto myself. He was a callous and indiscriminate lecher, and thank god he did not try to lodge her in his room in my house! That would have provoked a riot in Kabir Street, and god knows to what extremes our people might have gone if anything had happened there.

Luckily, nothing came of it—the girl seemed to come through her escapade unscathed. She resumed her studies and attended college regularly; this I verified from time to time through discreet inquiries at the Town Hall library. The old man was always happy to talk of his granddaughter. 'Oh, she is too studious nowadays. After her school hours, she just comes home, and writes and reads all evening. Her grandmother is rather worried about her, and wants her to go out and relax with her friends. But she seems to have lost interest in her friends and has become very serious-minded.'

In my narrative about Rann at the Boardless, I gave a modified version of the story and generally slurred over all the incidents connected with the girl to save her from gossip. If anyone questioned me concerning the floating rumours about Rann and Girija, I dismissed their curiosity with contempt as being morbid. But no amount of hedging could keep Rann's abrupt exit from being discussed.

Varma was the first to question me. 'So the lady abducted her own husband from the meeting! Wonderful! What happened after that?'

'I may say that they lived happily ever after, from a letter just received yesterday from Commandant Sarasa. She is keeping him in check. I don't think he will try to get away again. After all, husband and wife quarrel, but it can't last: a sound couple will always get over that phase.'

Varma was impressed with the wife's determined pursuit and capture of her husband.

'It reminds one of Savitri and Satyavan of our legends. How Savitri persistently followed Yama, the God of Death, when he plucked away her husband's life; how she dogged his steps as he tried to move off, pleading and pleading until he yielded, and how Satyavan, whose body had lain inert in the forest, revived and joined his wife. I think this Commandant is a similar one.'

I left him and his cronies to draw whatever conclusion they pleased, without contradicting anyone. I suspected that somewhere in his thirty-year collection of calendars Varma surely had a sheet in colour litho of Savitri pestering Yama; most of his philosophical conclusions were derived from such representations on his walls.

The fiasco at the Town Hall was a passing sensation as far as the Boardless community was concerned; the confusion was a result of some thugs who had got into the hall only to disturb and break chairs. But one of the members explained: 'It seems the lecturer threatened to blow up the earth with an atom bomb. I was not there, of course, but my nephew, who is studying at Albert Mission, told me that the lecturer made a threatening speech.'

His listeners murmured an approval of the manner in which the function ended.

'But the Deputy Minister's speech was wholesome and inspiring, I learn,' added someone else.

I never corrected any statement or defended Rann. Not my business.

But I constantly speculated on Rann's present plight—the tethered domesticity, which he must be facing in far-off Delhi. I was hoping to hear from him, but he never wrote probably resenting the manner in which he had ended his lecture and fallen into a trap.

Six months later one evening while posting a letter in the mail van of 7 Down, the station master came excitedly to announce, 'The lady is in the waiting room—arrived in a jeep this afternoon!' I looked and there she stood, filling up the threshold of the waiting room in her khaki uniform, an overwhelming presence. She waved to me and turned in, opened the door a few minutes later and came out in civilian dress—a pale yellow saree. She looked enormously powerful as she greeted me with a laugh: 'You never expected to see me, but I am here now.' She had two chairs put out under the tree as before, looked at the station master hovering around to do her bidding. She told him:

'Masterji—I hope the timetable is unchanged, and we won't be disturbed till the goods train arrives at eleven.'

'Yes madam, how well you remember!'

'Tell your good wife, I shall need nothing more than a banana and a glass of milk—advised to avoid all food at all times! I shall call for my milk and fruit by and by—till then please leave us alone, we have to talk over important matters.' Turning to me, she said, 'TM, no excuses today. You will have to sit through and listen to me fully. I'm pressed for time. I've been sent south for a survey of rural areas—last two days I was busy travelling around in a jeep. Painful business, jeep travel. I'm pressed for time, leaving for Trichy airport at five in the morning and then on to Delhi by noon. Have to tell you a lot. Sit down and stay down. If you feel hungry, I'll ask the master to give you something to eat. But don't go. You have to listen to me.'

Without coming to the point she was talking in general terms, since she suspected that the station master and Muni must still be around, ready to listen to our talks. When she was sure they were gone, she leaned forward and whispered, her voice quivering, 'Your friend has vanished again!'

I had sensed that some such statement was coming and said involuntarily, 'I thought so.'

She begged, 'If he is here, please give him up again—I agreed to this trip in the hope that he might be here again, although I knew it was a hopeless hope.'

'I wish with all my heart I could help you again. But believe me, he is not here. I have no information. I've not heard from him at all.'

I repeated it several times to emphasize that I was speaking the truth. She fished out of her handbag a tiny kerchief, touched her eyes, blew her nose and said, 'These few months have been our happiest ones. It seemed a revival of our far-off days in Madras—he managed to convey the same charm and warmth. But for our physical changes and age, which the outside world might notice. As far as we were concerned, we were back in the days of my father's carpentry, on the bench under the tree, whispering to each other. Such revived moments made one forget the present conditions. The joy in each other's company and the sense of fulfilment were complete and indescribable. At such moments I thought of you with profound gratitude. But alas, I could not give him enough time. I left home for the Parade Ground at six in the morning, returned home off and on, being mostly out on various official duties. Sometimes I had to be away for a couple of days or more touring the countryside. Heavy work, I liked it. He appreciated my work and was full of praise and encouragement, and looked after himself and the home. Such a domesticated creature one could not imagine. He lived a very well-regulated life, sought no society-life or diversion, being completely absorbed in his writing and studies. He mentioned that his work was progressing smoothly, at a faster rate than at any time in his life, and regretted that he should have missed this wonderful life with me. We found time to sit and talk only late in the evening after I had shed my official uniform and changed into a saree. We had chairs put out in the garden and sat there till late at night, even carrying our supper out under the stars. At about eleven he would return to his study and shut himself in, worked, I suppose far into the night. He often said that his book, when it came out, would shake all our ideas to the foundation. He jogged in the morning in the park nearby, went for a stroll in the evening through shopping crowds at the market, and demanded nothing more nor sought any other company. I left him absolutely alone, respected his desire for privacy. When I noticed letters coming to him from different countries, I feared he might be in touch with his old friends, but I suppressed that suspicion as unworthy—he was a man to be loved, respected and above all trusted.'

She laughed now bitterly. 'All wrong ideas and misleading notions. I tell you he had unsuspected depths of duplicity. At the initial stages I did not trust him so fully and had his movements watched, but I gave that up in due course, for it seemed unnecessary and mean. Thus we passed our time. It was pleasant but I was also feeling apprehensive without any reason, only because it seemed too good to last. And it actually turned out so.

'Ten days ago I had to be away in Jaipur for three days on special duty. I couldn't take leave of him—he hadn't opened his door yet. It was my usual practice to leave without disturbing him. When I returned home three days later, it was all over, the old story again. The cook told me that he had gone soon after breakfast the day I left, taking a suitcase and a trunk with him. A car came for him with a woman in it. I wondered who she might be and where she came from, and how he could have arranged all this. He had left a letter on the hall table for me.'

She held out the letter for me to read. It just said: 'Good-bye dearest. I have to be off again. It was lovely while it lasted—thanks!'

'What do you make of it?' she asked.

'He must have received a sudden call connected with his research, I think.'

She laughed bitterly. 'But who is the woman?'

'Perhaps a research assistant?'

'No, a nurse from Matilda's. I checked everywhere for missing persons, and one Komal at Matilda's had vanished suddenly, resigning her job. Don't ask me how he could have organized it all, or how he managed to cultivate the nurse or how long it must have gone on. He was an expert in the art of deception. Now I realize that all along he must have lived a parallel secret life while creating the impression of living with me. I visited various airlines and the airport, and got the information that he had taken a flight to Rome on the same day I left for Jaipur. From Rome he could radiate on to any continent with his latest companion! I can only conclude from the description I got at one of the airline counters that the passenger was your Rann of Malgudi, a special name he seems to have conjured up for your edification. God alone knows under how many names he goes about and how many passports he has manufactured. An expert, really, in his own field. I pray to god that some day he may be caught at least for his passport frauds and made to spend the rest of his life in some hellish prison. I've no hope of seeing him again.'

At this point she broke down, and began to sob uncontrollably. Between her fits of sobbing she managed to say, 'I should have been far happier if I had never met you or noticed your news item about the Timbuctoo man. Or it would have been best if I'd listened to my father's advice to keep away from him.'

It was distressing to see a mighty personality, generally self-possessed, crumbling down. My eyes were wet too. Presently finding it embarrassing to continue in my presence, she abruptly got up, rushed back to the waiting room, and bolted the door.

POSTSCRIPT

I had planned *Talkative Man* as a full-length novel, and grandly titled it, 'Novel No. 14'. While it progressed satisfactorily enough, it would not grow beyond 116 typewritten sheets, where it just came to a halt, like a motor car run out of petrol. Talkative Man, the narrator, had nothing more to say, he seemed to feel. What more do you expect? This is only the story of a wife's attempt to reclaim her erratic, elusive husband who is a wanderer, a philanderer on a global scale, abandoning women right and left. I have told you his story as far as I could confine and observe him as a curio in Kabir Street, but I had to manoeuvre to get him out of Malgudi hurriedly, when I found that he was planning to seduce and abduct a young, innocent schoolgirl known to me. So there we are, and 'finis' on page 116 inevitably.

Why *not* only 116 pages, I question. While a poet or dramatist rarely exceeds a hundred pages even in his most ambitious work, and is accepted without anyone commenting on the length of his composition, a writer of fiction is often subject to a quantitative evaluation.

The difficulty lies perhaps in classification. *Talkative Man* is too long to be a short story, but is it too short for a novel? I prefer the shorter form, because it gives me scope for elaboration of details, but within certain limits; I can take up a variety of subjects and get through each in a reasonable time, while a novel ties me down to a single theme for at least two years! When I am at work on a novel, I imagine that I am keeping a crowd of characters waiting outside my door, who are in search of their author.

At the beginning of my career I was advised by my literary agent in London to bear in mind that a novel should run to at least 70,000 words, the minimum standard for fiction in those days. The failure of my first novel, *Swami and Friends*, was attributed to its length: 'Fifty thousand words are an awkward length for a novel,' my agent wrote. A bookbuyer investing 7/6d (in that Golden Age) liked to have his money's worth of reading, I was told. When I mentioned this to Graham Greene in a letter, he wrote back to say, 'I hope you will get a subject next time which will run to a full-length book. But that's on the knees of the gods. Only if you see a choice of subjects and lengths ahead of you, do next time go for the longer.' A welcome advice. Otherwise, I feared that I might be compelled to inflate my stories with laboured detail and description of dress, deportment, facial features, furniture, food and drinks—passages I ruthlessly skip when reading a novel. While writing, I prefer to keep such details to a minimum in order to save my readers the bother of skipping. Also, I have the habit of pruning and trimming, when I look over the first draft, and then in a second draft a further lopping off is certain, until I am satisfied that the narrative progresses smoothly.

The present work has turned out the shortest among my novels, but if I were to blow it up, I could perhaps push it forward from the point where it now ends, with Commandant Sarasa setting out on an odyssey in search of her slippery husband, across several continents and in many societies and hide-and-seek situations; until she tracks him down, corners him, and finally incarcerates him in the prison of domesticity. Thus I might generate 100,000 words or more and give the volume a respectable girth, fit to top a best-seller list. To achieve this end, perhaps I should acquire a word processor, and learn how to handle it without blowing its fuse or allowing it to outwit me by gushing forth phrases faster than I can spell. But alas, I am not inclined to acquire new skills; I cannot handle any mechanical or electronic device. I have given up even typing, finding the typewriter a nuisance and a distraction when its keys stick or the ribbon gets tangled. Apart from this, still bearing in mind Graham Greene's advice of half a century ago, I do not concern myself with quantity while writing.

I speculate, however, what Commandant Sarasa would say if Talkative Man had advised her to set forth in search of her husband. In her present mood, she would probably retort, 'No. Let *him* undertake the pursuit this time when he is finally let out of prison. It will be a long time, though, before that happens. Prison life will have shorn him of his Adolphe Menjou style and his three-piece suit, no woman would even give him a glance, and he will have nowhere to go. At that point he will think of me, but he won't find me. I am going away presently on a UN assignment to a developing country. Your friend won't know where I am gone. Nor am I going to leave my address with you since you are a talkative man and will not keep a secret. The faded Dr Rann, I'm sure, will ultimately seek refuge in your Kabir Street unless he ends up on a footpath in Calcutta or Bombay.'

An Astrologer's Day

Punctually at midday he opened his bag and spread out his professional equipment, which consisted of a dozen cowrie shells, a square piece of cloth with obscure mystic charts on it, a notebook and a bundle of palmyra writing. His forehead was resplendent with sacred ash and vermilion, and his eyes sparkled with a sharp abnormal gleam which was really an outcome of a continual searching look for customers, but which his simple clients took to be a prophetic light and felt comforted. The power of his eyes was considerably enhanced by their position—placed as they were between the painted forehead and the dark whiskers which streamed down his cheeks: even a half-wit's eyes would sparkle in such a setting. To crown the effect he wound a saffron-coloured turban around his head. This colour scheme never failed. People were attracted to him as bees are attracted to cosmos or dahlia stalks. He sat under the boughs of a spreading tamarind tree which flanked a path running through the Town Hall Park. It was a remarkable place in many ways: a surging crowd was always moving up and down this narrow road morning till night. A variety of trades and occupations was represented all along its way: medicine-sellers, sellers of stolen hardware and junk, magicians and, above all, an auctioneer of cheap cloth, who created enough din all day to attract the whole town. Next to him in vociferousness came a vendor of fried groundnuts, who gave his ware a fancy name each day, calling it Bombay Ice-Cream one day, and on the next Delhi Almond, and on the third Raja's Delicacy, and so on and so forth, and people flocked to him. A considerable portion of this crowd dallied before the astrologer too. The astrologer transacted his business by the light of a flare which crackled and smoked up above the groundnut heap nearby. Half the enchantment of the place was due to the fact that

102

it did not have the benefit of municipal lighting. The place was lit up by shop lights. One or two had hissing gaslights, some had naked flares stuck on poles, some were lit up by old cycle lamps and one or two, like the astrologer's, managed without lights of their own. It was a bewildering criss-cross of light rays and moving shadows. This suited the astrologer very well, for the simple reason that he had not in the least intended to be an astrologer when he began life; and he knew no more of what was going to happen to others than he knew what was going to happen to himself next minute. He was as much a stranger to the stars as were his innocent customers. Yet he said things which pleased and astonished everyone: that was more a matter of study, practice and shrewd guesswork. All the same, it was as much an honest man's labour as any other, and he deserved the wages he carried home at the end of a day.

He had left his village without any previous thought or plan. If he had continued there he would have carried on the work of his forefathers—namely, tilling the land, living, marrying, and ripening in his cornfield and ancestral home. But that was not to be. He had to leave home without telling anyone, and he could not rest till he left it behind a couple of hundred miles. To a villager it is a great deal, as if an ocean flowed between.

He had a working analysis of mankind's troubles: marriage, money and the tangles of human ties. Long practice had sharpened his perception. Within five minutes he understood what was wrong. He charged three pies per question and never opened his mouth till the other had spoken for at least ten minutes, which provided him enough stuff for a dozen answers and advices. When he told the person before him, gazing at his palm, 'In many ways you are not getting the fullest results for your efforts,' nine out of ten were disposed to agree with him. Or he questioned: 'Is there any woman in your family, maybe even a distant relative, who is not well disposed towards you?' Or he gave an analysis of character: 'Most of your troubles are due to your nature. How can you be otherwise with Saturn where he is? You have an impetuous nature and a rough exterior.' This endeared him to their hearts immediately, for even the mildest of us loves to think that he has a forbidding exterior.

The nuts-vendor blew out his flare and rose to go home. This was a signal for the astrologer to bundle up too, since it left him in darkness except for a little shaft of green light which strayed in from somewhere and touched the ground before him. He picked up his cowrie shells and paraphernalia and was putting them back into his bag when the green shaft of light was blotted out; he looked up and saw a man standing before him. He sensed a possible client and said: 'You look so careworn. It will do you good to sit down for a while and chat with me.' The other grumbled some vague reply. The astrologer pressed his invitation; whereupon the other thrust his palm under his nose, saying: 'You call yourself an astrologer?' The astrologer felt challenged and said, tilting the other's palm towards the green shaft of light: 'Yours is a nature...'

'Oh, stop that,' the other said. 'Tell me something worthwhile...'

Our friend felt piqued. 'I charge only three pies per question, and what you get ought to be good enough for your money...' At this the other withdrew his arm, took out an anna and flung it out to him, saying, 'I have some questions to ask. If I prove you are bluffing, you must return that anna to me with interest.'

'If you find my answers satisfactory, will you give me five rupees?'

'No.'

'Or will you give me eight annas?'

'All right, provided you give me twice as much if you are wrong,' said the stranger. This pact was accepted after a little further argument. The astrologer sent up a prayer to heaven as the other lit a cheroot. The astrologer caught a glimpse of his face by the matchlight. There was a pause as cars hooted on the road, *jutka* drivers swore at their horses and the babble of the crowd agitated the semi-darkness of the park. The other sat down, sucking his cheroot, puffing out, sat there ruthlessly. The astrologer felt very uncomfortable. 'Here, take your anna back. I am not used to such challenges. It is late for me today...' He made preparations to bundle up. The other held his wrist and said, 'You can't get out of it now. You dragged me in while I was passing.' The astrologer shivered in his grip; and his voice shook and became faint. 'Leave me today. I will speak to you tomorrow.' The other thrust his palm in his face and said, 'Challenge is challenge. Go on.' The astrologer proceeded with his throat drying up. 'There is a woman…'

'Stop,' said the other. 'I don't want all that. Shall I succeed in my present search or not? Answer this and go. Otherwise I will not let you go till you disgorge all your coins.' The astrologer muttered a few incantations and replied, 'All right. I will speak. But will you give me a rupee if what I say is convincing? Otherwise I will not open my mouth, and you may do what you like.' After a good deal of haggling the other agreed. The astrologer said, 'You were left for dead. Am I right?'

'Ah, tell me more.'

'A knife has passed through you once?' said the astrologer.

'Good fellow!' He bared his chest to show the scar. 'What else?'

'And then you were pushed into a well nearby in the field. You were left for dead.'

'I should have been dead if some passer-by had not chanced to peep into the well,' exclaimed the other, overwhelmed by enthusiasm. 'When shall I get at him?' he asked, clenching his fist.

'In the next world,' answered the astrologer. 'He died four months ago in a far-off town. You will never see any more of him.' The other groaned on hearing it. The astrologer proceeded.

'Guru Nayak—'

'You know my name!' the other said, taken aback.

'As I know all other things. Guru Nayak, listen carefully to what I have to say. Your village is two days' journey due north of this town. Take the next train and be gone. I see once again great danger to your life if you go from home.' He took out a pinch of sacred ash and held it out to him. 'Rub it on your forehead and go home. Never travel southward again, and you will live to be a hundred.'

'Why should I leave home again?' the other said reflectively. 'I was only going away now and then to look for him and to choke out his life if I met him.' He shook his head regretfully. 'He has escaped my hands. I hope at least he died as he deserved.' 'Yes,' said the astrologer. 'He was crushed under a lorry.' The other looked gratified to hear it.

The place was deserted by the time the astrologer picked up his articles and put them into his bag. The green shaft was also gone, leaving the place in darkness and silence. The stranger had gone off into the night, after giving the astrologer a handful of coins.

It was nearly midnight when the astrologer reached home. His wife was waiting for him at the door and demanded an explanation. He flung the coins at her and said, 'Count them. One man gave all that.'

'Twelve and a half annas,' she said, counting. She was overjoyed. 'I can buy some jaggery and coconut tomorrow. The child has been asking for sweets for so many days now. I will prepare some nice stuff for her.'

'The swine has cheated me! He promised me a rupee,' said the astrologer. She looked up at him. 'You look worried. What is wrong?'

'Nothing.'

After dinner, sitting on the *pyol*, he told her, 'Do you know a great load is gone from me today? I thought I had the blood of a man on my hands all these years. That was the reason why I ran away from home, settled here and married you. He is alive.'

She gasped. 'You tried to kill!'

'Yes, in our village, when I was a silly youngster. We drank, gambled and quarrelled badly one day—why think of it now? Time to sleep,' he said, yawning, and stretched himself on the *pyol*.

A Horse and Two Goats

OF THE seven hundred thousand villages dotting the map of India, in which the majority of India's five hundred million live, flourish and die, Kritam was probably the tiniest. It was indicated on the district survey map by a microscopic dot, the map being meant more for the revenue official out to collect tax than for the guidance of the motorist, who in any case could not hope to reach it since it sprawled far from the highway at the end of a rough track furrowed up by the iron-hooped wheels of bullock carts. But its size did not prevent it giving itself the grandiose name Kritam, which meant in Tamil 'coronet' or 'crown' on the brow of this subcontinent. The village consisted of less than thirty houses, only one of them built with brick and cement. Painted a brilliant yellow and blue all over with gorgeous carvings of gods and gargoyles on its balustrade, it was known as the Big House. The other houses, distributed in four streets, were generally of bamboo thatch, straw, mud, and other unspecified material. Muni's was the last house in the fourth street, beyond which stretched the fields. In his prosperous days Muni had owned a flock of forty sheep and goats and sallied forth every morning driving the flock to the highway a couple of miles away. There he would sit on the pedestal of a clay statue of a horse while his cattle grazed around. He carried a crook at the end of a bamboo pole and snapped foliage from the avenue trees to feed his flock; he also gathered faggots and dry sticks, bundled them, and carried them home for fuel at sunset.

His wife lit the domestic fire at dawn, boiled water in a mud pot, threw into it a handful of millet flour, added salt, and gave him his first nourishment for the day. When he started out, she would put in his hand a packed lunch, once again the same millet cooked into a little ball, which he could swallow with a raw onion at midday. She was old, but he was older and needed all the attention she could give him in order to be kept alive.

His fortunes had declined gradually, unnoticed. From a flock of forty which he drove into a pen at night, his stock had now come down to two goats which were not worth the rent of a half rupee a month which the Big House charged for the use of the pen in their backyard. And so the two goats were tethered to the trunk of a drumstick tree which grew in front of his hut and from which occasionally Muni could shake down drumsticks. This morning he got six. He carried them in with a sense of triumph. Although no one could say precisely who owned the tree, it was his because he lived in its shadow.

She said, 'If you were content with the drumstick leaves alone, I could boil and salt some for you.'

'Oh, I am tired of eating those leaves. I have a craving to chew the drumstick out of sauce, I tell you.'

'You have only four teeth in your jaw, but your craving is for big things. All right, get the stuff for the sauce, and I will prepare it for you. After all, next year you may not be alive to ask for anything. But first get me all the stuff, including a measure of rice or millet, and I will satisfy your unholy craving. Our store is empty today. Dal, chili, curry leaves, mustard, coriander, gingelley oil, and one large potato. Go out and get all this.' He repeated the list after her in order not to miss any item and walked off to the shop in the third street.

He sat on an upturned packing case below the platform of the shop. The shopman paid no attention to him. Muni kept clearing his throat, coughing and sneezing until the shopman could not stand it any more and demanded, 'What ails you? You will fly off that seat into the gutter if you sneeze so hard, young man.' Muni laughed inordinately, in order to please the shopman, at being called 'young man'. The shopman softened and said, 'You have enough of the imp inside to keep a second wife busy, but for the fact that the old lady is still alive.' Muni laughed appropriately again at this joke. It completely won the shopman over; he liked his sense of humour to be appreciated. Muni engaged his attention in local gossip for a few minutes, which always ended with a reference to the postman's wife, who had eloped to the city some months before.

The shopman felt most pleased to hear the worst of the postman, who had cheated him. Being an itinerant postman, he returned home to Kritam only once in ten days and every time managed to slip away again without passing the shop in the third street. By thus humouring the shopman, Muni could always ask for one or two items of food, promising payment later. Some days the shopman was in a good mood and gave in, and sometimes he would lose his temper suddenly and bark at Muni for daring to ask for credit. This was such a day, and Muni could not progress beyond two items listed as essential components. The shopman was also displaying a remarkable memory for old facts and figures and took out an oblong ledger to support his observations. Muni felt impelled to rise and flee but his self-respect kept him in his seat and made him listen to the worst things about himself. The shopman concluded, 'If you could find five rupees and a quarter, you would pay off an ancient debt and then could apply for admission to swarga. How much have you got now?'

'I will pay you everything on the first of the next month.'

'As always, and whom do you expect to rob by then?'

Muni felt caught and mumbled, 'My daughter has sent word that she will be sending me money.'

'Have you a daughter?' sneered the shopman. 'And she is sending you money! For what purpose, may I know?'

'Birthday, fiftieth birthday,' said Muni quietly.

'Birthday! How old are you?'

Muni repeated weakly, not being sure of it himself, 'Fifty.' He always calculated his age from the time of the great famine when he stood as high as the parapet around the village well, but who could calculate such things accurately nowadays with so many famines occuring? The shopman felt encouraged when other customers stood around to watch and comment. Muni thought helplessly, 'My poverty is exposed to everybody. But what can I do?'

'More likely you are seventy,' said the shopman. 'You also forget that you mentioned a birthday five weeks ago when you wanted castor oil for your holy bath.'

'Bath! Who can dream of a bath when you have to scratch the tank-bed for a bowl of water? We would all be parched and dead but for the Big House, where they let us take a pot of water from their well.' After saying this Muni unobtrusively rose and moved off.

He told his wife, 'That scoundrel would not give me anything. So go out and sell the drumsticks for what they are worth.'

He flung himself down in a corner to recoup from the fatigue of his visit to the shop. His wife said, 'You are getting no sauce today, nor anything else. I can't find anything to give you to eat. Fast till evening, it'll do you good. Take the goats and be gone now,' and added, 'Don't come back before the sun is down.' He knew that if he obeyed her she would somehow conjure up some food for him in the evening. Only he must be careful not to argue and irritate her. Her temper was undependable in the morning but improved by evening time. She was sure to go out and work—grind corn in the Big House, sweep or scrub somewhere, and earn enough to buy some food and keep a dinner ready for him in the evening.

Unleashing the goats from the drumstick tree, Muni started out, driving them ahead and uttering weird cries from time to time in order to urge them on. He passed through the village with his head bowed in thought. He did not want to look at anyone or be accosted. A couple of cronies lounging in the temple corridor hailed him, but he ignored their call. They had known him in the days of affluence when he lorded over a flock of fleecy sheep, and not the miserable gawky goats that he had today. Of course, he also used to have a few goats for those who fancied them, but the real wealth lay in sheep; they bred fast and people came and bought the fleece in the shearing season; and then that famous butcher from the town came over on the weekly market days bringing him betel leaves, tobacco, and often enough some bhang, which they smoked in a hut in the coconut grove, undisturbed by wives and well-wishers. After a smoke one felt light and elated and inclined to forgive everyone including that brother-in-law of his who had once tried to set fire to his home. But all this seemed like the memories of a previous birth. Some pestilence afflicted his cattle (he could of course guess who had laid his animals under a curse) and

even the friendly butcher would not touch one at half the price...
and now here he was left with the two scraggy creatures. He wished
someone would rid him of their company too. The shopman had said
that he was seventy. At seventy, one only waited to be summoned by
god. When he was dead what would his wife do? They had lived in
each other's company since they were children. He was told on their
day of wedding that he was ten years old and she was eight. During
the wedding ceremony they had had to recite their respective ages and
names. He had thrashed her only a few times in their career, and later
she had had the upper hand. Progeny, none. Perhaps a large progeny
would have brought him the blessing of the gods. Fertility brought
merit. People with fourteen sons were always so prosperous and at
peace with the world and themselves. He recollected the thrill he
had felt when he mentioned a daughter to that shopman. Although
it was not believed, what if he did not have a daughter?—his cousin
in the next village had many daughters, and any one of them was
as good as his; he was fond of them all and would buy them sweets
if he could afford it. Still, everyone in the village whispered behind
their backs that Muni and his wife were a barren couple. He avoided
looking at anyone; they all professed to be so high up. And everyone
else in the village had more money than he. 'I am the poorest fellow
in our caste and no wonder that they spurn me, but I won't look
at them either,' and so he passed on along the edge of the street,
with his eyes downcast and people also left him alone, commenting
only to the extent, 'Ah, there he goes with his two great goats; if he
slits their throats, he may have more peace of mind'; 'What has he
to worry about anyway? They live on nothing and have nobody to
worry about.' Thus people commented when he passed through the
village. Only on the outskirts did he lift his head and look up. He
urged and bullied the goats until they meandered along to the foot
of the horse statue on the edge of the village. He sat on its pedestal
for the rest of the day. The advantage of this was that he could watch
the highway and see the lorries and buses pass through to the hills,
and it gave him a sense of belonging to a larger world. The pedestal
of the statue was broad enough for him to move around as the sun

travelled up and westward; or he could also crouch under the belly of the horse, for shade.

The horse was nearly life-size, moulded out of clay, baked, burnt and brightly coloured, and reared its head proudly, prancing with its forelegs in the air and flourishing its tail in a loop. Beside the horse stood a warrior with scythe-like mustachios, bulging eyes and aquiline nose. The old image-makers believed in indicating a man of strength by making his eyes bulge and sharpening his moustache tips. They had also decorated the man's chest with beads which looked today like blobs of mud through the ravages of sun and wind and rain (when it came), but Muni would insist that he had known the beads to sparkle like the nine gems at one time in his life. The horse itself was said to have been as white as a *dhobi*-washed sheet, and had had on its back a cover of pure brocade of red-and-black lace, matching the multicoloured sash around the waist of the warrior. But none in the village remembered the splendour as no one noticed its existence. Even Muni, who spent all his waking hours at its foot, never bothered to look up. It was untouched by the young vandals of the village who gashed tree trunks with knives and tried to topple off milestones and inscribed lewd designs on all the walls. This statue had been closer to the population of the village at one time, when this spot bordered the village; but when the highway was laid (or perhaps when the tank and wells dried up completely here) the village moved a couple of miles inland.

Muni sat at the foot of the statue, watching his two goats graze in the arid soil among the cactus and lantana bushes. He looked at the sun; it had tilted westward no doubt, but it was not yet time to go back home; if he went too early his wife would have no food for him. Also, he must give her time to cool off her temper and feel sympathetic, and then she would scrounge and manage to get some food. He watched the mountain road for a time signal. When the green bus appeared around the bend he could leave, and his wife would feel pleased that he had let the goats feed long enough.

He noticed now a new sort of vehicle coming down at full speed. It looked both like a motor car and a bus. He used to be intrigued by the novelty of such spectacles, but of late work was going on at the source of the river on the mountain and an assortment of people and traffic went past him, and he took it all casually and described to his wife, later in the day, not everything as he once did, but only some things, if he noticed anything special. Today, while he observed the yellow vehicle coming down, he was wondering how to describe it later when it sputtered and stopped in front of him. A red-faced foreigner who had been driving it got down and went round it, stooping, looking, and poking under the vehicle; then he straightened himself up, looked at the dashboard, stared in Muni's direction, and approached him. 'Excuse me, is there a gas station nearby, or do I have to wait until another car comes—' He suddenly looked up at the clay horse and cried, 'Marvellous!' without completing his sentence. Muni felt he should get up and run away, and cursed his age. He could not really put his limbs into action; some years ago he could outrun a cheetah, as happened once when he went to the forest to cut fuel and it was then that two of his sheep were mauled—a sign that bad times were coming. Though he tried, he could not extricate himself easily from his seat, besides which there was also the problem of the goats. He could not leave them behind.

The red-faced man wore khaki clothes—evidently a policeman or a soldier. Muni said to himself, 'He will chase or shoot if I start running. Sometimes dogs chase only those who run—O Shiva protect me. I don't know why this man should be after me.' Meanwhile the foreigner cried 'Marvellous!' again, nodding his head. He paced around the statue with his eyes fixed on it. Muni sat frozen for a while, and then fidgeted and tried to edge away. Now the other man suddenly pressed his palms together in a salute, smiled, and said, 'Namaste! How do you do?'

At which Muni spoke the only English expression he had learnt, 'Yes, no.' Having exhausted his English vocabulary, he started in Tamil: 'My name is Muni. These two goats are mine, and no one can gainsay it—though our village is full of slanderers these days who will not hesitate to say that what belongs to a man doesn't belong to him.' He rolled his eyes and shuddered at the thought of the evil-minded men and women peopling his village.

The foreigner faithfully looked in the direction indicated by Muni's fingers, gazed for a while at the two goats and the rocks, and with a puzzled expression took out his silver cigarette-case and lit a cigarette. Suddenly remembering the courtesies of the season, he asked, 'Do you smoke?' Muni answered, 'Yes, no.' Whereupon the red-faced man took a cigarette and gave it to Muni, who received it with surprise, having had no offer of a smoke from anyone for years now. Those days when he smoked bhang were gone with his sheep and the large-hearted butcher. Nowadays he was not able to find even matches, let alone bhang. (His wife went across and borrowed a fire at dawn from a neighbour.) He had always wanted to smoke a cigarette; only once had the shopman given him one on credit, and he remembered how good it had tasted. The other flicked the lighter open and offered a light to Muni. Muni felt so confused about how to act that he blew on it and put it out. The other, puzzled but undaunted, flourished his lighter, presented it again, and lit Muni's cigarette. Muni drew a deep puff and started coughing; it was racking, no doubt, but extremely pleasant. When his cough subsided he wiped his eyes and took stock of the situation, understanding that the other man was not an inquisitor of any kind. Yet, in order to make sure, he remained wary. No need to run away from a man who gave such a potent smoke. His head was reeling from the effect of the strong American cigarette made with roasted tobacco. The man said, 'I come from New York,' took out a wallet from his hip pocket, and presented his card.

Muni shrank away from the card. Perhaps he was trying to present a warrant and arrest him. Beware of khaki, one part of his mind warned. Take all the cigarettes or bhang or whatever is offered, but don't get caught. Beware of khaki. He wished he weren't seventy as the shopman had said. At seventy one didn't run, but surrendered to whatever came. He could only ward off trouble by talk. So he went on, all in the chaste Tamil for which Kritam was famous. (Even the worst detractors could not deny that the famous poetess Avvaiyar was born in this area, although no one could say whether it was in Kritam or Kuppam, the adjoining village.) Out of this heritage the Tamil language gushed through Muni in an unimpeded flow. He said, 'Before god, sir, bhagavan, who sees everything, I tell you, sir, that we know nothing of the case. If the murder was committed, whoever did it will not escape. Bhagavan is all-seeing. Don't ask me about it. I know nothing.' A body had been found mutilated and thrown under a tamarind tree at the border between Kritam and Kuppam a few weeks before, giving rise to much gossip and speculation. Muni added an explanation, 'Anything is possible there. People over there will stop at nothing.' The foreigner nodded his head and listened courteously though he understood nothing.

'I am sure you know when this horse was made,' said the red man and smiled ingratiatingly.

Muni reacted to the relaxed atmosphere by smiling himself, and pleaded, 'Please go away, sir. I know nothing. I promise we will hold him for you if we see any bad character around, and we will bury him up to his neck in a coconut pit if he tries to escape; but our village has always had a clean record. Must definitely be the other village.'

Now the red man implored, 'Please, please, I will speak slowly, please try to understand me. Can't you understand even a simple word of English? Everyone in this country seems to know English. I have got along with English everywhere in this country, but you don't speak it. Have you any religious or spiritual scruples for avoiding the English speech?'

Muni made some indistinct sounds in his throat and shook his head. Encouraged, the other went on to explain at length, uttering each syllable with care and deliberation. Presently he sidled over and took a seat beside the old man, explaining, 'You see, last August, we probably had the hottest summer in history, and I was working in my shirtsleeves in my office on the fortieth floor of the Empire State Building. You must have heard of the power failure, and there I was stuck for four hours, no elevator, no air-conditioning. All the way in the train I kept thinking, and the minute I reached home in Connecticut, I told my wife Ruth, "We will visit India this winter, it's time to look at other civilizations." Next day she called the travel agent first thing and told him to fix it, and so here I am. Ruth came with me but is staying back at Srinagar, and I am the one doing the rounds and joining her later.'

Muni looked reflective at the end of this long peroration and said, rather feebly, 'Yes, no,' as a concession to the other's language, and went on in Tamil, 'When I was this high,' he indicated a foot high, 'I heard my uncle say...'

No one can tell what he was planning to say as the other interrupted him at this stage to ask, 'Boy, what is the secret of your teeth? How old are you?'

The old man forgot what he had started to say and remarked, 'Sometimes we too lose our cattle. Jackals or cheetahs may carry them off, but sometimes it is just theft from over in the next village, and then we will know who has done it. Our priest at the temple can see in the camphor flame the face of the thief, and when he is caught...' He gestured with his hands a perfect mincing of meat.

The American watched his hands intently and said, 'I know what you mean. Chop something? Maybe I am holding you up and you want to chop wood? Where is your axe? Hand it to me and show me what to chop. I do enjoy it, you know, just a hobby. We get a lot of driftwood along the backwater near my house, and on Sundays I do nothing but chop wood for the fireplace. I really feel different when I watch the fire in the fireplace, although it may take all the sections of the Sunday *New York Times* to get a fire started,' and he smiled at this reference.

Muni felt totally confused but decided the best thing would be to make an attempt to get away from this place. He tried to edge out, saying, 'Must go home,' and turned to go. The other seized his shoulder and said desperately, 'Is there no one, absolutely no one here, to translate for me?' He looked up and down the road, which was deserted in this hot afternoon. A sudden gust of wind churned up the dust and dead leaves on the roadside into a ghostly column and propelled it towards the mountain road. The stranger almost pinioned Muni's back to the statue and asked, 'Isn't this statue yours? Why don't you sell it to me?'

The old man now understood the reference to the horse, thought for a second, and said in his own language, 'I was an urchin this high when I heard my grandfather explain the story of this horse and warrior, and my grandfather himself was this high when he heard his grandfather, whose grandfather...'

The other man interrupted him with, 'I don't want to seem to have stopped here for nothing. I will offer you a good price for this,' he said, indicating the horse. He had concluded without the least doubt that Muni owned this mud horse. Perhaps he guessed by the way he sat at its pedestal, like other souvenir-sellers in this country presiding over their wares.

Muni followed the man's eyes and pointing fingers and dimly understood the subject matter and, feeling relieved that the theme of the mutilated body had been abandoned at least for the time being, said again, enthusiastically, 'I was this high when my grandfather told me about this horse and the warrior, and my grandfather was this high when he himself...' and he was getting into a deeper bog of remembering each time he tried to indicate the antiquity of the statue.

The Tamil that Muni spoke was stimulating even as pure sound, and the foreigner listened with fascination. 'I wish I had my tape-recorder here,' he said, assuming the pleasantest expression. 'Your language sounds wonderful. I get a kick out of every word you utter, here'—he indicated his ears—'but you don't have to waste your breath in sales talk. I appreciate the article. You don't have to explain its points.'

'I never went to a school, in those days only brahmins went to schools, but we had to go out and work in the fields morning till night, from sowing to harvest time...and when Pongal came and we had cut the harvest, my father allowed me to go out and play with others at the tank, and so I don't know the Parangi language you speak, even little fellows in your country probably speak the Parangi language, but here only learned men and officers know it. We had a postman in our village who could speak to you boldly in your language, but his wife ran away with someone and he does not speak to anyone at all nowadays. Who would, if a wife did what she did? Women must be watched; otherwise they will sell themselves and the home,' and he laughed at his own quip.

The foreigner laughed heartily, took out another cigarette, and offered it to Muni, who now smoked with ease, deciding to stay on if the fellow was going to be so good as to keep up his cigarette supply. The American now stood up on the pedestal in the attitude of a demonstrative lecturer and said, running his finger along some of the carved decorations around the horse's neck, speaking slowly and uttering his words syllable by syllable, 'I could give a sales talk for this better than anyone else... This is a marvellous combination of yellow and indigo, though faded now... How do you people of this country achieve these flaming colours?'

Muni, now assured that the subject was still the horse and not the dead body, said, 'This is our guardian, it means death to our adversaries. At the end of Kali Yuga, this world and all other worlds will be destroyed, and the Redeemer will come in the shape of a horse called Kalki; then this horse will come to life and gallop and trample down all bad men.' As he spoke of bad men the figures of the shopman and his brother-in-law assumed concrete forms in his mind, and he revelled for a moment in the predicament of the fellow under the horse's hoof: served him right for trying to set fire to his home...

While he was brooding on this pleasant vision, the foreigner utilized the pause to say, 'I assure you that this will have the best home in the USA. I'll push away the bookcase, you know I love books and am a member of five book clubs, and the choice and bonus volumes really mount up to a pile in our living-room, as high as this horse itself. But they'll have to go. Ruth may disapprove, but I will convince her. The TV may have to be shifted too. We can't have everything in the living room. Ruth will probably say what about when we have a party? I'm going to keep him right in the middle of the room. I don't see how that can interfere with the party—we'll stand around him and have our drinks.'

Muni continued his description of the end of the world. 'Our pundit discoursed at the temple once how the oceans are going to close over the earth in a huge wave and swallow us—this horse will grow bigger than the biggest wave and carry on its back only the good people and kick into the floods the evil ones—plenty of them about,' he said reflectively. 'Do you know when it is going to happen?' he asked.

The foreigner now understood by the tone of the other that a question was being asked and said, 'How am I transporting it? I can push the seat back and make room in the rear. That van can take in an elephant'—waving precisely at the back of the seat.

Muni was still hovering on visions of avatars and said again, 'I never missed our pundit's discourses at the temple in those days during every bright half of the month, although he'd go on all night, and he told us that Vishnu is the highest god. Whenever evil men trouble us, he comes down to save us. He has come many times. The first time he incarnated as a great fish, and lifted the scriptures on his back when the floods and sea waves...'

'I am not a millionaire, but a modest businessman. My trade is coffee.'

Amidst all this wilderness of obscure sounds Muni caught the word 'coffee' and said, 'If you want to drink "kapi", drive further up, in the next town, they have Friday markets, and there they open "kapi-otels"—so I learn from passers-by. Don't think I wander about. I go nowhere and look for nothing.' His thoughts went back to the avatars. 'The first avatar was in the shape of a little fish in a bowl of water, but every hour it grew bigger and bigger and became in the end a huge whale which the seas could not contain, and on the back of the whale the holy books were supported, saved and carried.' Having launched on the first avatar it was inevitable that he should go on to the next, a wild boar on whose tusk the earth was lifted when a vicious conqueror of the earth carried it off and hid it at the bottom of the sea. After describing this avatar Muni concluded, 'God will always save us whenever we are troubled by evil beings. When we were young we staged at full moon the story of the avatars. That's how I know the stories; we played them all night until the sun rose, and sometimes the European collector would come to watch, bringing his own chair. I had a good voice and so they always taught me songs and gave me the women's roles. I was always Goddess Laxmi, and they dressed me in a brocade sari, loaned from the Big Hous...'

The foreigner said, 'I repeat I am not a millionaire. Ours is a modest business; after all, we can't afford to buy more than sixty minutes' TV time in a month, which works out to two minutes a day, that's all, although in the course of time we'll maybe sponsor a one-hour show regularly if our sales graph continues to go up...'

Muni was intoxicated by the memory of his theatrical days and was about to explain how he had painted his face and worn a wig and diamond earrings when the visitor, feeling that he had spent too much time already, said, 'Tell me, will you accept a hundred rupees or not for the horse? I'd love to take the whiskered soldier also but I've no space for him this year. I'll have to cancel my air ticket and take a boat home, I suppose. Ruth can go by air if she likes, but I will go with the horse and keep him in my cabin all the way if necessary,' and he smiled at the picture of himself voyaging across the seas hugging this horse. He added, 'I will have to pad it with straw so that it doesn't break...'

'When we played *Ramayana*, they dressed me as Sita,' added Muni. 'A teacher came and taught us the songs for the drama and we gave him fifty rupees. He incarnated himself as Rama, and he alone could destroy Ravana, the demon with ten heads who shook all the worlds; do you know the story of *Ramayana*?'

'I have my station wagon as you see. I can push the seat back and take the horse in if you will just lend me a hand with it.'

'Do you know *Mahabharata*? Krishna was the eighth avatar of Vishnu, incarnated to help the Five Brothers regain their kingdom. When Krishna was a baby he danced on the thousand-hooded giant serpent and trampled it to death; and then he suckled the breasts of the demoness and left them flat as a disc though when she came to him her bosoms were large, like mounds of earth on the banks of a dug-up canal.' He indicated two mounds with his hands. The stranger was completely mystified by the gesture. For the first time he said, 'I really wonder what you are saying because your answer is crucial. We have come to the point when we should be ready to talk business.'

'When the tenth avatar comes, do you know where you and I will be?' asked the old man.

'Lend me a hand and I can lift off the horse from its pedestal after picking out the cement at the joints. We can do anything if we have a basis of understanding.'

At this stage the mutual mystification was complete, and there was no need even to carry on a guessing game at the meaning of words. The old man chattered away in a spirit of balancing off the credits and debits of conversational exchange, and said in order to be on the credit side, 'O honourable one, I hope god has blessed you with numerous progeny. I say this because you seem to be a good man, willing to stay beside an old man and talk to him, while all day I have none to talk to except when somebody stops by to ask for a piece of tobacco. But I seldom have it, tobacco is not what it used to be at one time, and I have given up chewing. I cannot afford it nowadays.' Noting the other's interest in his speech, Muni felt encouraged to ask, 'How many children have you?' with appropriate gestures with his hands. Realizing that a question was being asked, the red man replied, 'I said a hundred,' which encouraged Muni to go into details, 'How many of your children are boys and how many girls? Where are they? Is your daughter married? Is it difficult to find a son-in-law in your country also?'

In answer to these questions the red man dashed his hand into his pocket and brought forth his wallet in order to take immediate advantage of the bearish trend in the market. He flourished a hundred-rupee currency note and asked, 'Well, this is what I meant.'

The old man now realized that some financial element was entering their talk. He peered closely at the currency note, the like of which he had never seen in his life; he knew the five and ten by their colours although always in other people's hands, while his own earning at any time was in coppers and nickels. What was this man flourishing the note for? Perhaps asking for change. He laughed to himself at the notion of anyone coming to him for changing a thousand—or ten-thousand-rupee note. He said with a grin, 'Ask our village headman, who is also a moneylender; he can change even a lakh of rupees in gold sovereigns if you prefer it that way; he thinks nobody knows, but dig the floor of his puja room and your head will reel at the sight of the hoard. The man disguises himself in rags just to mislead the public. Talk to the headman yourself because he goes mad at the sight of me. Someone took away his pumpkins with the creeper and he, for some reason, thinks it was me and my goats...that's why I never let my goats be seen anywhere near the farms.' His eyes travelled to the goats nosing about, attempting to wrest nutrition from the minute greenery peeping out of rock and dry earth.

The foreigner followed his look and decided that it would be a sound policy to show an interest in the old man's pets. He went up casually to them and stroked their backs with every show of courteous attention. Now the truth dawned on the old man. His dream of a lifetime was about to be realized. He understood that the red man was actually making an offer for the goats. He had reared them up in the hope of selling them some day and, with the capital, opening a small shop on this very spot. Sitting here, watching the hills, he had often dreamt how he would put up a thatched roof here, spread a gunny sack out on the ground, and display on it fried nuts, coloured sweets and green coconut for the thirsty and famished wayfarers on the highway, which was sometimes very busy. The animals were not prize ones for a cattle show, but he had spent his occasional savings to provide them some fancy diet now and then, and they did not look too bad. While he was reflecting thus, the red man shook his hand and left on his palm one hundred rupees in tens now. 'It is all for you or you may share it if you have a partner.'

The old man pointed at the station wagon and asked, 'Are you carrying them off in that?'

'Yes, of course,' said the other, understanding the transportation part of it.

The old man said, 'This will be their first ride in a motor car. Carry them off after I get out of sight, otherwise they will never follow you, but only me even if I am travelling on the path to Yama Loka.' He laughed at his own joke, brought his palms together in a salute, turned around and went off, and was soon out of sight beyond a clump of thicket.

The red man looked at the goats grazing peacefully. Perched on the pedestal of the horse, as the westerly sun touched the ancient faded colours of the statue with a fresh splendour, he ruminated, 'He must be gone to fetch some help, I suppose!' and settled down to wait.

When a truck came downhill, he stopped it and got the help of a couple of men to detach the horse from its pedestal and place it in his station wagon. He gave them five rupees each, and for a further payment they siphoned off gas from the trucks and helped him to start his engine.

Muni hurried homeward with the cash securely tucked away at his waist in his *dhoti*. He shut the street door and stole up softly to his wife as she squatted before the lit oven wondering if by a miracle food would drop from the sky. Muni displayed his fortune for the day. She snatched the notes from him, counted them by the glow of the fire, and cried, 'One hundred rupees! How did you come by it? Have you been stealing?'

'I have sold our goats to a red-faced man. He was absolutely crazy to have them, gave me all this money and carried them off in his motor car!'

Hardly had these words left his lips when they heard bleating outside. She opened the door and saw the two goats at her door. 'Here they are!' she said. 'What's the meaning of all this?'

He muttered a great curse and seized one of the goats by its ear and shouted, 'Where is that man? Don't you know you are his? Why did you come back?' The goat only wriggled in his grip. He asked the same question of the other too. The goat shook itself off. His wife glared at him and declared, 'If you have thieved, the police will come tonight and break your bones. Don't involve me. I will go away to my parents...'

Under the Banyan Tree

The village Somal, nestling away in the forest tracts of Mempi, had a population of less than three hundred. It was in every way a village to make the heart of a rural reformer sink. Its tank, a small expanse of water, right in the middle of the village, served for drinking, bathing, and washing the cattle, and it bred malaria, typhoid, and heaven knew what else. The cottages sprawled anyhow and the lanes twisted and wriggled up and down and strangled each other. The population used the highway as the refuse ground and in the backyard of every house drain water stagnated in green puddles.

Such was the village. It is likely that the people of the village were insensitive: but it is more than likely that they never noticed their surroundings because they lived in a kind of perpetual enchantment. The enchanter was Nambi the storyteller. He was a man of about sixty or seventy. Or was he eighty or one hundred and eighty? Who could say? In a place so much cut off as Somal (the nearest bus-stop was ten miles away), reckoning could hardly be in the familiar measures of time. If anyone asked Nambi what his age was he referred to an ancient famine or an invasion or the building of a bridge and indicated how high he had stood from the ground at the time.

He was illiterate, in the sense that the written word was a mystery to him; but he could make up a story, in his head, at the rate of one a month; each story took nearly ten days to narrate.

His home was the little temple which was at the very end of the village. No one could say how he had come to regard himself as the owner of the temple. The temple was a very small structure with red-striped walls, with a stone image of the Goddess Shakti in the sanctum. The front portion of the temple was Nambi's home. For aught it mattered any place might be his home; for he was without possessions. All that he possessed was a broom with which he swept the temple; and he had also a couple of *dhotis* and upper cloth. He spent most of the day in the shade of the banyan which spread out its branches in front of the temple. When he felt hungry he walked into any house that caught his fancy and joined the family at dinner. When he needed new clothes they were brought to him by the villagers. He hardly ever had to go out in search of company; for the banyan shade served as a clubhouse for the village folk. All through the day people came seeking Nambi's company and squatted under the tree. If he was in a mood for it he listened to their talk and entertained them with his own observations and anecdotes. When he was in no mood he looked at the visitors sourly and asked, 'What do you think I am? Don't blame me if you get no story at the next moon. Unless I meditate how can the goddess give me a story? Do you think stories float in the air?' And he moved out to the edge of the forest and squatted there, contemplating the trees.

On Friday evenings the village turned up at the temple for worship, when Nambi lit a score of mud lamps and arranged them around the threshold of the sanctuary. He decorated the image with flowers, which grew wildly in the backyard of the temple. He acted as the priest and offered to the goddess fruits and flowers brought in by the villagers.

On the nights he had a story to tell he lit a small lamp and placed it in a niche in the trunk of the banyan tree. Villagers as they returned home in the evening saw this, went home, and said to their wives, 'Now, now, hurry up with the dinner, the storyteller is calling us.' As the moon crept up behind the hillock, men, women, and children gathered under the banyan tree. The storyteller would not appear yet. He would be sitting in the sanctum, before the goddess, with his eyes shut, in deep meditation. He sat thus as long as he liked and when he came out, with his forehead ablaze with ash and vermilion, he took his seat on a stone platform in front of the temple. He opened the story with a question. Jerking his finger towards a vague, faraway destination, he asked, 'A thousand years ago, a stone's throw in that direction, what do you think there was? It was not the weed-covered waste it is now, for donkeys to roll in. It was not the ash-pit it is now. It was the capital of the king...' The king would be Dasaratha, Vikramaditya, Asoka, or anyone that came into the old man's head; the capital was called Kapila, Kridapura, or anything. Opening thus, the old man went on without a pause for three hours. By then brick by brick the palace of the king was raised. The old man described the dazzling durbar hall where sat a hundred vassal kings, ministers, and subjects; in another part of the palace all the musicians in the world assembled and sang; and most of the songs were sung over again by Nambi to his audience; and he described in detail the pictures and trophies that hung on the walls of the palace...

It was story-building on an epic scale. The first day barely conveyed the setting of the tale, and Nambi's audience as yet had no idea who were coming into the story. As the moon slipped behind the trees of Mempi Forest Nambi said, 'Now friends, Mother says this will do for the day.' He abruptly rose, went in, lay down, and fell asleep long before the babble of the crowd ceased.

The light in the niche would again be seen two or three days later, and again and again throughout the bright half of the month. Kings and heroes, villains and fairy-like women, gods in human form, saints and assassins, jostled each other in that world which was created under the banyan tree. Nambi's voice rose and fell in an exquisite rhythm and the moonlight and the hour completed the magic. The villagers laughed with Nambi, they wept with him, they adored the heroes, cursed the villains, groaned when the conspirator had his initial success, and they sent up to the gods a heartfelt prayer for a happy ending...

On the day when the story ended, the whole gathering went into the sanctum and prostrated before the goddess...

By the time the next moon peeped over the hillock Nambi was ready with another story. He never repeated the same kind of story or brought in the same set of persons, and the village folk considered Nambi a sort of miracle, quoted his words of wisdom, and lived on the whole in an exalted plane of their own, though their life in all other respects was hard and drab.

And yet it had gone on for years and years. One moon he lit the lamp in the tree. The audience came. The old man took his seat and began the story. '…When King Vikramaditya lived, his minister was…' He paused. He could not get beyond it. He made a fresh beginning. 'There was the king…' he said, repeated it, and then his words trailed off into a vague mumbling. 'What has come over me?' he asked pathetically. 'Oh, Mother, great Mother, why do I stumble and falter? I know the story. I had the whole of it a moment ago. What was it about? I can't understand what has happened.' He faltered and looked so miserable that his audience said, 'Take your own time. You are perhaps tired.'

'Shut up!' he cried. 'Am I tired? Wait a moment; I will tell you the story presently.' Following this there was utter silence. Eager faces looked up at him. 'Don't look at me!' he flared up. Somebody gave him a tumbler of milk. The audience waited patiently. This was a new experience. Some persons expressed their sympathy aloud. Some persons began to talk among themselves. Those who sat in the outer edge of the crowd silently slipped away. Gradually, as it neared midnight, others followed this example. Nambi sat staring at the ground, his head bowed in thought. For the first time he realized that he was old. He felt he would never more be able to control his thoughts or express them cogently. He looked up. Everyone had gone except his friend Mari the blacksmith. 'Mari, why aren't you also gone?'

Mari apologized for the rest: 'They didn't want to tire you; so they have gone away.'

Nambi got up. 'You are right. Tomorrow I will make it up. Age, age. What is my age? It has come on suddenly.' He pointed at his head and said, 'This says, "Old fool, don't think I shall be your servant any more. You will be my servant hereafter." It is disobedient and treacherous.'

He lit the lamp in the niche next day. The crowd assembled under the banyan faithfully. Nambi had spent the whole day in meditation. He had been fervently praying to the goddess not to desert him. He began the story. He went on for an hour without a stop. He felt greatly relieved, so much so that he interrupted his narration to remark, 'Oh, friends. The Mother is always kind. I was seized with a foolish fear…' and continued the story. In a few minutes he felt

dried up. He struggled hard: 'And then…and then…what happened?'
He stammered. There followed a pause lasting an hour. The audience
rose without a word and went home. The old man sat on the stone
brooding till the cock crew. 'I can't blame them for it,' he muttered
to himself. 'Can they sit down here and mope all night?' Two days
later he gave another instalment of the story, and that, too, lasted
only a few minutes. The gathering dwindled. Fewer persons began to
take notice of the lamp in the niche. Even these came only out of
a sense of duty. Nambi realized that there was no use in prolonging
the struggle. He brought the story to a speedy and premature end.

He knew what was happening. He was harrowed by the thoughts
of his failure. I should have been happier if I had dropped dead years
ago, he said to himself, Mother, why have you struck me dumb…?
He shut himself up in the sanctum, hardly ate any food, and spent
the greater part of the day sitting motionless in meditation.

The next moon peeped over the hillock, Nambi lit the lamp in
the niche. The villagers as they returned home saw the lamp, but only
a handful turned up at night. 'Where are the others?' the old man
asked. 'Let us wait.' He waited. The moon came up. His handful of
audience waited patiently. And then the old man said, 'I won't tell
the story today, nor tomorrow unless the whole village comes here.
I insist upon it. It is a mighty story. Everyone must hear it.' Next
day he went up and down the village street shouting, 'I have a most
wonderful tale to tell tonight. Come one and all; don't miss it…' This
personal appeal had a great effect. At night a large crowd gathered
under the banyan. They were happy that the storyteller had regained
his powers. Nambi came out of the temple when everyone had settled
and said: 'It is the Mother who gives the gifts; and it is she who takes
away the gifts. Nambi is a dotard. He speaks when the Mother has
anything to say. He is struck dumb when she has nothing to say. But
what is the use of the jasmine when it has lost its scent? What is the
lamp for when all the oil is gone? Goddess be thanked… These are
my last words on this earth; and this is my story.' He rose and went
into the sanctum. His audience hardly understood what he meant.
They sat there till they became weary. And then some of them got

up and stepped into the sanctum. There the storyteller sat with eyes shut. 'Aren't you going to tell us a story?' they asked. He opened his eyes, looked at them, and shook his head. He indicated by gesture that he had spoken his last words.

When he felt hungry he walked into any cottage and silently sat down for food, and walked away the moment he had eaten. Beyond this he had hardly anything to demand of his fellow beings. The rest of his life (he lived for a few more years) was one great consummate silence.

The Guide

1

Raju welcomed the intrusion—something to relieve the loneliness of the place. The man stood gazing reverentially on his face. Raju felt amused and embarrassed. 'Sit down if you like,' Raju said, to break the spell. The other accepted the suggestion with a grateful nod and went down the river steps to wash his feet and face, came up wiping himself dry with the end of a chequered yellow towel on his shoulder, and took his seat two steps below the granite slab on which Raju was sitting cross-legged as if it were a throne, beside an ancient shrine. The branches of the trees canopying the river course rustled and trembled with the agitation of birds and monkeys settling down for the night. Upstream beyond the hills the sun was setting. Raju waited for the other to say something. But he was too polite to open a conversation.

Raju asked, 'Where are you from?' dreading lest the other should turn round and ask the same question.

The man replied, 'I'm from Mangal.'

'Where is Mangal?'

The other waved his arm, indicating a direction across the river, beyond the high steep bank. 'Not far from here,' he added. The man volunteered further information about himself. 'My daughter lives nearby. I had gone to visit her; I am now on my way home. I left her after food. She insisted that I should stay on to dinner, but I refused. It'd have meant walking home at nearly midnight. I'm not afraid of anything, but why should we walk when we ought to be sleeping in bed?'

'You are very sensible,' Raju said.

They listened for a while to the chatter of monkeys, and the man added as an afterthought, 'My daughter's married to my own sister's son, and so there is no problem. I often visit my sister and also my daughter; and so no one minds it.'

'Why should anyone mind in any case if you visit a daughter?'

'It's not considered proper form to pay too many visits to a son-in-law,' explained the villager.

Raju liked this rambling talk. He had been all alone in this place for over a day. It was good to hear the human voice again. After this the villager resumed the study of his face with intense respect. And Raju stroked his chin thoughtfully to make sure that an apostolic beard had not suddenly grown there. It was still smooth. He had had his last shave only two days before and paid for it with the hard-earned coins of his jail life.

Loquacious as usual and with the sharp blade scraping the soap, the barber had asked, 'Coming out, I suppose?' Raju rolled his eyes and remained silent. He felt irritated at the question, but did not like to show it with the fellow holding the knife. 'Just coming out?' repeated the barber obstinately.

Raju felt it would be no use being angry with such a man. Here he was in the presence of experience. He asked, 'How do you know?'

'I have spent twenty years shaving people here. Didn't you observe that this was the first shop as you left the jail gate? Half the trick is to have your business in the right place. But that raises other people's jealousies!' he said, waving off an army of jealous barbers.

'Don't you attend to the inmates?'

'Not until they come out. It is my brother's son who is on duty there. I don't want to compete with him and I don't want to enter the jail gates every day.'

'Not a bad place,' said Raju through the soap.

'Go back then,' said the barber and asked, 'What was it? What did the police say?'

'Don't talk of it,' snapped Raju and tried to maintain a sullen, forbidding silence for the rest of the shave.

But the barber was not to be cowed so easily. His lifelong contact with tough men had hardened him. He said, 'Eighteen months or twenty-four? I can bet it's one or the other.'

Raju felt admiration for the man. He was a master. It was no use losing one's temper. 'You are so wise and knowing. Why do you ask questions?'

The barber was pleased with the compliment. His fingers paused in their operations; he bent round to face Raju and say, 'Just to get it out of you, that is all. It's written on your face that you are a two-year sort, which means you are not a murderer.'

'How can you tell?' Raju said.

'You would look different if you had been in for seven years, which is what one gets for murder only half-proved.'

'What else have I not done?' Raju asked.

'You have not cheated in any big way; but perhaps only in a small, petty manner.'

'Go on. What next?'

'You have not abducted or raped anyone, or set fire to a house.'

'Why don't you say exactly why I was sent to jail for two years? I'll give you four annas for a guess.'

'No time now for a game,' said the barber and went on, 'What you do next?'

'I don't know. Must go somewhere, I suppose,' said Raju thoughtfully.

'In case you like to go back to your old company, why don't you put your hand in someone's pocket at the market, or walk through an open door and pick out some trash and let the people howl for the police? They'll see you back where you want to be.'

'Not a bad place,' Raju repeated, nodding slightly in the direction of the jail wall. 'Friendly people there, but I hate to be awakened every morning at five.'

'An hour at which a night-prowler likes to return home to bed, I suppose,' said the barber with heavy insinuation. 'Well, that's all. You may get up,' he said, putting away the razor. 'You look like a maharaja now'—surveying Raju at a distance from his chair.

The villager on the lower step looked up at his face with devotion, which irked Raju. 'Why do you look at me like that?' he asked brusquely.

The man replied, 'I don't know. I don't mean to offend you, sir.' Raju wanted to blurt out, 'I am here because I have nowhere else to go. I want to be away from people who may recognize me.' But he hesitated, wondering how he should say it. It looked as though he would be hurting the other's deepest sentiment if he so much as whispered the word 'jail'. He tried at least to say, 'I am not so great as you imagine. I am just ordinary.' Before he could fumble and reach the words, the other said, 'I have a problem, sir.'

'Tell me about it,' Raju said, the old, old habit of affording guidance to others asserting itself. Tourists who recommended him to one another would say at one time, 'If you are lucky enough to be guided by Raju, you will know everything. He will not only show you all the worthwhile places, but also help you in every way.' It was in his nature to get involved in other people's interests and activities. 'Otherwise,' Raju often reflected, 'I should have grown up like a thousand other normal persons, without worries in life.'

My troubles would not have started (Raju said in the course of narrating his life-story to this man who was called Velan at a later stage) but for Rosie. Why did she call herself Rosie? She did not come from a foreign land. She was just an Indian, who should have done well with Devi, Meena, Lalitha, or any one of the thousand names we have in our country. She chose to call herself Rosie. Don't imagine on hearing her name that she wore a short skirt or cropped her hair. She looked just the orthodox dancer that she was. She wore sarees of bright hues and gold lace, had curly hair which she braided and beflowered, wore diamond earrings and a heavy gold necklace. I told her at the first opportunity what a great dancer she was and how she fostered our cultural traditions, and it pleased her.

Thousands of persons must have said the same thing to her since, but I happened to be the first in the line. Anyone likes to hear flattering sentiments, and more than others, I suppose, dancers. They like to be told every hour of the day how well they keep their steps. I praised her art whenever I could snatch a moment alone with her and whisper in her ear, out of range of that husband of hers. Oh, what a man! I have not met a more grotesque creature in my life. Instead of calling herself Rosie, she could more logically have called him Marco Polo. He dressed like a man about to undertake an expedition, with his thick coloured glasses, thick jacket, and a thick helmet over which was perpetually stretched a green, shiny, waterproof cover, giving him the appearance of a space-traveller. I have, of course, no idea of the original Marco Polo's appearance, but I wanted to call this man Marco at first sight, and I have not bothered to associate him with any other name since.

The moment I set eyes on him, on that memorable day at our railway station, I knew that here was a lifelong customer for me. A man who preferred to dress like a permanent tourist was just what a guide passionately looked for all his life.

You may want to ask why I became a guide or when. I was a guide for the same reason as someone else is a signaller, porter, or guard. It is fated thus. Don't laugh at my railway associations. The railways got into my blood very early in life. Engines, with their tremendous clanging and smoke, ensnared my senses. I felt at home on the railway platform, and considered the station master and porter the best company for man, and their railway talk the most enlightened. I grew up in their midst. Ours was a small house opposite the Malgudi station. The house had been built by my father with his own hands long before trains were thought of. He chose this spot because it was outside the town and he could have it cheap. He had dug the earth, kneaded the mud with water from the well, and built the walls, and roofed them with coconut thatch. He planted papaya trees around, which yielded fruit, which he cut up and sold in slices: a single fruit brought him eight annas if he carved it with dexterity. My father had a small shop built of dealwood planks and gunny sack; and all day he sat there selling peppermint, fruit, tobacco, betel leaf, parched gram (which he measured out in tiny bamboo cylinders), and whatever else the wayfarers on the Trunk Road demanded. It was known as the 'hut shop'. A crowd of peasants and drivers of bullock-wagons were always gathered in front of his shop. A very busy man indeed. At midday he called me when he went in for his lunch and made a routine statement at the same hour. 'Raju, take my seat. Be sure to receive the money for whatever you give. Don't eat off all that eating stuff, it's kept for sale; call me if you have doubts.'

And I kept calling aloud, 'Father, green peppermints, how many for half an anna?' while the customer waited patiently.

'Three,' he shouted from the house, with his mouth stuffed with food. 'But if he is buying for three-quarters of an anna, give him...' He mentioned some complicated concession, which I could never apply.

I appealed to the customer, 'Give me only half an anna,' and gave him three peppermints in return. If by chance I had happened to take four greens out of the big bottle, I swallowed the fourth in order to minimize complications.

An eccentric cockerel in the neighbourhood announced the daybreak when probably it felt that we had slept long enough. It let out a shattering cry which made rny father jump from his bed and wake me up.

I washed myself at the wall, smeared holy ash on my forehead, stood before the framed pictures of gods hanging high up on the wall, and recited all kinds of sacred verse in a loud, ringing tone. After watching my performance for a while, my father slipped away to the back yard to milk the buffalo. Later, coming in with the pail, he always remarked, 'Something really wrong with that animal this time. She wouldn't yield even half a measure today.'

My mother invariably answered, 'I know, I know. She is getting wrong-headed, that is all. I know what she will respond to,' she said in a mysterious, sinister manner, receiving the pail and carrying it into the kitchen. She came out in a moment with a tumblerful of hot milk for me.

The sugar was kept in an old tin can, which looked rusty but contained excellent sugar. It was kept on a wooden ledge on the smoke-stained wall of the kitchen, out of my reach. I fear that its position was shifted up and up as I grew older, because I remember that I could never get at that rusty can at any time except with the cooperation of my elders.

When the sky lightened, my father was ready for me on the *pyol*.

There he sat with a thin broken twig at his side. The modern notions of child psychology were unknown then; the stick was an educator's indispensable equipment. 'The unbeaten brat will remain unlearned,' said my father, quoting an old proverb. He taught me the Tamil alphabet. He wrote the first two letters on each side of my slate at a time. I had to go over the contours of the letters with my pencil endlessly until they became bloated and distorted beyond recognition. From time to time my father snatched the slate from my hand, looked at it, glared at me, and said, 'What a mess! You will never prosper in life if you disfigure the sacred letters of the alphabet.' Then he cleaned the slate with his damp towel, wrote the letters again, and gave it to me with the injunction, 'If you spoil this, you will make me wild. Trace them exactly as I have written. Don't try any of your tricks on them,' and he flourished his twig menacingly.

I said meekly, 'Yes, Father,' and started to write again. I can well picture myself, sticking my tongue out, screwing my head to one side, and putting my entire body weight on the pencil; the slate pencil screeched as I tried to drive it through and my father ordered, 'Don't make all that noise with that horrible pencil of yours. What has come over you?'

Then followed arithmetic. Two and two, four; four and three, something else. Something into something, more; some more into less. Oh god, numbers did give me a headache. While the birds were out chirping and flying in the cool air, I cursed the fate that confined me to my father's company. His temper was rising every second. As if in answer to my silent prayer, an early customer was noticed at the door of the hut shop and my lessons came to an abrupt end. My father left me with the remark, 'I have better things to do of a morning than make a genius out of a clay-head.'

Although the lessons had seemed interminable to me, my mother said the moment she saw me, 'So you have been let off! I wonder what you can learn in half an hour!'

I told her, 'I'll go out and play and won't trouble you. But no more lessons for the day, please.' With that I was off to the shade of a tamarind tree across the road. It was an ancient, spreading tree, dense with leaves, amidst which monkeys and birds lived, bred, and chattered incessantly, feeding on the tender leaves and fruits. Pigs and piglets came from somewhere and nosed about the ground, thick with fallen leaves, and I played there all day. I think I involved the pigs in some imaginary game and even fancied myself carried on their backs. My father's customers greeted me as they passed that way. I had marbles, an iron hoop to roll, and a rubber ball, with which I occupied myself. I hardly knew what time of the day it was or what was happening around me.

Sometimes my father took me along to the town when he went shopping. He stopped a passing bullock-cart for the trip. I hung about anxiously with an appealing look in my eyes (I had been taught not to ask to be taken along) until my father said, 'Climb in, little man.' I clambered in before his sentence was completed. The bells around the bull's neck jingled, the wooden wheels grated and ground the dust off the rough road; I clung to the staves on the sides and felt my bones shaken. Still, I enjoyed the smell of the straw in the cart and all the scenes we passed. Men and vehicles, hogs and boys—the panorama of life enchanted me.

At the market my father made me sit on a wooden platform within sight of a shopman known to him, and went about to do his shopping. My pockets would be filled with fried nuts and sweets; munching, I watched the activities of the market—people buying and selling, arguing and laughing, swearing and shouting. While my father was gone on his shopping expedition, I remember, a question kept drumming in my head: 'Father, you are a shopkeeper yourself. Why do you go about buying in other shops?' I never got an answer. As I sat gazing on the afternoon haze, the continuous din of the marketplace lulled my senses, the dusty glare suddenly made me drowsy, and I fell asleep, leaning on the wall of that unknown place where my father had chosen to put me.

'I have a problem, sir,' said the man.

Raju nodded his head and said, 'So has everyone,' in a sudden access of pontificality. Ever since the moment this man had come and sat before him, gazing on his face, he had experienced a feeling of importance. He felt like an actor who was always expected to utter the right sentence. Now the appropriate sentence was, 'If you show me a person without a problem, then I'll show you the perfect world. Do you know what the great Buddha said?' The other edged nearer. 'A woman once went wailing to the great Buddha, clasping her dead baby to her bosom. The Buddha said, "Go into every home in this city and find one where death is unknown; if you find such a place, fetch me a handful of mustard from there, and then I'll teach you how to conquer death."'

The man clicked his tongue in appreciation and asked, 'And what happened to the dead baby, sir?'

'She had to bury it, of course,' said Raju. 'So also,' he concluded, while doubting in his mind the relevance of the comparison, 'if you show me a single home without a problem, I shall show you the way to attain a universal solution to all problems.'

The man was overwhelmed by the weightiness of this statement. He performed a deep obeisance and said, 'I have not told you my name, sir. I am Velan. My father in his lifetime married thrice. I am the first son of his first wife. The youngest daughter of his last wife is also with us. As the head of the family, I have given her every comfort at home, provided her with all the jewellery and clothes a girl needs, but...' He paused slightly before bringing out the big surprise. But Raju completed the sentence for him, 'The girl shows no gratitude.'

'Absolutely, sir!' said the man.

'And she will not accept your plans for her marriage?'

'Oh, too true, sir,' Velan said, wonderstruck. 'My cousin's son is a fine boy. Even the date of the wedding was fixed, but do you know, sir, what the girl did?'

'Ran away from the whole thing,' said Raju, and asked, 'How did you bring her back?'

'I searched for her three days and nights and spotted her in a festival crowd in a distant village. They were pulling the temple chariot around the streets and the population of fifty villages was crowded into one. I searched every face in the crowd and at last caught her while she was watching a puppet show. Now, do you know what she does?' Raju decided to let the other have the satisfaction of saying things himself, and Velan ended his story with, 'She sulks in a room all day. I do not know what to do. It is possible that she is possessed. If I could know what to do with her, it'd be such a help, sir.'

Raju said with a philosophic weariness, 'Such things are common in life. One should not let oneself be bothered unduly by anything.'

'What am I to do with her, sir?'

'Bring her over; let me speak to her,' Raju said grandly.

Velan rose, bowed low, and tried to touch Raju's feet. Raju recoiled at the attempt. 'I'll not permit anyone to do this. God alone is entitled to such a prostration. He will destroy us if we attempt to usurp His rights.' He felt he was attaining the stature of a saint. Velan went down the steps meekly, crossed the river, climbed the opposite bank, and was soon out of sight. Raju ruminated. 'I wish I had asked him what the age of the girl was. Hope she is uninteresting. I have had enough trouble in life.'

He sat there for a long time, watching the river flow into the night; the rustle of the peepul and banyan trees around was sometimes loud and frightening. The sky was clear. Having nothing else to do, he started counting the stars. He said to himself, 'I shall be rewarded for this profound service to humanity. People will say, "Here is the man who knows the exact number of stars in the sky. If you have any trouble on that account, you had better consult him. He will be your night guide for the skies."' He told himself, 'The thing to do is to start from a corner and go on patch by patch. Never work from the top to the horizon, but always the other way.' He was evolving a theory. He started the count from above a fringe of palmyra trees on his left-hand side, up the course of the river, over to the other side. 'One... two...fifty-five...' He suddenly realized that if he looked deeper a new cluster of stars came into view; by the time he assimilated it into his reckoning, he realized he had lost sight of his starting point and found himself entangled in hopeless figures. He felt exhausted. He stretched himself on the stone slab and fell asleep under the open sky.

The eight o'clock sun shone fully on his face. He opened his eyes and saw Velan standing respectfully away on a lower step. 'I have brought my sister,' he said and thrust up a young girl of fourteen, who had tightly braided her hair and decorated herself with jewellery. Velan explained, 'These jewels were given by me, bought out of my own money, for she is after all my sister.'

Raju sat up, rubbing his eyes. He was as yet unprepared to take charge of the world's affairs. His immediate need was privacy for his morning ablutions. He said to them, 'You may go in there and wait for me.'

He found them waiting for him in the ancient, pillared hall. Raju sat himself down on a slightly elevated platform in the middle of the hall. Velan placed before him a basket filled with bananas, cucumbers, pieces of sugar cane, fried nuts, and a copper vessel brimming with milk.

Raju asked, 'What is all this for?'

'It will please us very much if you will accept them, sir.'

Raju sat looking at the hamper. It was not unwelcome. He could eat anything and digest it now. He had learned not to be fussy. Formerly he would have said, 'Who will eat this? Give me coffee and *idli*, please, first thing in the day. These are good enough for munching later.' But prison life had trained him to swallow anything at any time. Sometimes a colleague in the cell, managing to smuggle in, through the kindness of a warder, something unpalatable like mutton-puff made six days ago, with its oil going rancid, shared it with Raju, and Raju remembered how he ate it with gusto at three in the morning—a time chosen before the others could wake up and claim a share. Anything was welcome now. He asked, 'Why do you do all this for me?'

'They are grown in our fields and we are proud to offer them to you.'

Raju did not have to ask further questions. He had gradually come to view himself as a master of these occasions. He had already begun to feel that the adulation directed to him was inevitable. He sat in silence, eyeing the gift for a while. Suddenly he picked up the basket and went into an inner sanctum. The others followed. Raju stopped before a stone image in the dark recess. It was a tall god with four hands, bearing a mace and wheel, with a beautifully chiselled head, but abandoned a century ago. Raju ceremoniously placed the basket of edibles at the feet of the image and said, 'It's His first. Let the offering go to Him, first; and we will eat the remnants. By giving to God, do you know how it multiplies, rather than divides? Do you know the story?' He began narrating the story of Devaka, a man of ancient times who begged for alms at the temple gate every day and would not use any of his collections without first putting them at the feet of the god. Halfway through the story he realized that he could not remember either its course or its purport. He lapsed into silence. Velan patiently waited for the continuation. He was of the stuff disciples are made of; an unfinished story or an incomplete moral never bothered him; it was all in the scheme of life. When Raju turned and strode majestically back to the river step, Velan and his sister followed him mutely.

How could I recollect the story heard from my mother so long ago? She told me a story every evening while we waited for Father to close the shop and come home. The shop remained open till midnight. Bullock-carts in long caravans arrived late in the evening from distant villages, loaded with coconut, rice, and other commodities for the market. The animals were unyoked under the big tamarind tree for the night, and the cart-men drifted in twos and threes to the shop, for a chat or to ask for things to eat or smoke. How my father loved to discuss with them the price of grain, rainfall, harvest, and the state of irrigation channels. Or they talked about old litigations. One heard repeated references to magistrates, affidavits, witnesses in the case, and appeals, punctuated with roars of laughter—possibly the memory of some absurd legality or loophole tickled them.

My father ignored food and sleep when he had company. My mother sent me out several times to see if he could be made to turn in. He was a man of uncertain temper and one could not really guess how he would react to interruptions, and so my mother coached me to go up, watch his mood, and gently remind him of food and home. I stood under the shop awning, coughing and clearing my throat, hoping to catch his eye. But the talk was all-absorbing and he would not glance in my direction, and I got absorbed in their talk, although I did not understand a word of it.

After a while my mother's voice came gently on the night air, calling, 'Raju, Raju,' and my father interrupted his activities to look at me and say, 'Tell your mother not to wait for me. Tell her to place a handful of rice and buttermilk in a bowl, with just one piece of lime pickle, and keep it in the oven for me. I'll come in later.' It was almost a formula with him five days in a week. He always added, 'Not that I'm really hungry tonight.' And then I believe he went on to discuss health problems with his cronies.

But I didn't stop to hear further. I made a swift dash back home. There was a dark patch between the light from the shop and the dim lantern shedding its light on our threshold, a matter of about ten yards, I suppose, but the passage through it gave me a cold sweat. I expected wild animals and supernatural creatures to emerge and grab me. My mother waited on the doorstep to receive me and said, 'Not hungry, I suppose! That'll give him an excuse to talk to the village folk all night, and then come in for an hour's sleep and get up with the crowing of that foolish cock somewhere. He will spoil his health.'

I followed her into the kitchen. She placed my plate and hers side by side on the floor, drew the rice-pot within reach, and served me and herself simultaneously, and we finished our dinner by the sooty tin lamp, stuck on a nail in the wall. She unrolled a mat for me in the front room, and I lay down to sleep. She sat at my side, awaiting Father's return. Her presence gave me a feeling of inexplicable cosiness. I felt I ought to put her proximity to good use, and complained, 'Something is bothering my hair,' and she ran her fingers through my hair and scratched the nape of my neck. And then I commanded, 'A story.'

Immediately she began, 'Once upon a time there was a man called Devaka...' I heard his name mentioned almost every night. He was a hero, saint, or something of the kind. I never learned fully what he did or why, sleep overcoming me before my mother was through even the preamble.

Raju sat on the step and watched the river dazzling in the morning sun. The air was cool, and he wished he were alone. His visitors sat patiently on a lower step, waiting for him to attend to them, like patients in a doctor's room. Raju had many problems of his own to think of. He suddenly felt irritated at the responsibility that Velan was thrusting on him, and said frankly, 'I am not going to think of your problems, Velan; not now.'

'May I know why?' he asked humbly.

'It is so,' Raju said with an air of finality.

'When may I trouble you, sir?' he asked.

Raju replied grandly, 'When the time is ripe for it.' This took the matter from the realms of time into eternity. Velan accepted his answer with resignation and rose to go. It was rather touching. Raju felt indebted to him for the edibles he had brought, so he said pacifyingly, 'Is this the sister you told me about?'

'Yes, sir; it is.'

'I know what your problem is, but I wish to give the matter thought. We cannot force vital solutions. Every question must bide its time. Do you understand?'

'Yes, sir,' Velan said. He drew his fingers across his brow and said, 'Whatever is written here will happen. How can we ever help it?'

'We may not change it, but we may understand it,' Raju replied grandly. 'And to arrive at a proper understanding, time is needed.' Raju felt he was growing wings. Shortly, he felt, he might float in the air and perch himself on the tower of the ancient temple. Nothing was going to surprise him. He suddenly found himself asking, 'Have I been in a prison or in some sort of transmigration?'

Velan looked relieved and proud to hear so much from his master. He looked significantly at his difficult sister, and she bowed her head in shame. Raju declared, looking fixedly at the girl, 'What must happen must happen; no power on earth or in heaven can change its course, just as no one can change the course of that river.' They gazed on the river, as if the clue to their problems lay there, and turned to go. Raju watched them cross the river and climb the opposite bank. Soon they were out of sight.

2

We noticed much activity in the field in front of our house. A set of men arrived from the town every morning and were busy in the field all day. We learned that they were building a railway track. They came to my father's shop for refreshments. My father inquired anxiously, 'When shall we have the trains coming in here?'

If they were in a good mood, they answered, 'About six or eight months, who can say?' Or if they were in a black mood, 'Don't ask us. Next you will tell us to drive a locomotive to your shop!' And they laughed grimly.

Work was going on briskly. I lost to some extent my freedom under the tamarind tree, because trucks were parked there. I climbed into them and played. No one minded me. All day I was climbing in and out of the trucks, and my clothes became red with mud. Most of the trucks brought red earth which was banked up on the field. In a short while, a small mountain was raised in front of our house. It was enchanting. When I stood on the top of this mound I could see far-off places, the hazy outlines of Mempi Hills. I became as busy as the men. I spent all my time in the company of those working on the track, listening to their talk and sharing their jokes. More trucks came, bringing timber and iron. A variety of goods was piling up on every side. Presently I began to collect sawn-off metal bits, nuts and bolts, and I treasured them in my mother's big trunk, where a space was allotted to me amidst her ancient silk sarees, which she never wore.

A boy grazing his cows approached the spot just below the mound on which I was playing a game by myself. His cows were munching the grass right below the mound on which the men were working, and the little fellow had dared to step on the slope where I played. I was beginning to have a sense of ownership of the railway, and I didn't want trespassers there. I frowned at the boy and barked, 'Get out.'

'Why?' he asked. 'My cows are here, I'm watching them.'

'Begone with your cows,' I said. 'Otherwise they will be run over by the train, which will be here shortly.'

'Let them be. What do you care?' he said, which irritated me so much that I let out a yell and pounced on him with 'You son of a...' and a variety of other expressions recently picked up. The boy, instead of knocking me down, ran screaming to my father, 'Your son is using bad language.'

My father sprang up on hearing this. Just my misfortune. He came rushing toward me as I was resuming my game and asked, 'What did you call this boy?' I had the good sense not to repeat it. I blinked, wordlessly, at which the boy repeated exactly what I had said. This produced an unexpectedly violent effect on my father. He grabbed my neck within the hollow of his hand, and asked, 'Where did you pick that up?' I pointed at the men working on the track. He looked up, remained silent for a second, and said, 'Oh, that is so, is it? You will not idle about picking up bad words any more. I will see to it. You will go to a school tomorrow and every day.'

'Father!' I cried. He was passing a harsh sentence on me. To be removed from a place I loved, to a place I loathed!

A tremendous fuss was made before I started for my school each day. My mother fed me early and filled up a little aluminium vessel with refreshment for the afternoon. She carefully put my books and slate into a bag and slung it across my shoulder. I was dressed in clean shorts and shirt; my hair was combed back from the forehead, with all the curls falling on my nape. For the first few days I enjoyed all this attention, but soon developed a normal aversion; I preferred to be neglected and stay at home to being fussed over and sent to a school. But my father was a stern disciplinarian; perhaps he was a snob who wanted to brag before others that his son was going to a school. He kept an eye on my movements till I was safely on the road each morning. He sat in his shop and kept calling every few minutes, 'Boy, have you left?'

I walked endlessly to reach my school. No other boy went in my direction. I talked to myself on the way, paused to observe the passers-by or a country cart lumbering along, or a grasshopper going under a culvert. My progress was so halting and slow that when I turned into the Market Street I could hear my classmates shouting their lessons in unison, for the old man, our master, who taught us, believed in getting the maximum noise out of his pupils.

I don't know on whose advice my father chose to send me here for my education, while the fashionable Albert Mission School was quite close by. I'd have felt proud to call myself an Albert Mission boy. But I often heard my father declare, 'I don't want to send my boy there; it seems they try to convert our boys into Christians and are all the time insulting our gods.' I don't know how he got the notion; anyway, he was firmly convinced that the school where I was sent was the best under the sun. He was known to boast, 'Many students who have passed through the hands of this ancient master are now big officials at Madras, collectors and men like that...' It was purely his own imagining or the invention of the old man who taught me. No one could dream that this was in any sense a school, let alone an outstanding school. It was what was called a *pyol* school, because the classes were held on the *pyol* of the gentleman's house. He lived in Kabir Lane, in a narrow old house with a cement *pyol* in front, with the street drain running right below it. He gathered a score of young boys of my age every morning on the *pyol*, reclined on a cushion in a corner, and shouted at the little fellows, flourishing a rattan cane all the time. All the classes were held there at the same time, and he bestowed attention on each group in turn. I belonged to the youngest and most elementary set, just learning the alphabet and numbers. He made us read aloud from our books and copy down the letters on our slates, and looked through each and gave corrections and flicks from the cane for those who repeated their follies. He was a very abusive man. My father, who wanted to save me from the language of the railway trackmen, had certainly not made a safer choice in sending me to this old man, who habitually addressed his pupils as donkeys and traced their genealogies on either side with thoroughness.

The thing that irritated him was not merely the mistakes that we made but our very presence. Seeing us, such short, clumsy youngsters, always fumbling and shuffling, I think got on his nerves. Of course, we made a lot of noise on his *pyol*. When he went into his house for a moment's nap or for his food or for any of a dozen domestic calls, we rolled over each other, fought, scratched, bleated, yelled. Or we tried to invade his privacy and peep in. Once we slipped in and passed from room to room until we came to the kitchen and saw him sitting before the oven, baking something. We stood at the doorway and said, 'Oh, master, you know how to cook also!' and giggled, and a lady who was standing nearby also giggled at our remark.

He turned on us fiercely and ordered, 'Get out, boys; don't come here; this is not your classroom,' and we scampered back to our place, where he found us later and twisted our ears until we screamed. He said, 'I am admitting you devils here because I want you to become civilized, but what you do is...' and he catalogued our sins and misdeeds.

We were contrite, and he softened and said, 'Hereafter let me not catch you anywhere beyond that threshold. I will hand you over to the police if you come in.' That settled it. We never peeped again, but when his back was turned confined our attention to the drain that flowed beneath the *pyol*. We tore off loose leaves from our notebooks, made boats, and floated them down the drain, and in a short while it became established practice, and a kind of boat-racing developed out of it; we lay on our bellies and watched the boats float away on the drainwater. He warned us, 'If you fall off into the gutter, you will find yourselves in the Sarayu River, remember, and I shall have to tell your father to go out and look for you there, I suppose!' and he laughed at the grim prospect.

His interest in us was one rupee a month and anything else in kind we cared to carry. My father sent him every month two cubes of jaggery, others brought in rice and vegetables and anything else he might demand from time to time. Whenever his store at home ran out, he called one or another to his side and said, 'Now if you are a good boy, you will run to your house and fetch me just a little, only so much, mind you, of sugar. Come, let me see if you are smart!' He adopted a kindly, canvassing tone on such occasions, and we felt honoured to be able to serve him, and pestered our parents to give us the gifts and fought for the honour of serving him. Our parents showed an excessive readiness to oblige this master, grateful probably because he kept us in his charge for the major part of the day, from morning till four in the afternoon, when he dismissed us and we sprinted homeward.

In spite of all the apparent violence and purposelessness, I suppose we did make good under our master, for within a year I proved good enough for the first standard in the Board High School; I could read heavier books, and do multiplication up to twenty in my head. The old master himself escorted me to the Board School, which had just established itself, and admitted me there; he saw me off in my new class, seated me and two others, and blessed us before taking leave of us. It was a pleasant surprise for us that he could be so kind.

Velan was bursting with news of a miracle. He stood before Raju with folded hands, and said, 'Sir, things have turned out well.'

'I'm so happy. How?'

'My sister came before our family gathering and admitted her follies. She has agreed...' He went on to explain. The girl had all of a sudden appeared before the assembled family that morning. She faced everyone straight and said, 'I have behaved foolishly all these days. I will do what my brother and the other elders at home tell me to do. They know what is best for us.'

'I could hardly believe my ears,' explained Velan. 'I pinched myself to see whether I was dreaming or awake. This girl's affair had cast a gloom on our home. If you left out our partition suit and all the complications arising from it, we had no worry to equal this. You see, we are fond of the girl, and it pained us to watch her sulk in a dark room, without minding her appearance or dress or caring for food. We did our best to make her cheerful and then had to leave her alone. We had all been very miserable on account of her, and so we were surprised this morning when she came before us with her hair oiled and braided, with flowers in it. Looking bright, she said, "I have been a bother to you all these days. Forgive me, all of you. I shall do whatever my elders order me to do." Naturally, after we got over the surprise, we asked, "Are you prepared to marry your cousin?" She did not answer at once, but stood with bowed head. My wife took her aside and asked whether we might send word to the other family, and she agreed. We have sent the happy message around, and there will soon be a marriage in our house. I have money, jewellery, and everything ready. I will call the pipers and drummers tomorrow morning and get through it all quickly. I have consulted the astrologer already, and he says that this is an auspicious time. I do not want to delay even for a second the happy event.'

'For fear that she may change her mind once again?' Raju asked. He knew why Velan was rushing it through at this pace. It was easy to guess why. But the remark threw the other into a fit of admiration, and he asked, 'How did you know what I had in mind, sir?'

Raju remained silent. He could not open his lips without provoking admiration. This was a dangerous state of affairs. He was in a mood to debunk himself a little. He told Velan sharply, 'There is nothing extraordinary in my guess,' and promptly came the reply, 'Not for you to say that, sir. Things may look easy enough for a giant, but ordinary poor mortals like us can never know what goes on in other people's minds.'

To divert his attention, Raju simply asked, 'Have you any idea of the views of the bridegroom? Is he ready for you? What does he think of her refusal?'

'After the girl came round, I sent our priest to discuss it with him, and he has come back to say that the boy is willing. He prefers not to think of what is past. What is gone is gone.'

'True, true,' Raju said, having nothing else to say and not wishing to utter anything that might seem too brilliant. He was beginning to dread his own smartness nowadays. He was afraid to open his lips. A vow of silence was indicated, but there was greater danger in silence.

All this prudence did not save him. Velan's affairs were satisfactorily ended. One day he came to invite Raju to his sister's marriage, and Raju had to plead long and hard before he could make him leave him alone. However, Velan brought him fruit on huge trays covered with silk cloth, the sort of offering which Raju would conjure up for the edification of his tourists when he took them through an ancient palace or hall. He accepted the gift gracefully.

He avoided the girl's marriage. He did not want to be seen in a crowd, and he did not want to gather a crowd around him as a man who had worked a change in an obstinate girl. But his aloofness did not save him. If he would not go to the wedding, the wedding was bound to come to him. At the earliest possible moment Velan brought the girl and her husband and a huge concourse of relatives to the temple. The girl herself seemed to have spoken of Raju as her saviour. She had told everyone, 'He doesn't speak to anyone, but if he looks at you, you are changed.'

His circle was gradually widening. Velan, at the end of his day's agricultural toil, came and sat on the lower step. If Raju spoke, he listened; otherwise he accepted the silence with equal gratitude, got up without a word when darkness fell, and moved away. Gradually, unnoticed, a few others began to arrive very regularly. Raju could not very well question who they were; the river bank was a public place, and he himself was an intruder. They just sat there on the lower step and looked at Raju, and kept looking at him. He didn't have to say a word to anyone; he just sat there at the same place, looking away at the river, at the other bank, and tried hard to think where he should go next and what to do. They did not so much as whisper a word for fear that it might disturb him. Raju was beginning to feel uncomfortable on these occasions; and wondered if he could devise some means of escape from their company. Throughout the day he was practically left alone, but late in the evening, after doing their day's work, the villagers would come.

One evening before the company arrived, he moved himself to the back yard of the temple and hid himself behind a gigantic hibiscus bush full of red flowers. He heard them arrive, heard their voices on the river step. They were talking in low, hushed voices. They went round the building and passed by the hibiscus bush. Raju's heart palpitated as he crouched there like an animal at bay. He held his breath and waited. He was already planning to offer an explanation if they should discover his presence there. He would say that he was in deep thought and that the hibiscus shade was congenial for such contemplation. But fortunately they did not look for him there. They stood near the bush talking in a hushed, awed whisper. Said one, 'Where could he have gone?'

'He is a big man, he may go anywhere; he may have a thousand things to do.'

'Oh, you don't know. He has renounced the world; he does nothing but meditate. What a pity he is not here today!'

'Just sitting there for a few minutes with him—ah, what a change it has brought about in our household! Do you know, that cousin of mine came round last night and gave me back the promissory note. As long as he held it, I felt as if I had put a knife in his hand for stabbing us.'

'We won't have to fear anything more; it is our good fortune that this great soul should have come to life in our midst.'

'But he has disappeared today. Wonder if he has left us for good.'

'It would be our misfortune if he went away.'

'His clothes are still all there in the hall.'

'He has no fears.'

'The food I brought yesterday has been eaten.'

'Leave there what you have brought now; he is sure to come back from his outing and feel hungry.' Raju felt grateful to this man for his sentiment.

'Do you know sometimes these yogis can travel to the Himalayas just by a thought?'

'I don't think he is that kind of yogi,' said another.

'Who can say? Appearances are sometimes misleading,' said someone. They then moved off to their usual seat and sat there. For a long time Raju could hear them talking among themselves. After a while they left. Raju could hear them splashing the water with their feet. 'Let us go before it gets too dark. They say that there is an old crocodile in this part of the river.'

'A boy known to me was held up by his ankle once, at this very spot.'

'What happened, then?'

'He was dragged down, next day...'

Raju could hear their voices far off. He cautiously peeped out of his hiding. He could see their shadowy figures on the other bank. He waited till they vanished altogether from sight. He went in and lit a lamp. He was hungry. They had left his food wrapped in a banana leaf on the pedestal of the old stone image. Raju was filled with gratitude and prayed that Velan might never come to the stage of thinking that he was too good for food and that he subsisted on atoms from the air.

Next morning he rose early and went through his ablutions, washed his clothes in the river, lit the stove, made himself coffee, and felt completely at ease with the world. He had to decide on his future today. He should either go back to the town of his birth, bear the giggles and stares for a few days, or go somewhere else. Where could he go? He had not trained himself to make a living out of hard work. Food was coming to him unasked now. If he went away somewhere else certainly nobody was going to take the trouble to bring him food in return for just waiting for it. The only other place where it could happen was the prison. Where could he go now? Nowhere. Cows grazing on the slopes far off gave the place an air of sublime stillness. He realized that he had no alternative: he must play the role that Velan had given him.

With his mind made up he prepared himself to meet Velan and his friends in the evening. He sat as usual on the stone slab with beatitude and calm in his face. The thing that had really bothered him was that he might sound too brilliant in everything he said. He had observed silence as a precaution. But that fear was now gone. He decided to look as brilliant as he could manage, let drop gems of thought from his lips, assume all the radiance available, and afford them all the guidance they required without stint. He decided to arrange the stage for the display with more thoroughness. With this view he transferred his seat to the inner hall of the temple. It gave one a better background. He sat there at about the time he expected Velan and others to arrive. He anticipated their arrival with a certain excitement. He composed his features and pose to receive them.

The sun was setting. Its tint touched the wall with pink. The tops of the coconut trees around were aflame. The bird cries went up in a crescendo before dying down for the night. Darkness fell. Still there was no sign of Velan or anyone. They did not come that night. He was left foodless; that was not the main worry, he still had a few bananas. Suppose they never came again? What was to happen? He became panicky. All night he lay worrying. All his old fears came back. If he returned to the town he would have to get his house back from the man to whom he had mortgaged it. He would have to fight for a living space in his own home or find the cash to redeem it.

He debated whether to step across the river, walk into the village, and search for Velan. It didn't seem a dignified thing to do. It might make him look cheap, and they might ignore him altogether.

He saw a boy grazing his sheep on the opposite bank. He clapped his hands and cried, 'Come here.' He went down the steps and cried across the water, 'I am the new priest of this temple, boy, come here. I have a plantain for you. Come and take it.' He flourished it, feeling that this was perhaps a gamble; it was the last piece of fruit in his store and might presently be gone, as might the boy, and Velan might never know how badly he was wanted, while he, Raju, lay starving there until they found his bleached bones in the temple and added them to the ruins around. With these thoughts he flourished the banana. The boy was attracted by it and soon came across the water. He was short and was wet up to his ears. Raju said, 'Take off your turban and dry yourself, boy.'

'I am not afraid of water,' he said.

'You should not be so wet.'

The boy held out his hand for the plantain and said, 'I can swim. I always swim.'

'But I have never seen you here before,' Raju said.

'I don't come here. I go farther down and swim.'

'Why don't you come here?'

'This is a crocodile place,' he said.

'But I have never seen any crocodile.'

'You will sometime,' the boy said. 'My sheep generally graze over there. I came to see if a man was here.'

'Why?'

'My uncle asked me to watch. He said, "Drive your sheep before that temple and see if a man is there." That is why I came here today.'

Raju gave the boy the banana and said, 'Tell your uncle that the man is back here and tell him to come here this evening.'

He did not wait to ask who the uncle was. Whoever he might be, he was welcome. The boy peeled the plantain, swallowed it whole, and started munching the peel also. 'Why do you eat the peel? It will make you sick,' Raju said.

'No, it won't,' the boy replied. He seemed to be a resolute boy who knew his mind.

Raju vaguely advised, 'You must be a good boy. Now be off. Tell your uncle—'

The boy was off, after cautioning him, 'Keep an eye on those till I get back.' He indicated his flock on the opposite slope.

3

One fine day, beyond the tamarind tree, the station building was ready. The steel tracks gleamed in the sun; the signal posts stood with their red and green stripes and their colourful lamps; and our world was neatly divided into this side of the railway line and that side. Everything was ready. All our spare hours were spent in walking along the railway track up to the culvert half a mile away. We paced up and down our platform. A gold mohur sapling was planted in the railway yard. We passed through the corridor, peeping into the room meant for the station master.

One day we were all given a holiday. 'The train comes to our town today,' people said excitedly. The station was decorated with festoons and bunting. A piper was playing, bands were banging away. Coconuts were broken on the railway track, and an engine steamed in, pulling a couple of cars. Many of the important folk of the town were there. The Collector and the Police Superintendent and the Municipal Chairman, and many of the local tradesmen, who flourished green invitation cards in their hands, were assembled at the station. The police guarded the platform and did not allow the crowds in. I felt cheated by this. I felt indignant that anyone should prohibit my entry to the platform. I squeezed myself through the railings at the farthest end, and by the time the engine arrived I was there to receive it. I was probably so small that no one noticed my presence.

Tables were laid and official gentlemen sat around refreshing themselves, and then several men got up and lectured. I was aware only of the word 'Malgudi' recurring in their speeches. There was a clapping of hands. The band struck up, the engine whistled, the bell rang, the guard blew his whistle, and the men who had been consuming refreshments climbed into the train. I was half inclined to follow their example, but there were many policemen to stop me. The train moved and was soon out of sight. A big crowd was now allowed to come on to the platform. My father's shop had record sales that day.

By the time a station master and a porter were installed in their little stone house at the back of the station, facing our house, my father had become so prosperous that he acquired a *jutka* and a horse in order to go to the town and do his shopping.

My mother had been apathetic. 'Why should you have all this additional bother in this household, horse and horse-gram and all that, while the buffalo pair is a sufficient bother?'

He did not answer her in any detail, just swept off her objections with, 'You know nothing about these things, I have so much to do every day in the town. I have to visit the bank so often.' He uttered the word 'bank' with a proud emphasis, but it did not impress my mother.

And so there was an addition of a thatch-roofed shed to our yard, in which a brown pony was tied up, and my father had picked up a groom to look after it. We became the folk of the town with this horse and carriage, but my mother never reconciled herself to it. She viewed it as an extraordinary vanity on my father's part and no amount of explanation from him ever convinced her otherwise. Her view was that my father had overestimated his business, and she nagged him whenever he was found at home and the horse and carriage were not put to proper use. She expected him to be always going round the streets in his vehicle. He had not more than an hour's job any day in the town and he always came back in time to attend to his shop, which he was now leaving in charge of a friend for a few hours in the day. My mother was developing into a successful nagger, I suppose, for my father was losing much of his aggressiveness and was becoming very apologetic about his return home whenever the horse and the carriage were left unused under the tamarind tree. 'You take it and go to the market, if you like,' he often said, but my mother spurned the offer, explaining, 'Where should I go every day? Some day it may be useful for going to the temple on a Friday. But ought you to maintain an extravagant turnout all through the year, just for a possible visit to the temple? Horse-gram and grass, do you know what they cost?' Fortunately, it did not prove such a liability after all. Worn out by Mother's persistent opposition, my father seriously considered disposing of the horse and (a fantastic proposal) converting the carriage into a single bullock-cart with a 'bow spring' mounted over the wheel, which a blacksmith of his acquaintance at the market gate had promised to do for him.

The groom who minded the horse laughed at the idea and said that it was an impossible proposition, convincing my father that the blacksmith would reduce the carriage to a piece of furniture fit for lounging under the tamarind tree. 'You could as well listen to a promise to turn the horse into a bullock!' he said, and then he made a proposal which appealed to my father's business instinct. 'Let me ply it for hire in the market. All gram and grass my charge—only let me use your shed. I will hand you two rupees a day and one rupee a month for the use of the shed, and anything I earn over two rupees should be mine.'

This was a delightful solution. My father had the use of the carriage whenever he wanted it, and earned a sum for it each day, and no liabilities. As the days passed, the driver came along and pleaded lack of engagements. A great deal of argument went on in the front part of my house, in semi-darkness, between my father and the driver as my father tried to exact his two rupees. Finally my mother too joined in, saying, 'Don't trust these fellows. Today with all that festival crowd, he says he has not made any money. How can we believe him?'

My mother was convinced that the cart-driver drank his earnings. My father retorted, 'What if he drinks? It is none of our business.'

Every day this went on. Every night the man stood under the tree and cringed and begged for remission. It was evident that he was misappropriating our funds. For within a few weeks the man came and said, 'This horse is growing bony and will not run properly, and is becoming wrong-headed. It is better we sell it off soon and take another, because all the passengers who get into this *jutka* complain and pay less at the end because of the discomfort suffered. And the springs over the wheels must also be changed.' The man was constantly suggesting that the turnout had better be sold off and a new one taken. Whenever he said it within my mother's hearing she lost her temper and shouted at him, saying that one horse and carriage were sufficient expense. This reduced my father to viewing the whole arrangement as a hopeless liability, until the man hinted that he had an offer of seventy rupees for both horse and carriage. My father managed to raise this to seventy-five and finally the man brought the cash and drove off the turnout himself. Evidently he had saved a lot of our own money for this enterprise. Anyway, we were glad to be rid of the thing. This was a nicely calculated transaction, for as soon as the trains began to arrive regularly at our station we found our *jutka* doing a brisk business carrying passengers to the town.

My father was given the privilege of running a shop at the railway station. What a shop it was! It was paved with cement, with shelves built in. It was so spacious that when my father had transferred all the articles from the hut-shop, the place was only one-quarter filled; there were so many blank spaces all along the wall that he felt depressed at the sight of it. For the first time he was beginning to feel that he had not been running a very big business after all.

My mother had come out to watch the operation and taunted him, 'With this stock you think of buying motor cars and what not.' He had not at any time proposed buying a motor car but she liked to nag him.

Father said, rather weakly, 'Why drag in all that now?' He was ruminating. 'I shall need at least another five hundred rupees' worth of articles to fill up all this space.'

The station master, an old man wearing a green turban round his head and silver-rimmed spectacles, came along to survey the shop. My father became extremely deferential at the sight of him. Behind him stood Karia the porter in in his blue shirt and turban. My mother withdrew unobtrusively and went back home. The station master viewed the shop from a distance with his head on one side as if he were an artist viewing a handiwork. The porter, ever faithful, followed his example, keeping himself in readiness to agree with whatever he might say. The station master said, 'Fill up all that space, otherwise the ATS might come round and ask questions, poking his nose into all our affairs. It has not been easy to give you this shop.'

My father sat me in the shop and went over to the town to make the purchases. 'Don't display too much rice and other stuff—keep the other shop for such things,' advised the station master. 'Railway passengers won't be asking for tamarind and lentils during the journey.' My father implicitly accepted his directions. The station master was his palpable god now and he cheerfully obeyed all his commands. And so, presently there hung down from nails in my father's other shop bigger bunches of bananas, stacks of Mempu oranges, huge troughs of fried stuff, and colourful peppermints and sweets in glass containers, loaves of bread, and buns. The display was most appetizing, and he had loaded several racks with packets of cigarettes. He had to anticipate the demand of every kind of traveller and provide for it.

He left me in charge of his hut-shop. His old customers came down to gossip and shop, as had been their habit. But they found me unequal to it. I found it tedious to listen to their talk of litigation and irrigation. I was not old enough to appreciate all their problems and the subtleties of their transactions. I listened to them without response, and soon they discovered that I was no good as companion for them. They left me in peace and wandered off to the other shop, seeking my father's company. But they found it untenable. They felt strange there. It was too sophisticated a surrounding for them. Very soon, unobtrusively, my father was back in his seat at the hut-shop, leaving me to handle the business in the new shop. As soon as a certain bridge off Malgudi was ready, regular service began on our rails; it was thrilling to watch the activities of the station master and the blue-shirted porter as they 'received' and 'line-cleared' two whole trains each day, the noon train from Madras and the evening one from Trichy. I became very active indeed in the shop. As you might have guessed, all this business expansion in our family helped me achieve a very desirable end—the dropping off from my school unobtrusively.

4

The banana worked a miracle. The boy went from house to house, announcing that the saint was back at his post. Men, women and children arrived in a great mass. All that they wanted was to be allowed to look at him and watch the radiance on his face. The children stood around and gazed in awe. Raju tried to manage the situation by pinching a few cheeks and saying some inanities, or even indulging in baby-talk in order to soften the awkwardness of the situation. He went up to young boys and asked, 'What are you studying?' in the manner of big men he had seen in cities. But it was stupid to imitate that question here, because the boys giggled, looked at one another, and said, 'No school for us.'

'What do you do all day?' he asked, without any real interest in their problems.

One of the elders interposed to say, 'We cannot send our boys to the school as you do in towns; they have to take the cattle out for grazing.'

Raju clicked his tongue in disapproval. He shook his head. The gathering looked pained and anxious. Raju explained grandly, 'Boys must read, first. They must, of course, help their parents, but they must also find the time to study.' He added on an inspiration, 'If they cannot find the time to read during the day, why should they not gather in the evenings and learn?'

'Where?' asked someone.

'Maybe here.' Raju added, pointing at the vast hall, 'Maybe you could ask one of your masters. Is there no schoolmaster in your midst?'

'Yes, yes,' several voices cried in unison. 'Ask him to see me,' Raju commanded authoritatively, with the air of a president summoning a defaulting assistant master. Next afternoon a timid man, who wore a short tuft with a turban over it, turned up at the temple hall. Raju had just finished his repast and was enjoying a siesta in the hall, stretching himself on its cool, granite floor. The timid man stood beside an ancient pillar and cleared his throat. Raju opened his eyes and looked at him blankly. It was not the custom there, in that society, to ask who or why, when so many came and went. Raju flourished an arm to indicate to the other to sit down and resumed his sleep. When he awoke later, he saw the man sitting close to him.

'I'm the teacher,' the man said, and in the muddled state of half-sleep Raju's old fears of schoolteachers returned: he forgot for a split second that he had left all those behind years ago. He sat up. The master was rather surprised. He said, 'Don't disturb yourself. I can wait.'

'That's all right,' said Raju, recovering his composure and understanding his surroundings better. 'You are the schoolmaster?' he asked patronizingly. He brooded for a moment, then asked in a general way, 'How is everything?'

The other merely replied, 'No different from what it used to be.'

'How do you like it?'

'What does it matter?' the other said. 'I only try to do my best and do it sincerely.'

'Otherwise, what's the use of doing anything at all?' asked Raju. He was marking time. He was not very clear-headed yet after the deep sleep, and the problem of boys' education was not uppermost in his mind at the moment. He said tentatively, 'After all, one's duty—'

'I do my utmost,' said the other defensively, not wishing to give way. After these parleys, which lasted for half an hour, the village master himself clarified the position. 'It seems you suggested that the boys should be assembled here and taught at nights.'

'Oh! eh!' Raju said. 'Yes, I did, of course, but it's a matter in which the decision should be purely yours. After all, self-help is the best help; I may be here today and gone tomorrow. It's up to you to arrange it. I meant that if you want a place—you can have it.' He swept his arm about with the air of one conferring a gift on a whole community.

The teacher looked thoughtful for a moment and began, 'I'm not sure, however—'

But Raju suddenly became argumentative and definite. He said with a lot of authority, 'I like to see young boys become literate and intelligent.' He added with fervour because it sounded nice, 'It's our duty to make everyone happy and wise.'

This overwhelming altruism was too much for the teacher. 'I'll do anything,' he said, 'under your guidance.' Raju admitted the position with, 'I'm but an instrument accepting guidance myself.'

The result was that the teacher went back to the village a changed man. Next day he was back at the pillared hall with a dozen children of the village. They had their foreheads smeared with sacred ash, and their slates creaked in the silent night, while the teacher lectured to them, and Raju, seated on his platform, looked on benignly. The teacher was apologetic about the numbers: he could muster only about a dozen boys. 'They are afraid of crossing the river in the dark; they have heard of a crocodile hereabouts.'

'What can a crocodile do to you if your mind is clear and your conscience is untroubled?' Raju said grandly. It was a wonderful sentiment to express. He was surprised at the amount of wisdom welling from the depths of his being. He said to the teacher, 'Don't be dispirited that there are only a dozen. If you do your work sincerely by a dozen, it'll be equivalent, really, to serving a hundred times that number.'

The teacher suggested, 'Do not mistake me, but will you speak to these boys whenever you can?' This gave Raju a chance to air his views on life and eternity before the boys. He spoke to them on godliness, cleanliness, spoke on the *Ramayana*, the characters in the epics; he addressed them on all kinds of things. He was hypnotized by his own voice; he felt himself growing in stature as he saw the upturned faces of the children shining in the half-light when he spoke. No one was more impressed with the grandeur of the whole thing than Raju himself.

Now that I reflect upon it, I am convinced I was not such a dud after all. It seems to me that we generally do not have a correct measure of our own wisdom. I remember how I was equipping my mind all the time. I read a certain amount of good stuff in my railway-shopkeeping days. I sat in that shop, selling loaves of bread and aerated water. Sometimes schoolboys left their books with me for sale. Though my father thought very highly of our shop, I could not share his view. Selling bread and biscuits and accepting money in exchange seemed to me a tame occupation. I always felt that I was too good for the task.

My father died during the rainy part of that year. His end was sudden. He had been selling and talking to his cronies in his hut-shop till late at night; then he counted the cash, came into the house, consumed his rice and buttermilk, laid himself down to sleep, and never woke again.

My mother adjusted herself to the status of a widow. My father left her enough to live on comfortably. I gave her as much of my time as possible. With her consent, I closed down my father's shop and set up at the railway station. It was then that I began to develop new lines. I stocked old magazines and newspapers, and bought and sold schoolbooks. Of course my customers were not many, but the train brought in more and more school-going population, and the 10.30 local was full of young men going off to Albert Mission College, which had just been started at Malgudi. I liked to talk to people. I liked to hear people talk. I liked customers who would not open their mouths merely to put a plantain in, and would say something on any subject other than the state of crops, price of commodities, and litigation. I am afraid, after my father's death, his old friends wilted away and disappeared one by one, chiefly for want of an audience.

Students gathered at my shop while they waited for the trains. Gradually books appeared where there were coconuts before. People dumped old books and stolen books and all kinds of printed stuff on me. I bargained hard, showed indifference while buying and solicitude while selling. Strictly speaking, it was an irregular thing to do. But the station master was a friendly man who not only obtained unlimited credit for anything he and his children took from my shop, but also enjoyed the privilege of drawing his reading material from the stack growing in front of my shop.

My bookselling business was an unexpected offshoot of my search for old wrapping-paper. When people bought something I hated to see them carry it off in their hands. I liked to wrap it up nicely, as well as I could, but as long as my father was in control he said, 'If anyone brings a piece of paper, he is welcome to wrap up anything; but I can't do it for him. Profit being what it is, we can't afford to spend it on wrapping-paper. If a man buys oil, let him bring a pot to carry it in. Do we provide him with that?' While he practised this philosophy it was impossible for anyone to find even a scrap of paper in our shop. After his death I adopted a new policy. I made it known far and wide that I was looking for old paper and books, and soon gathered a big dump. In my off-hours I sat sorting it out. During the interval between trains, when the platform became quiet, there was nothing more pleasing than picking up a bundle of assorted books and lounging in my seat and reading, occasionally breaking off to watch through the doorway the immense tamarind tree in the field. I read stuff that interested me, bored me, baffled me, and dozed off in my seat. I read stuff that pricked up a noble thought, a philosophy that appealed, I gazed on pictures of old temples and ruins and new buildings and battleships, and soldiers, and pretty girls around whom my thoughts lingered. I learned much from scrap.

The children were enchanted by the talk they had had in their class from Raju (even their master sat absorbed in open-mouthed wonder). They went home and described the wonders they had been told about. They were impatient to be back on the following evening and listen to more. Very soon the parents joined their children. They explained apologetically, 'Children come home rather late, you see, master, and are afraid to return home, especially crossing the river at night.'

'Excellent, excellent,' Raju said. 'I wanted to suggest it myself. I'm glad you have thought of it. There is no harm. In fact, you may also benefit by keeping your ears open. Keep your ears open and mouth shut, that'll take you far,' he said, hitting upon a brilliant aphorism.

A circle formed around him. They sat there looking on. The children sat there looking on. The master sat there looking on. The pillared hall was bright with the lanterns the villagers had brought with them. It looked like a place where a great assembly was about to begin. Raju felt like an actor who had come on the stage, and, while the audience waited, had no lines to utter or gestures to make. He said to the master, 'I think you may take the children away to their corner for their usual lessons; take one of the lamps with you.'

Even as he said it he could not help thinking how he was issuing an order about the boys who were not his, to the teacher who need not obey him, pointing to a lamp which again was not his. The teacher started to obey him, but the boys lingered on. He said, 'You must read your lessons first and then I will come and speak to you. Now I will first speak to your elders; what I say to them will not interest you.' And the children got up and went away with the teacher to a farther corner of the pillared hall.

Velan ventured to suggest, 'Give us a discourse, sir.' And as Raju listened without showing any emotion, but looking as if he were in deep contemplation, Velan added, 'So that we may have the benefit of your wisdom.' The others murmured a general approval.

Raju felt cornered. 'I have to play the part expected of me; there is no escape.' He racked his head secretly, wondering where to start. Could he speak about tourists' attractions in Malgudi, or should it be moral lessons? How once upon a time there was a so-and-so, so good or bad that when he came to do such-and-such a thing he felt so utterly lost that he prayed, and so on and so forth? He felt bored. The only subject on which he could speak with any authority now seemed to be jail life and its benefits, especially for one mistaken for a saint. They waited respectfully for his inspiration. 'Oh, fools,' he felt like crying out, 'why don't you leave me alone? If you bring me food, leave it there and leave me in peace, thank you.'

After a long, brooding silence, he brought out the following words: 'All things have to wait their hour.' Velan and his friends who were in the front row looked worried for a moment; they were deferential, no doubt, but they did not quite realize what he was driving at. After a further pause, he added grandiosely, 'I will speak to you, when another day comes.'

Someone asked, 'Why another day, sir?'

'Because it is so,' said Raju mysteriously. 'While you wait for the children to finish their lessons, I'd advise you to pass the hour brooding over all your speech and actions from morning till now.'

'What speech and actions?' someone asked, genuinely puzzled by the advice.

'Your own,' said Raju. 'Recollect and reflect upon every word you have uttered since daybreak—'

'I don't remember exactly...'

'Well, that is why I say reflect, recollect. When you don't remember your own words properly, how are you going to remember other people's words?' This quip amused his audience. There were bursts of subdued laughter. When the laughter subsided Raju said, 'I want you all to think independently, of your own accord, and not allow yourselves to be led about by the nose as if you were cattle.'

There were murmurs of polite disagreement over this advice. Velan asked, 'How can we do that, sir? We dig the land and mind the cattle—so far so good, but how can we think philosophies? Not our line, master. It is not possible. It is wise persons like your good self who should think for us.'

'And why do you ask us to recollect all that we have said since daybreak?'

Raju himself was not certain why he had advised that, and so he added, 'If you do it you will know why.' The essence of sainthood seemed to lie in one's ability to utter mystifying statements. 'Until you try, how can you know what you can or cannot do?' he asked. He was dragging those innocent men deeper and deeper into the bog of unclear thoughts.

'I can't remember what I said a few moments ago; so many other things come into one's head,' wailed one of his victims.

'Precisely. That is what I wish to see you get over,' said Raju. 'Until you do it, you will not know the pleasure of it.' He picked out three men from the gathering. 'When you come to me tomorrow or another day, you must each repeat to me at least six words that you have been speaking since the morning. I am asking you to remember only six words,' he said pleadingly as a man who was making a great concession, 'not six hundred.'

'Six hundred! Is there anyone who can remember six hundred, sir?' asked someone with wonder.

'Well, I can,' said Raju. And he got the appreciative clicking of tongues which he expected as his legitimate due. Soon the children were there, a great boon to Raju, who rose from his seat as if to say, 'That is all for the day,' and walked towards the river, the others following. 'These children must be feeling sleepy. Take them safely home, and come again.'

When the assembly met next, he provided it with a specific programme. He beat a soft rhythm with his hands and chanted a holy song with a refrain that could be repeated by his audience. The ancient ceiling echoed with the voices of men, women, and children repeating sacred texts in unison. Someone had brought in tall bronze lamps and lit them. Others fed them with oil; others had spent a whole day twisting bits of cotton into wicks for the lamps. People brought of their own accord little framed pictures of gods and hung them on the pillars. Very soon women started to come in batches during the day to wash the floor and decorate it with patterns in coloured flour; they hung up flowers and greenery and festoons everywhere. The pillared hall was transformed. Someone had also covered the platform in the middle of the hall with a soft, coloured carpet; mats were rolled out for the assembly to sit on.

Raju soon realized that his spiritual status would be enhanced if he grew a beard and long hair to fall on his nape. A clean-shaven, close-haired saint was an anomaly. He bore the various stages of his make-up with fortitude, not minding the prickly phase he had to pass through before a well-authenticated beard could cover his face and come down to his chest. By the time he arrived at the stage of stroking his beard thoughtfully, his prestige had grown beyond his wildest dreams. His life had lost its personal limitations; his gatherings had become so large that they overflowed into the outer corridors and people sat right up to the river's edge.

With the exception of Velan and a few others, Raju never bothered to remember faces or names or even to know to whom he was talking. He seemed to belong to the world now. His influence was unlimited. He not only chanted holy verses and discoursed on philosophy, he even came to the stage of prescribing medicine; children who would not sleep peacefully at night were brought to him by their mothers; he pressed their bellies and prescribed a herb, adding, 'If he still gets no relief, bring him again to me.' It was believed that when he stroked the head of a child, the child improved in various ways. Of course, people brought him their disputes and quarrels over the division of ancestral property. He had to set apart several hours of his afternoon for these activities. He could hardly afford a private life now. There came a stage when he had to be up early and rush through all his own personal routine before his visitors should arrive. It was a strain. He sighed a deep sigh of relief and longed to be himself, eat like an ordinary human being, shout and sleep like a normal man, after the voices on the river had ceased for the night.

5

I came to be called Railway Raju. Perfect strangers, having heard of my name, began to ask for me when their train arrived at the Malgudi railway station. It is written on the brow of some that they shall not be left alone. I am one such, I think. Although I never looked for acquaintances, they somehow came looking for me. Men who had just arrived always stopped at my shop for a soda or cigarettes and to go through the book stack, and almost always they asked, 'How far is…?' or 'Are there many historical spots here?' or 'I heard that your River Sarayu has its source somewhere on those hills and that it is a beauty spot.' This sort of inquiry soon led me to think that I had not given sufficient thought to the subject. I never said, 'I don't know.' Not in my nature, I suppose. If I had had the inclination to say, 'I don't know what you are talking about,' my life would have taken a different turn. Instead, I said, 'Oh, yes, a fascinating place. Haven't you seen it? You must find the time to visit it, otherwise your whole trip here would be a waste.' I am sorry I said it, an utter piece of falsehood. It was not because I wanted to utter a falsehood, but only because I wanted to be pleasant.

Naturally, they asked me the way. I said, 'If you just go that way down to the Market Square and ask one of those taxi-drivers...' This was not a very satisfactory direction. Soon a man wanted me to show him the way to the Market Square and the taxi. There was a young son of the porter doing points-signalling duty whenever a train was about to arrive, who had no specified work to do at other times. I asked the young fellow to mind the shop while I helped the traveller to find a taxi.

At the market fountain stood the old shark Gaffur, looking for a victim. He made a speciality of collecting all the derelict vehicles in the country and rigging them up; he breathed new life into them and ran them on the mountain roads and into the forests. His usual seat was on the parapet of the fountain, while his car basked on the roadside beside the gutter. 'Gaffur,' I called out. 'Here is a very good gentleman, a friend of mine. He wants to see... You must take him out and bring him back safely—that is why I have brought him to you personally, although this is not an hour when I should be away from my shop.' We haggled over the prices; I allowed the customer to mention his figure and always tried to beat Gaffur down to it. When he demurred at the sight of the vehicle, I took up Gaffur's brief and explained, 'Gaffur is no fool to have this kind of car. He searched far and wide to find this particular model; this is the only car which can go up to all those places where in some parts there are no roads at all, but Gaffur will take you there and bring you back in time for dinner tonight. Can't you, Gaffur?'

'Well,' he drawled, 'it is seventy miles each way; it is one o'clock now. If we leave at once and if there are no punctures on the way...' But I hustled him so much that Gaffur never really completed his sentence. When they returned it could not exactly be called dinner-time, unless you stretched it to include midnight, but Gaffur did bring him back intact, honked his car to wake me up, took his cash, and departed. The next train for the man would be at eight on the following morning. He had to stretch himself under the awning on the platform of my shop and spend the night thus. If he felt hungry, I opened my store and sold him fruits and such things.

Travellers are an enthusiastic lot. They do not mind any inconvenience as long as they have something to see. Why anyone should want to forgo food and comfort and jolt a hundred-odd miles to see some place, I could never understand, but it was not my business to ask for reasons; just as I did not mind what people ate or smoked in my shop, my business being only to provide the supply and nothing more. It seemed to me silly to go a hundred miles to see the source of the Sarayu when it had taken the trouble to tumble down the mountain and come to our door. I had not even heard of its source till that moment; but the man who had gone was all praise for the spot. He said, 'I am only sorry I did not bring my wife and mother to see the place.' Later in life I found that everyone who saw an interesting spot always regretted that he hadn't come with his wife or daughter, and spoke as if he had cheated someone out of a nice thing in life. Later, when I had become a full-blown tourist guide, I often succeeded in inducing a sort of melancholia in my customer by remarking, 'This is something that should be enjoyed by the whole family,' and the man would swear that he would be back with his entire brood in the coming season.

The man who had gone to the source of the river spoke all night about it: how there was a small shrine on the peak right at the basin. 'It must be the source of the Sarayu mentioned in the mythological stories of goddess Parvathi jumping into the fire; the carving on one of the pillars of the shrine actually shows the goddess plunging into the fire and water arising from the spot,' etcctera. Sometimes someone with a scholarly turn of mind would come and make a few additions to the facts, such as that the dome of the shrine must have been built in the third century before Christ or that the style of drapery indicated the third century after Christ. But it was all the same to me, and the age I ascribed to any particular place depended upon my mood at that hour and the type of person I was escorting. If he was the academic type I was careful to avoid all mention of facts and figures and to confine myself to general descriptions, letting the man himself do the talking. You may be sure he enjoyed the opportunity. On the other hand, if an innocent man happened to be at hand, I let myself go freely. I pointed out to him something as the greatest, the highest, the only one in the world. I gave statistics out of my head. I mentioned a relic as belonging to the thirteenth century before Christ or the thirteenth century after Christ, according to the mood of the hour. If I felt fatigued or bored with the person I was conducting, I sometimes knocked the whole glamour out by saying, 'Must be something built within the last twenty years and allowed to go to rack and ruin. There are scores of such spots all over the place.' But it was years before I could arrive at that stage of confidence and nonchalance.

The porter's son sat in the shop all day. I spent a little time each night to check the cash and stock. There was no definite arrangement about what he should be paid for his trouble. I gave him a little money now and then. Only my mother protested. 'Why do you want him to work for you, Raju? Either give him a definite commission or do it yourself instead of all this wandering in the country. What good does it do you, anyway?'

'You don't know, Mother,' I said, eating my late dinner. 'This is a far better job I am doing than the other one. I am seeing a lot of places and getting paid for it; I go with them in their car or bus, talk to them, I am treated to their food sometimes, and I get paid for it. Do you know how well known I am? People come asking for me from Bombay, Madras, and other places, hundreds of miles away. They call me Railway Raju and have told me that even in Lucknow there are persons who are familiar with my name. It is something to become so famous, isn't it, instead of handing out matches and tobacco?'

'Well, wasn't it good enough for your father?'

'I don't say anything against it. I will look after the shop also.'

This pleased the old lady. Occasionally she threw in a word about her brother's daughter in the village before blowing out the lamp. She was always hoping that some day I would consent to marry the girl, though she never directly said so. 'Do you know Lalitha has got a prize in her school? I had a letter from my brother today about it.'

Even as the train steamed in at the outer signal, I could scent a customer. I had a kind of water-diviner's instinct. If I felt the pull of good business I drifted in the direction of the coming train; I could stand exactly where a prospective tourist would alight and look for me: it was not only the camera or binoculars slung on a shoulder that indicated to me the presence of a customer; even without any of that I could spot him. If you found me straying away in the direction of the barrier while the engine was still running through the lines onto the platform you might be sure that there was no customer for me on the train. In a few months I was a seasoned guide. I had viewed myself as an amateur guide and a professional shopman, but now gradually I began to think of myself as a part-time shopkeeper and a full-time tourist guide. Even when I had no tourist to guide I did not go back to my shop, but to Gaffur on the fountain parapet, and listened to his talk about derelict automobiles.

I had classified all my patrons. They were very varied, I can tell you. Some were passionate photographers; these men could never look at any object except through their viewfinders. The moment they got down from the train, even before lifting their baggage, they asked, 'Is there a place where they develop films?'

'Of course, Malgudi Photo Bureau. One of the biggest...'

'And if I want roll-films? I have, of course, enough stock with me, but if I run out... Do you think super-panchro three-colour something-or-other is available there?'

'Of course. That's his special line.'

'Will he develop and show me a print while I wait?'

'Of course, before you count twenty. He is a wizard.'

'That is nice. Now, where are you going to take me first?'

These were routine questions from a routine type. I had all the satisfactory answers ready. I generally took time to answer the latter question as to where I was going to take him first. It depended. I awaited the receipt of certain data before venturing to answer. The data were how much time and money he was going to spend. Malgudi and its surroundings were my special show. I could let a man have a peep at it or a whole panorama. It was adjustable. I could give them a glimpse of a few hours or soak them in mountain and river scenery or archaeology for a whole week. I could not really decide how much to give or withhold until I knew how much cash the man carried or, if he carried a cheque-book, how good it was. This was another delicate point. Sometimes a traveller offered to write a cheque for this man or that, and, of course, our Gaffur or the photo store or the keeper of the forest bungalow on top of Mempi Hills would not trust a stranger enough to accept his cheque. I had to put off such an offer with the utmost delicacy by saying, 'Oh, the banking system in our town is probably the worst you can think of. Sometimes they take twenty days to realize a cheque, but these poor fellows, how can they wait?'—rather a startling thing to say, but I didn't care if the banking reputation of our town suffered.

As soon as a tourist arrived, I observed how he dealt with his baggage, whether he engaged a porter at all or preferred to hook a finger to each piece. I had to note all this within a split second, and then, outside, whether he walked to the hotel or called a taxi or haggled with the one-horse *jutka*. Of course, I undertook all this on his behalf, but always with detachment. I did all this for him simply for the reason that he asked for Railway Raju the moment he stepped down on the platform and I knew he came with good references, whether he came from north or south or far or near. And at the hotel it was my business to provide him with the best room or the worst room, just as he might prefer. Those who took the cheapest dormitory said, 'After all, it's only for sleeping, I am going to be out the whole day. Why waste money on a room which is anyway going to be locked up all day? Don't you agree?'

'Surely, yes, yes,' I nodded, still without giving an answer to 'Where are you going to take me first?' I might still be said to be keeping the man under probation, under careful scrutiny. I never made any suggestion yet. No use expecting a man to be clearheaded who is fresh from a train journey. He must wash, change his clothes, refresh himself with *idli* and coffee, and only then can we expect anyone in south India to think clearly on all matters of this world and the next. If he offered me any refreshment, I understood that he was a comparatively liberal sort, but did not accept it until we were a little further gone in friendship. In due course, I asked him point blank, 'How much time do you hope to spend in this town?'

'Three days at the most. Could we manage everything within the time?'

'Certainly, although it all depends upon what you most wish to see.' And then I put him in the confessional, so to speak. I tried to draw out his interests. Malgudi, I said, had many things to offer, historically, scenically, from the point of view of modern developments, and so on and so forth; or if one came as a pilgrim I could take him to a dozen temples all over the district within a radius of fifty miles; I could find holy waters for him to bathe in all along the course of the Sarayu, starting, of course, with its source on Mempi Peaks.

One thing I learned in my career as a tourist guide was that no two persons were interested in the same thing. Tastes, as in food, differ also in sightseeing. Some people want to be seeing a waterfall, some want a ruin (oh, they grow ecstatic when they see cracked plaster, broken idols, and crumbling bricks), some want a god to worship, some look for a hydro-electric plant, and some want just a nice place, such as the bungalow on top of Mempi with all-glass sides, from where you could see a hundred miles and observe wild game prowling around. Of those again there were two types, one the poet who was content to watch and return, and the other who wanted to admire nature and also get drunk there. I don't know why it is so: a fine poetic spot like the Mempi Peak House excites in certain natures unexpected reactions. I know some who brought women there; a quiet, wooded spot looking over a valley one would think fit for contemplation or poetry, but it only acted as an aphrodisiac. Well, it was not my business to comment. My business stopped with taking them there, and to see that Gaffur went back to pick them up at the right time.

I was sort of scared of the man who acted as my examiner, who had a complete list of all the sights and insisted on his money's worth.

'What is the population of this town?' 'What is the area?' 'Don't bluff. I know when exactly that was built—it is not second-century but the twelfth.' Or he told me the correct pronunciation of words. 'R-o-u-t is not…' I was meek, self-effacing in his presence and accepted his corrections with gratitude, and he always ended up by asking, 'What is the use of your calling yourself a guide if you do not know…?' etcetera, etcetera.

You may well ask what I made out of all this? Well, there is no fixed answer to it. It depended upon the circumstances and the types of people I was escorting. I generally specified ten rupees as the minimum for the pleasure of my company, and a little more if I had to escort them far; over all this Gaffur, the photo store, the hotel manager, and whoever I introduced a customer to expressed their appreciation, according to a certain schedule. I learned while I taught and earned while I learned, and the whole thing was most enjoyable.

There were special occasions, such as the trapping of an elephant herd. During the winter months the men of the Forest Department put through an elaborate scheme for trapping elephants. They watched, encircled, and drove a whole herd into stockades, and people turned up in great numbers to watch the operation. On the day fixed for the drive, people poured in from all over the country and applied to me for a ringside seat in the spacious bamboo jungles of Mempi. I was supposed to have special influence with the men who were in charge of the drive: it meant several advance trips to the forest camp, and doing little services for the officials by fetching whatever they required from the town, and when the time came to arrange for the viewing of the elephant-drive only those who came with me were allowed to pass through the gates of the special enclosures. It kept all of us happy and busy and well-paid. I escorted visitors in bunches and went hoarse repeating, 'You see, the wild herd is watched for months…' and so forth. Don't imagine that I cared for elephants personally; anything that interested my tourists was also my interest. The question of my own preferences was secondary. If someone wanted to see a tiger or shoot one, I knew where to arrange it: I arranged for the lamb to bait the tiger, and had high platforms built so that the brave hunters might pop off the poor beast when it came to eat the lamb, although I never liked to see either the lamb or the tiger die. If someone wanted to see a king cobra spread out its immense hood, I knew the man who could provide the show.

There was a girl who had come all the way from Madras and who asked the moment she set foot in Malgudi, 'Can you show me a cobra—a king cobra it must be—which can dance to the music of a flute?'

'Why?' I asked.

'I'd like to see one. That's all,' she said.

Her husband said, 'We have other things to think of, Rosie. This can wait.'

'I'm not asking this gentleman to produce it at once. I am not demanding it. I'm just mentioning it, that's all.'

'If it interests you, you can make your own arrangements. Don't expect me to go with you. I can't stand the sight of a snake; your interests are morbid.'

I disliked this man. He was taunting such a divine creature. My sympathies were all for the girl; she was so lovely and elegant. After she arrived I discarded my khaki bush-coat and *dhoti* and took the trouble to make myself presentable. I wore a silk *jibba* and lace *dhoti* and groomed myself so well that my mother remarked when she saw me leave the house, 'Ah, like a bridegroom!' and Gaffur winked and said many an insinuating thing when I went to meet them at the hotel.

Her arrival had been a sort of surprise for me. The man was the first to appear. I had put him up at the Anand Bhavan Hotel. After a day of sightseeing he suddenly said one afternoon, 'I must meet the Madras train. Another person is coming.'

He didn't even stop to ask me what time the train would arrive. He seemed to know everything beforehand. He was a very strange man, who did not always care to explain what he was doing. If he had warned me that he was going to meet such an elegant creature at our station I should perhaps have decorated myself appropriately. As it was, I wore my usual khaki bush-coat and *dhoti,* a horrible unprepossessing combination at any time, but the most sensible and convenient for my type of work. The moment she got down from the train I wished I had hidden myself somewhere. She was not very glamorous, if that is what you expect, but she did have a figure, a slight and slender one, beautifully fashioned, eyes that sparkled, a complexion not white, but dusky, which made her only half visible—as if you saw her through a film of tender coconut juice. Forgive me if you find me waxing poetic. I gave some excuse and sent them off to the hotel, and stayed back to run home and tidy up my appearance.

I conducted a brief research with the help of Gaffur. He took me to a man in Ellaman Street, who had a cousin working in the municipal office said to know a charmer with a king cobra. I carried on the investigation while I left the visitor to decipher episodes from the *Ramayana* carved on the stone wall in Iswara Temple in North Extension—there were hundreds of minute carvings all along the wall. They kept the man fully occupied as he stooped and tried to study each bit. I knew all those panels and could repeat their order blindfolded, but he spared me the labour, he knew all about it.

When I returned from my brief investigation, I found the girl standing apart with every sign of boredom in her face. I suggested, 'If you can come out for an hour, I can show you a cobra.'

She looked delighted. She tapped the man on the shoulder as he was stooping over the frieze and asked, 'How long do you want to be here?'

'At least two hours,' he said without turning.

'I'll go out for a while,' she said.

'Please yourself,' he said. Then to me, 'Go to the hotel direct. I'll find my way back.'

We picked up our guide at the municipal office. The car rolled along the sand, crossed the stretch at Nallappa's Grove, and climbed the opposite bank, the entire route carved by the wheels of wooden bullock-carts. Gaffur looked sourly at the man sitting by his side. 'Do you want me to reduce this to a bullock-cart, dragging us about these places? Where are we going? I see no other place than the cremation ground there,' he said, pointing at the smoke above a forlorn, walled area on the other side of the river. I didn't like such inauspicious words to be uttered before the angel in the back-seat. I tried to cover them up hastily by saying something else aloud.

We arrived at a group of huts on the other side of the river. Many heads peeped out of the huts as soon as our car stopped, and a few bare-bodied children came and stood around the car, gaping at the occupants. Our guide jumped out and went at a trot to the farthest end of the village street and returned with a man who had a red turban around his head, his only other piece of clothing being a pair of drawers.

'This man has a king cobra?' I looked him up and down and said hesitantly, 'Let me see it.'

At which the young boys said, 'He has a very big one in his house; it is true.' And I asked the lady, 'Shall we go and see it?'

We set off. Gaffur said, 'I'll stay here, otherwise these monkeys will make short work of this automobile.'

I let the other two go forward and whispered to Gaffur, 'Why are you in such a bad mood today, Gaffur? After all, you have gone over worse roads and never complained!'

'I have new springs and shock-absorbers. You know what they cost?'

'Oh, you will recover their cost soon; be cheerful.'

'What some of our passengers need is a tractor and not a motor car. That fellow!' He was vaguely discontented. I knew his wrath was not against us, but against our guide, because he said, 'I think it will be good to make him walk back to the town. Why should anyone want to come so far to see a reptile?' I left him alone; it was no use trying to make him cheerful. Perhaps his wife had nagged him when he started out.

The girl stood under the shade of a tree while the man prodded a snake to make it come out of its basket. It was fairly large, and hissed and spread out its hood, while the boys screamed and ran off and returned. The man shouted at them, 'If you excite it, it will chase you all!'

I told the boys to keep quiet, and asked the man, 'You are sure you will not let it slip through?'

The girl suggested, 'You must play on the flute, make it rear its head and dance.' The man pulled out his gourd flute and played on it shrilly, and the cobra raised itself and darted hither and thither and swayed. The whole thing repelled me, but it seemed to fascinate the girl. She watched it swaying with the raptest attention. She stretched out her arm slightly and swayed it in imitation of the movement; she swayed her whole body to the rhythm—for just a second, but that was sufficient to tell me what she was, the greatest dancer of the century.

It was nearly seven in the evening when we got back to the hotel. As soon as she got down, she paused to murmur a 'Thanks' to no one in particular and went up the staircase. Her husband, waiting at the porch, said, 'That's all for the day. You could give me a consolidated account, I suppose, later. I shall want the car at ten o'clock tomorrow.' He turned and went back to his room.

I felt annoyed with him at this stage. What did he take me for? This fellow, telling me that he wanted the car at this hour or that hour. Did he think that I was a tout? It made me very angry, but the fact was that I really was a tout, having no better business than hanging around between Gaffur and a snake-charmer and a tourist and doing all kinds of things. The man did not even care to tell me anything about himself, or where he wanted to go on the following morning; an extraordinary fellow!

A hateful fellow. I had never hated any customer so much before. I told Gaffur as we were driving back, 'Tomorrow morning! He asks for the car as if it were his grandfather's property! Any idea where he wants to go?'

'Why should I bother about it? If he wants the car he can have it if he pays for it. That is all. I don't care who pays for a thing as long as they engage me...' He rambled on into a personal philosophy which I didn't care to follow.

My mother waited for me as usual. While serving me food she said, 'Where have you been today? What are the things you have done today?'

I told her about the visit to the snake-charmer. She said, 'They are probably from Burma, people who worship snakes.' She said, 'I had a cousin living in Burma once and he told me about the snake women there.'

'Don't talk nonsense, Mother. She is a good girl, not a snake-worshipper. She is a dancer, I think.'

'Oh, dancer! Maybe, but don't have anything to do with these dancing women. They are all a bad sort.' I ate my food in silence, trying to revive in my mind the girl's scent-filled presence.

At ten next day I was at the hotel. Gaffur's car was already at the porch; he cried, 'Aha! again,' at the sight of me. 'Big man! Hm, trying improvements!' His idiom was still as if he spoke of automobiles. He winked at me.

I ignored everything and asked in a businesslike manner, 'Are they in?'

'I suppose so. They have not come out yet, that's all I know,' said Gaffur. Twenty words where one would do. Something was wrong with him. He was becoming loquacious. And then I felt a sudden stab of jealousy as I realized that perhaps he too had been affected by the presence of the damsel and was desirous of showing off in her presence. I grew jealous and unhappy and said to myself, 'If this is how Gaffur is going to conduct himself in the future, I shall get rid of him and find someone else, that's all.' I had no use for a loquacious, nose-poking taxi-driver.

I went upstairs to Room 28 on the second floor of the hotel and knocked authoritatively. 'Wait,' said the voice from inside. It was the man's, not the girl's as I had hoped. I waited for a few minutes and fretted. I looked at my watch. Ten o'clock. And this man said, 'Wait.' Was he still in bed with her? It was a fit occasion, as it seemed to me, to tear the door down and go in. The door opened, and he came out, dressed and ready. He shut the door behind him. I was aghast. I was on the point of demanding, 'What about her?' But I checked my impulse. I went sheepishly down with him.

He gave me a look of approval, as if I had dressed to please *him*. Before getting into the car he said, 'Today I want to study those friezes again for a short while.'

'All right, all right,' I thought, 'study the friezes or whatever else

you like. Why do you want me for that?' As if in answer to my
thoughts, he said, 'After that—' He took out of his pocket a piece
of paper and read.

This man would go on wall-gazing all his life and leave her to
languish in her hotel room. Strange man! Why did he not bring her
along with him? Probably he was absentminded. I asked, 'Is no one
else coming?'

'No,' he replied curtly, as if understanding my mind. He looked
at the paper in his hand and asked, 'Are you aware of the existence
of cave-paintings in these parts?'

I laughed off the question. 'Of course, everyone does not have the
taste to visit places like that, but there have been a few discriminating
visitors who insisted on seeing them. But—but—it will take a whole
day, and we may not be able to get back tonight.'

He went back to his room, returned after a few minutes with a
downcast face. Meanwhile I, with Gaffur's help, calculated the expense
involved in the trip. We knew that the path lay past the Peak House
forest bungalow. One would have to halt there for the night and walk
down a couple of miles. I knew where the caves were, but this was
the first time I was going to set eyes on them. Malgudi seemed to
unroll a new sightseeing place each time.

The man sat back in the car and said, 'You have probably no
notion how to deal with women, have you?'

I was pleased that he was becoming more human in his approach.
I said, 'I have no idea,' and laughed, thinking it might please him if
I seemed to enjoy his joke. Then I made bold to ask, 'What is the
trouble?' My new dress and deportment gave me a new courage. In
my khaki bush-coat I would not have dared to take a seat beside him
or talk to him in this way.

He looked at me with what seemed a friendly smile. He leaned
over and said, 'If a man has to have peace of mind it is best that he
forget the fair sex.' This was the first time in our association of three
days that he had talked to me so freely. He had always been curt and
taciturn. I judged that the situation must be pretty grave if it loosened
his tongue to this extent.

Gaffur sat in his seat with his chin in his hand. He was looking away from us. His whole attitude said, 'I am sorry to be wasting my morning with such time-killers as you two.' A courageous idea was developing in my head. If it succeeded it would lead to a triumphant end, if it failed the man might kick me out of his sight or call the police. I said, 'Shall I go and try on your behalf?'

'Would you?' he asked, brightening up. 'Go ahead, if you are bold enough.'

I didn't wait to hear further. I jumped out of the car and went up the steps four at a time. I paused at Number 28 to regain normal breath, and knocked.

'Don't trouble me, I don't want to come with you. Leave me alone,' came the girl's voice from within.

I hesitated, wondering how to speak. This was my first independent speech with the divine creature. I might either make a fool of myself or win the heavens. How should I announce myself? Would she know my famous name? I said, 'It's not he, but me.'

'What?' asked the sweet voice, puzzled and irritated.

I repeated, 'It is not him, but me. Don't you know my voice? Didn't I come with you yesterday to that cobra man? All night I didn't sleep,' I added, lowering my voice, and whispered through a chink in the door, 'The way you danced, your form and figure haunted me all night.'

Hardly had I finished my sentence when the door half opened and she looked at me. 'Oh, you!' she said, her eyes lighting up with understanding.

'My name is Raju,' I said.

She scrutinized me thoroughly. 'Of course, I know you.' I smiled affably, my best smile, as if I had been asked for it by a photographer. She said, 'Where is he?'

'Waiting in the car for you. Won't you get ready and come out?' She looked dishevelled, her eyes were red with recent tears, and she wore a faded cotton saree; no paint or perfume, but I was prepared to accept her as she was. I told her, 'You may come out as you are and no one will mind it.' And I added, 'Who would decorate a rainbow?'

She said, 'You think you can please me by all this? You think you can persuade me to change my mind?'

'Yes,' I said. 'Why not?'

'Why do you want me to go out with him? Leave me in peace,' she said, opening her eyes wide, which gave me another opportunity to whisper close to her face, 'Because life is so blank without your presence.'

She could have pushed my face back, crying, 'How dare you talk like this!' and shut the door on me. But she didn't. She merely said, 'I never knew you would be such a troublesome man. Wait a minute, then.' She withdrew into her room, I wanted to cry with all my being, 'Let me in,' and bang on the door, but I had the good sense to restrain myself. I heard footsteps and saw that her husband had come to see the results.

'Well, is she coming or not? I am not prepared to waste all—'

'Hush,' I said. 'She will be out in a moment. Please go back to the car.'

'Really!' he muttered in amazement. 'You are a wizard!' He noiselessly turned and went back to his car. Presently the lady did come out like a vision, and said, 'Let us go. But for you I would have given you all a few surprises.'

'What?'

'I would have taken the next train home.'

'We are going to a wonderful spot. Please be your usual sweet self, for my sake.'

'All right,' she said and went down the steps; I followed. She opened the door of the car, went straight in, and took her seat, as her husband edged away to make space for her. I came over to the other side and sat down beside him. I was not prepared to go and sit down beside Gaffur at this stage.

Gaffur now turned his head to ask whether we might go. 'We cannot return tonight if we are going to the Peak House.'

'Let us try and come back,' the man pleaded.

'We will try, but there is no harm in being prepared to stay over if necessary. Take a change of clothing. No harm in it. I am asking

Gaffur to stop at my house.'

The lady said, 'Just a minute, please.' She dashed upstairs and returned with a small suitcase. She said to the man, 'I have your clothes too in this.'

The man said, 'Very good,' and smiled, and she smiled and in the laughter the tension of the morning partly disappeared. Still, there was some uneasiness in the air.

I asked Gaffur to pull up at the railway station for a moment, the car facing away from my house. I didn't want them to see my house. 'Just a moment, please.' I dashed out. Directly the shop-boy sighted me he opened his mouth to say something. I ignored him, dashed up to my house, picked up a bag, and ran out, saying, 'I may stay out tonight. Don't wait,' to my mother in the kitchen.

We reached the Peak House at about four in the afternoon. The caretaker was delighted to see us. He was often rewarded by me unstintingly with my clients' money. I always made it a point to tell my clients beforehand, 'Keep that caretaker in good humour and he'll look after you and procure for you even the most impossible articles.' I repeated the formula now and the husband—he shall be referred to as Marco henceforth—said, 'Go ahead and do it. I look to you to help us through. You know I have only one principle in life. I don't want to be bothered with small things. I don't mind the expense.'

I told Joseph, the caretaker, to get us food and foodstuffs from his village, two miles away. I asked Marco, 'Will you leave some cash with me? I'll render accounts later. I need not worry you again and again for small payments.'

One could not foresee how he would react to such a request. He was unsteady—sometimes he announced aloud his indifference to money, the next minute he'd suddenly show every symptom of miserliness and behave like an auditor, but ultimately he'd pay for everything if, as I discovered, he got a voucher for payments. He would not yield an anna without a voucher, whereas if you gave him a slip of paper you could probably get him to write off his entire fortune.

Now I knew the trick. As I found him stumbling for words, I

said, 'I'll see that you get proper receipts for every payment.' It pleased him; he opened his purse.

I had to dispose of the taxi. Gaffur would come back on the following afternoon. I made Gaffur sign a receipt, and gave some money to Joseph to fetch us food from a hotel in the village. Now that I was in charge of the arrangements, I had not much time to gaze on my beloved's face, although I was darting glances in her direction.

'The caves are a mile off, down that way,' Joseph said. 'We can't go there now. Tomorrow morning. If you leave after breakfast, you can come back for lunch.'

The Peak House was perched on the topmost cliff on Mempi Hills—the road ended with the house; there was a glass wall covering the north veranda, through which you could view the horizon a hundred miles away. Below us the jungle stretched away down to the valley, and on a clear day you might see also the Sarayu sparkling in the sun and pursuing its own course far away. This was like heaven to those who loved wild surroundings and to watch the game, which prowled outside the glass wall at nights. The girl was in ecstasy. Our house was surrounded with rich vegetation. She ran like a child from plant to plant with cries of joy, while the man looked on with no emotion. Anything that interested her seemed to irritate him.

She suddenly halted, gazing on the sun-bathed plains thousands of feet below. I feared that when night came on she might get scared. We heard the jackals howling, and all kinds of grunts and roars. Joseph brought a hamper of food for us and left it on a table. He brought milk, coffee, and sugar, for the morning, and showed me where the coal stove was.

The lady cried, 'Nobody should get up till I call. I'll have coffee ready for everyone.'

Joseph said, 'Please lock the door inside,' and added, 'if you sit up on that veranda, you can watch tigers and other animals prowling about. But you must not make any noise; that's the secret of it.' We watched Joseph pick up a lantern and go down the steps; we could see his lantern faintly light the foliage on the way and disappear.

'Poor Joseph, how bold of him to go down alone!' the girl said, at which the husband replied casually, 'Nothing surprising. He has probably been born and bred here. Do you know him?' he asked, aiming to me.

'Yes; he was born in that village and came to mind this place is a boy. He must be at least sixty years old.'

'How has he come to be a Christian?'

'There was a mission somewhere here; missionaries go and settle down in all sorts of places, you know,' I said.

Joseph had given us two lamps, brass ones filled with kerosene. One I kept on the kitchen table, and the other I gave the man for his room, leaving the rest of the building in darkness. Outside through the glass we could see the stars in the sky. We sat around the table. I knew where the plates were. I set them on the table and served food—or, rather, attempted to serve food. It was about seven-thirty in the evening. We had seen a gorgeous sunset. We had seen the purple play of colour in the northern skies after that, and admired it; we saw the tops of the trees lit up by stray red rays even after the sun was out of view, and had found a common idiom to express our admiration.

The man just followed us about. I had become so lyrical that he suddenly said, 'Hey, Raju, so you are a poet too!' a compliment I accepted with becoming modesty.

At dinner, I picked up a dish and tried to serve. She said, 'No, no. Let me serve you both, and I will be the last to eat, like a good housewife.'

'Aha, that's a good idea,' the man said jocularly. She extended her hand for me to pass the dish to her. But I insisted on doing it myself. She suddenly darted forward and forcibly snatched it away from my hand. Oh, that touch made my head reel for a moment. I didn't see anything clearly. Everything disappeared into a sweet, dark haze, as under chloroform. My memory dwelt on the touch all through the dinner: I was not aware what we were eating or what they were saying. I sat with head bowed. I was nervous to see her face and meet her looks. I don't recollect when we finished eating and when she took away the dishes. I was only conscious of her soft movements. My thoughts dwelt on her golden touch. A part of my mind went an saying, 'No, no. It is not right. Marco is her husband, remember. It's not to be thought of.' But it was impossible to pull the thoughts back. 'He may shoot you,' said my wary conscience. 'Has he a gun?' commented another part of my mind.

After dinner she said, 'Let us go to the glass veranda. I must watch the game. Do you think they will come out at this hour?'

'Yes; if we are patient and lucky,' I said. 'But won't you be afraid? One has to wait in the dark.'

She laughed at my fears and invited Marco to go with her. But he said he wanted to be left alone. He pulled a chair to the lamp, took out his portfolio, and was soon lost in his papers. She said, 'Shield your lamp. I don't want my animals to be scared off.' She moved with light steps to the veranda, pulled up a chair, and sat down. On the way she had said to me, 'Have *you* documents to see to?'

'No, no,' I said, hesitating midway between my room and hers.

'Come along, then. Surely you aren't going to leave me to the mercy of prowling beasts?' I looked at the man to know what he would have to say, but he was absorbed in his papers. I asked, 'Do you want anything?'

'No.'

'I'll be on the veranda.'

'Go ahead,' he said without looking up from his papers.

She sat close to the glass pane, intently looking out. I softly placed a chair beside her, and sat down. After a while she said, 'Not a soul. Do animals come here at all, I wonder, or is it one of the usual stories?'

'No, lots of people have seen them—'

'What animals?'

'Lions.'

'Lions here?' she said and began laughing. 'I have read they were only in Africa. But this is really—'

'No, excuse me.' I had slipped. 'I meant tigers, and panthers, and bears, and sometimes elephants too are to be seen crossing the valley or coming for a drink of water at the pool.'

'I'm prepared to spend the whole night here,' she said. 'He will, of course, be glad to be left alone. Here at least we have silence and darkness, welcome things, and something to wait for out of that darkness.'

I couldn't find anything to say in reply. I was overwhelmed by her perfume. The stars beyond the glass shone in the sky.

'Can't an elephant break through the glass?' she asked, yawning.

'No; there is a moat on the other side. They can't approach us.'

Bright eyes shone amidst the foliage. She pulled my sleeve and whispered excitedly, 'Something—what can it be?'

'Probably a panther,' I said to keep up the conversation. Oh, the whispers, the stars, and the darkness—I began to breathe heavily with excitement.

'Have you caught a cold?' she asked.

I said, 'No.'

'Why are you breathing so noisily?'

I wanted to put my face close to her and whisper, 'Your dance was marvellous. You are gifted. Do it again sometime. God bless you. Won't you be my sweetheart?' But fortunately I restrained myself. Turning back, I saw that Marco had come with soft steps. 'What luck?' he asked in a whisper.

'Something came, but it's gone. Sit down, won't you?' I said, giving him the chair. He sat down, peering through the glass.

Next morning I found the atmosphere once again black and tense—all the vivacity of the previous evening was gone. When their room opened, only he came out, fully dressed and ready. I had made the coffee on the charcoal stove. He came over and mechanically held his hand out as if I were the man on the other side of a coffee bar. I poured him a cup of coffee. 'Joseph has brought tiffin. Will you not taste it?'

'No; let us be going. I'm keen on reaching the caves.'

'What about the lady?' I asked.

'Leave her alone,' he said petulantly. 'I can't afford to be fooling around, wasting my time.' In the same condition as yesterday! This seemed to be the spirit of their morning every day. How cordially he had come over and sat beside her last night on the veranda! How cordially they had gone into the hotel on that night! What exactly happened at night that made them want to tear at each other in the morning? Did they sit up in bed and fight, or did she fatigue him with a curtain lecture? I wanted to cry out, 'Oh, monster, what do you do to her that makes her sulk like this on rising? What a treasure you have in your hand, without realizing its worth—like a monkey picking up a rose garland!' Then a thrilling thought occurred to me—probably she was feigning anger again, so that I might intercede.

He put down his cup and said, 'Now let us go.' I was afraid to ask him again about his wife. He was swinging a small cane impatiently. Could it be that he had been using it on her at night?

Even in my wild state, I did not make the mistake of asking again, 'Shall I call her?' as that might have led to a very serious situation. I only asked, 'Does she know about coffee?'

'Yes, yes,' he cried impatiently. 'Leave it there; she'll take it. She has enough sense to look after herself.' He waved the switch, and we started out. Only once did I turn my head to look back, in the hope that she might appear at the window and call us back. 'Did I come all the way for this monster's company?' I asked myself as I followed him down the hill slope. How appropriate it would be if he should stumble and roll downhill! Bad thought, bad thought. He walked ahead of me. We were like a couple of African hunters—in fact, his dress, with his helmet and thick jacket, as I have already mentioned, was that of a wild African *shikari*.

Our path through grass and shrub led to the valley. The cave was halfway across it. I felt suddenly irritated at the speed of his walk, as if he knew the way, swinging his cane and hugging his portfolio. If he could show half the warmth of that hug elsewhere! I suddenly asked, 'Do you know the way?'

'Oh no,' he said.

'You are leading me!' I said, putting into it all the irony I was capable of.

He cried, 'Oh!' looked confused, and said, stepping aside, 'Well, lead us,' and through an irrelevant association added, 'kindly light.'

The entrance to the cave was beyond a thicket of lantana. A huge door on its rusty hinges stood open. And, of course, all the crumbling brick and plaster was there. It was a cave with a single rock covering its entire roof; why any man should have taken the trouble to build a thing like this in a remote spot was more than I could understand.

He stood outside and surveyed the entrance. 'You see, this entrance must have been a later improvisation; the cave itself, I know, must have been about first century AD. The entrance and the door are of a later date. You see, that kind of tall entrance and the carved doorway became a current fashion in the seventh or eighth century, when the South Indian rulers became fond of…' He went on talking. Dead and decaying things seemed to loosen his tongue and fire his imagination, rather than things that lived and moved and swung their limbs. I had little to do as a guide; he knew so much more of everything!

When he passed in, he completely forgot the world outside and its inhabitants. The roof was low, but every inch of the wall space was covered with painted figures. He flashed a torch on the walls. He took out of his pocket a mirror and placed it outside to catch the sunlight and throw a beam on the paintings. Bats were whirring about; the floor was broken and full of holes. But he minded nothing. He became busy measuring, writing down, photographing, all the time keeping up a chatter, not bothered in the least whether I listened or not.

I was bored with his ruin-collecting activities. The wall-painting represented episodes from the epics and mythology, and all kinds of patterns and motifs, with men, women, and kings and animals, in a curious perspective and proportion of their own, and ancient like the rocks. I had seen hundreds like them, and I saw no point in seeing more. I had no taste for them, just as he had no taste for other things.

'Be careful,' I said. 'There may be reptiles in those cracks.'

'Oh, no,' he said indifferently, 'reptiles don't generally come to such interesting places; moreover, I have this.' He flourished his stick. 'I can manage. I'm not afraid.'

I suddenly said, 'I seem to hear the sound of a car. If it's Gaffur, I'd like to be there at the bungalow, so do you mind if I go? I'll be back.'

He said, 'Keep him. Don't let him go away.'

'When you return, come the same way—so that we may not get lost.' He didn't answer, but resumed his studies.

I reached the house at a run and rested a while in the back yard to regain my breath. I went in, brushing back my hair with my hand and composing my features. As I entered, I heard her voice. 'Looking for me?' She was sitting on a boulder in the shade of a tree. She must have seen me come up. 'I saw you even half a mile way, but you couldn't see me,' she said like one who had discovered a fault.

'You were on the peak and I was in the valley,' I said. I went up to her and made some polite inquiries about her coffee. She looked both sad and profound. I sat down on a stone near her.

'You have returned alone. I suppose he is wall-gazing?' she said.

'Yes,' I replied briefly.

'He does that everywhere.'

'Well, I suppose he is interested, that's all.'

'What about me, interested in something else?'

'What is your interest?'

'Anything except cold, old stone walls,' she said.

I looked at my watch. I had already been away from him for nearly an hour. I was wasting time. Time was slipping through my fingers. If I were to make good, I should utilize this chance. 'Every night you generally sit up and quarrel, do you?' I asked boldly.

'When we are alone and start talking, we argue and quarrel over everything. We don't agree on most matters, and then he leaves me alone and comes back and we are all right, that's all.'

'Until it is night again,' I said.

'Yes, yes.'

'It's unthinkable that anyone should find it possible to quarrel or argue with you—being with you must be such bliss.'

She asked sharply, 'What do you mean?'

I explained myself plainly. I was prepared to ruin myself today if need be, but I was going to talk and tell her. If she wanted to kick me out, she could do it after listening to me. I spoke my mind. I praised her dancing. I spoke out my love, but sandwiched it conveniently between my appreciations of her art. I spoke of her as an artist in one breath, and continued in the next as a sweetheart. Something like, 'What a glorious snake dance! Oh, I keep thinking of you all night. World's artist number one! Don't you see how I am pining for you every hour!'

It worked. She said, 'You are a brother to me ('Oh, no,' I wanted to cry) and I'll tell you what happens.' She gave me an account of their daily quarrels.

'Why did you marry at all?' I asked recklessly.

She remained moody and said, 'I don't know. It just happened.'

'You married him because of his wealth,' I said, 'and you were advised by your uncle and the rest.'

'You see,' she began, plucking my sleeve. 'Can you guess to what class I belong?'

I looked her up and down and ventured, 'The finest, whatever it may be, and I don't believe in class or caste. You are an honour to your caste, whatever it may be.'

'I belong to a family traditionally dedicated to the temples as dancers; my mother, grandmother, and, before her, her mother. Even as a young girl I danced in our village temple. You know how our caste is viewed?'

'It's the noblest caste on earth,' I said.

'We are viewed as public women,' she said plainly, and I was thrilled to hear the words. 'We are not considered respectable; we are not considered civilized.'

'All that narrow notion may be true of old days, but it's different now. Things have changed. There is no caste or class today.'

'A different life was planned for me by my mother. She put me to school early in life; I studied well. I took my master's degree in economics. But after college, the question was whether I should become a dancer or do something else. One day I saw in our paper an advertisement—the usual kind you may have seen: "Wanted: an educated, good-looking girl to marry a rich bachelor of academic interests. *No caste restrictions*; good looks and university degree essential." I asked myself, "Have I looks?"'

'Oh, who could doubt it?'

'I had myself photographed clutching the scroll of the university citation in one hand, and sent it to the advertiser. Well, we met, he examined me and my certificate, we went to a registrar and got married.'

'Did you like him the moment you saw him?'

'Don't ask all that now,' she snubbed me. 'We had had many discussions before coming to a decision. The question was, whether it would be good to marry so much above our wealth and class. But all the women in my family were impressed, excited that a man like him was coming to marry one of our class, and it was decided that if it was necessary to give up our traditional art, it was worth the sacrifice. He had a big house, a motor car, he was a man of high social standing; he had a house outside Madras, he was living in it all alone, no family at all; he lived with his books and papers.'

'So you have no mother-in-law!' I said.

'I'd have preferred any kind of mother-in-law, if it had meant one real, live husband,' she said. I looked up at her to divine her meaning, but she lowered her eyes. I could only guess. She said, 'He is interested in painting and old art and things like that.'

'But not one which can move its limbs, I suppose,' I said.

I sighed deeply, overcome with the sadness of her life. I placed my hand on her shoulder and gently stroked it. 'I am really very unhappy to think of you, such a gem lost to the world. In his place I would have made you a queen of the world.' She didn't push away my hand. I let it travel and felt the softness of her ear and pushed my fingers through the locks of her hair.

Gaffur's car did not turn up. A passing truck-driver brought the message that it had had a breakdown and would be coming on the following day. No one in the party minded really. Joseph looked after us quite well. Marco said it gave him more time to study the walls. I did not mind. It gave me an occasion to watch the game beyond the sheet glass every night, holding her hand, while Marco sat in his room, poring over his notes.

When Gaffur's car did turn up Marco said, 'I want to stay on here; it is going to take more time than I thought. Could you fetch from my room in the hotel my black trunk? I have some papers in it. I'd prefer to have you here also, if it is all the same to you.'

I seemed to hesitate, and then looked up at the girl for a moment.

There was a mute appeal in her eyes. I said yes.

'You may treat it as a part of your professional work,' he said, 'unless you feel it's going to hurt your general business.'

'All right,' I said, hesitantly. 'It's true, but I'd also like to be of service to you. Once I take charge of anyone, I always feel that they are my responsibility till I see them off again safely.'

As I was getting into the car she said to her husband, 'I'll also go back to the town; I want a few things from my box.'

I added, 'We may not be able to return tonight.'

He asked his wife, 'Can you manage?'

'Yes,' she said.

As we were going down the mountain road I often caught Gaffur looking at us through the mirror, and we moved away from the range of his vision. We reached our hotel in the evening. I followed her to her room. 'Should we go back this evening?' I asked her.

'Why?' she asked. 'Suppose Gaffur's car stops on the way? Better not risk it on that road. I'll stay here tonight.'

I went home to change. My mother was full of information the moment she saw me, and full of inquiries. I brushed everything aside. I rushed through my washing and grooming and took out another set of special clothes. I gave my old clothes in a bundle to my mother. 'Will you tell that shop-boy to take them to the *dhobi* and have them washed and ironed neatly? I may want them tomorrow.'

'Becoming a dandy?' she said, surveying me. 'Why are you always on the run now?' I gave her some excuse and started out again.

I engaged Gaffur for my own rounds that day. I was a true guide. Never had I shown anyone the town with greater zest. I took Rosie all over the place, showed her the town hall tower; showed her the Sarayu, and we sat on the sands and munched a large packet of salted nuts. She behaved like a baby—excited, thrilled, appreciative of everything. I took her through the Suburban Stores and told her to buy anything she liked. This was probably the first time that she was seeing the world. She was in ecstasies. Gaffur warned me when he got me alone for a moment outside the store, 'She is a married woman, remember.'

'What of it?' I said. 'Why do you tell me this?'

'Don't be angry, sir,' he said. 'Go slow; that is all I can say.'

'You are unhealthy-minded, Gaffur. She is like a sister to me,' I said, and tried to shut him up.

All he said was, 'You are right. What is it to me? After all, that man is here, who has really married her. And I've my own wife to bother about.'

I left him and went back to the store. She had picked up a silver brooch, painted over and patterned like a peacock. I paid for it and pinned it on her saree. We dined on the terrace of the Taj, from where she could have a view of the River Sarayu winding away. When I pointed it out to her she said, 'It's good. But I have had views of valleys, trees, and brooks to last me a lifetime.' We laughed. We were getting into a state of perpetual giggling.

She liked to loaf in the market, eat in a crowded hotel, wander about, see a cinema—these common pleasures seemed to have been beyond her reach all these days. I had dismissed the car at the cinema. I did not want Gaffur to watch my movements. We walked to the hotel after the picture. We had hardly noticed what it was. I had taken a box. She wore a light-yellow crepe saree which made her so attractive that people kept looking at her.

Her eyes sparkled with vivacity and gratitude. I knew I had placed her in my debt.

It was nearing midnight. The man at the hotel desk watched us pass without showing any interest. Deskmen at hotels learn not to be inquisitive. At the door of Number 28 I hesitated. She opened the door, passed in, and hesitated, leaving the door half open. She stood looking at me for a moment, as on the first day.

'Shall I go away?' I asked in a whisper.

'Yes. Good night,' she said feebly.

'May I not come in?' I asked, trying to look my saddest.

'No, no. Go away,' she said. But on an impulse I gently pushed her out of the way, and stepped in and locked the door on the world.

6

Raju lost count of the time that passed in these activities, one day being like another and always crowded. Several months (or perhaps years) had passed. He counted the seasons by the special points that jutted out, such as the harvest in January, when his disciples brought him sugar cane and jaggery cooked with rice; when they brought him sweets and fruits, he knew that the Tamil New Year was on; when Dussera came they brought in extra lamps and lit them, and the women were busy all through the nine days, decorating the pillared hall with coloured paper and tinsel; and for Deepavali they brought him new clothes and crackers and he invited the children to a special session and fired the crackers. He kept a rough count of time thus, from the beginning of the year to its end, through its seasons of sun, rain, and mist. He kept count of three cycles and then lost count. He realized that it was unnecessary to maintain a calendar.

His beard now caressed his chest, his hair covered his back, and around his neck he wore a necklace of prayer beads. His eyes shone with softness and compassion, the light of wisdom emanated from them. The villagers kept bringing in so many things for him that he lost interest in accumulation. He distributed whatever he had to the gathering at the end of the day. They brought him huge chrysanthemum garlands, jasmine and rose petals in baskets. He gave them all back to the women and children.

He protested to Velan one day, 'I'm a poor man and you are poor men; why do you give me all this? You must stop it.' But it was not possible to stop the practice; they loved to bring him gifts. He came to be called Swami by his congregation, and where he lived was called the Temple. It was passing into common parlance. 'The Swami said this or that', or 'I am on my way to the Temple'. People loved this place so much that they lime-washed its walls and drew red bands on them.

In the first half of the year they had evening rains, which poured down fussily for a couple of hours to the tune of tremendous thunder; later in the year they had a quieter sort of rain, steadily pattering down.

But no rain affected the assembly. People came shielding themselves with huge bamboo mats or umbrellas or coconut thatch. The hall became more packed during the wet season, since the people could not overflow into the outer courtyard. But it made the gathering cosy, interesting, and cool; and the swish of rain and wind in the trees and the swelling river (which made them carry their children aloft on their shoulders and cross the river only at certain shallow points) lent a peculiar charm to the proceedings. Raju loved this season, for its greenness everywhere, for the variety of cloud-play in the sky, which he could watch through the columned halls.

But he suddenly noticed at the end of the year that the skies never dimmed with cloud. The summer seemed to continue. Raju inquired, 'Where are the rains?"

Velan pulled a long face. 'The first rains have totally kept off, Swamiji, and the millet crop, which we should have harvested by now, is all scorched on the stalks. It's a big worry.'

'A thousand banana seedlings are dead,' said another. 'If it continues, who knows?' They looked anxious.

Raju, ever a soothsayer, said consolingly, 'Such things are common; don't worry too much about them. Let us hope for the best.'

They became argumentative. 'Do you know, Swamiji, our cattle which go out to graze nose about the mud and dirt and come back, having no grass to eat?'

Raju had some soothing remark for every complaint. They went home satisfied. 'You know best, master,' they said and left. Raju recollected that for his bath nowadays he had to go down three more steps to reach the water. He went down and stood looking along the river course. He looked away to his left, where the river seemed to wind back to the mountain ranges of the Mempi, to its source, where he had often conducted tourists. Such a small basin, hardly a hundred square feet with its little shrine—what had happened there to make this river shrink so much here? He noticed that the borders were wide, more rocks were showing, and the slope on the other side seemed to have become higher.

Other signs too were presently to be noticed. At the Harvest

Festival, the usual jubilation was absent. 'Sugar canes have completely wilted; with difficulty we have brought in this bit. Please accept it.'

'Give it to the children,' Raju said. Their gifts were shrinking in size and volume.

'The astrologer says that we shall have very early rains in the coming year,' someone said. The talk was always about the rains. People listened to discourses and philosophy with only half-interest. They sat around, expressing their fears and hopes. 'Is it true, Swami, that the movement of aeroplanes disturbs the clouds and so the rains don't fall? Too many aeroplanes in the sky.' 'Is it true, Swami, that the atom bombs are responsible for the drying up of the clouds?' Science, mythology, weather reports, good and evil, and all kinds of possibilities were connected with the rain. Raju gave an explanation for each in the best manner he could manage, but he found his answers never diverted their minds.

He decreed, 'You must not think too much of it. The rain-god sometimes teases those who are obsessed with thoughts of him. How would you feel if someone went on mentioning and repeating your name all hours of the day and night for days and days on end?' They enjoyed the humour of the analogy, and went their ways. But a situation was developing which no comforting word or discipline of thinking could help. Something was happening on a different plane over which one had no control or choice, and where a philosophical attitude made no difference. Cattle were unable to yield milk; they lacked the energy to drag the plough through the furrows; flocks of sheep were beginning to look scurvy and piebald, with their pelvic bones sticking out.

The wells in the villages were drying up. Huge concourses of women with pitchers arrived at the river, which was fast narrowing. From morning to night they came in waves and took the water. Raju watched their arrival and departure as they passed in files on the high ground opposite, looking picturesque, but without the tranquillity inherent in a picture. They quarrelled at the water-hole for priorities, and there was fear, desperation, and lamentation in their voices.

The earth was fast drying up. A buffalo was found dead on a

foot-track. The news was brought to the Swami early one morning by Velan. He stood above him as he slept and said, 'Swami, I want you to come with us.'

'Why?'

'Cattle have begun to die,' he said with quiet resignation.

'What can I do about it?' Raju felt like asking, sitting up in his bed. But he could not say such a thing. He said soothingly, 'Oh, no; it can't be.'

'A buffalo was found dead on the forest path beyond our village.'

'Did you see it yourself?'

'Yes, Swami, I come from there.'

'Can't be as bad as that, Velan. It must have died of some other disease.'

'Please come along and see it, and if you can tell us why it is dead, it will relieve our minds. A learned man like you should see and tell.'

They were clearly losing their heads. They were entering a nightmare phase. The Swami knew so little of cattle, dead or alive, that it was of no practical use his going to see this one, but since they wanted it, he asked Velan to be seated for a few moments, and went down with him. The village street looked deserted. Children played about in the road dust, because the master had gone to town with a petition for relief addressed to the revenue authorities, and so the day-school was closed. Women were moving about with water-pots on their heads. In passing, 'Could hardly get half a pot today,' said some. 'What's the world coming to? You must show us the way, Swami.'

Raju merely raised a hand and waved it as if to say, 'Be peaceful; everything will be all right; I will fix it with the gods.' A small crowd followed him and Velan to the forest path, saying the same thing over and over again. Someone reported worse happenings in the next village; cholera was breaking out and thousands were dying, and so forth; he was snubbed by the rest as a scaremonger. Raju paid little attention to the jabber around him.

There it was outside the village, on a rough foot-track that led into the forest, a buffalo with bones sticking out. Crows and kites, already hovering about, flew off at the approach of men. There was a sickening odour, and henceforth Raju began to associate the season with it. It could not be mitigated with soothsaying. He held his upper cloth to his nostrils and gazed at the carcass for a while. 'Whose was this?' he asked.

They looked at one another. 'Not ours,' someone said. 'It belonged to the next village.' There was some relief at this thought. If it was one from the next village, it was far removed. Anything, any explanation, any excuse served to console people now.

'It belonged to no one,' said another. 'It looks like a wild buffalo.'

This was even better. Raju felt relieved at the possibility of there being other solutions and explanations. He added, peering at it again, 'It must have been bitten by a poisonous insect.' This was a comforting explanation, and he turned back without letting his eye dwell on the barren branches of trees, and the ground covered with bleached mud without a sign of green.

The piece of interpretations by the Swamiji pleased the public. It brought them untold comfort. The air of tension suddenly relaxed. When the cattle were penned for the night, they looked on them without anxiety. 'There is enough about for the cattle to feed on,' they said. 'Swami says that the buffalo died of a poisonous bite. He knows.' In support of it, many anecdotes were told of the death of animals from mysterious causes. 'There are snakes which bite into their hooves.' 'There are certain kinds of ants whose bite is fatal to animals.'

More cattle were found dead here and there. When the earth was scratched it produced only a cloud of fine dust. The granary of the previous year, in most of the houses, remained unreplenished and the level was going down. The village shopman was holding out for bigger prices. When people asked for a measure of rice he demanded fourteen annas for it. The man who wanted the rice lost his temper and slapped his face. The shopman came out with a chopper and attacked the customer; and those who sympathized with the man gathered in front of the shop and invaded it. The shopman's relatives and sympathizers came at night with crowbars and knives and started attacking the other group.

Velan and his men also picked up axes and knives and started out for the battle. Shrieks and cries and imprecations filled the air. The little hay that was left was set on fire, and the dark night was ablaze. Raju heard the cries, coming on the night air, and then he saw the blaze lighting up the landscape beyond the mound. Only a few hours before, everything had seemed peaceful and quiet. He shook his head, saying to himself, 'The village people do not know how to remain peaceful. They are becoming more and more agitated. At this rate, I think I'll look for a new place.' He went back to sleep, unable to take any further interest in their activities.

But news was brought to him early in the morning. Velan's brother told him while he was still half asleep that Velan was down with an injured skull and burns, and he gave a list of women and children hurt in the fight. They were mustering themselves to attack the other group tonight.

Raju was amazed at the way things were moving. He did not know what he was expected to do now, whether to bless their expedition or prevent it. Personally, he felt that the best thing for them would be to blow one another's brains out. That'd keep them from bothering too much about the drought. He felt a pity for Velan's condition. 'Is he seriously hurt?' he asked.

Velan's brother said, 'Oh, no. Just cut up here and there,' as though he wasn't satisfied with the marks.

Raju wondered for a while whether he should visit Velan, but he felt a tremendous reluctance to move. If Velan was hurt, he'd get healed; that was all. And now the brother's description of the injuries, whether false or true, suited his programme. There was no urgency to go and see Velan. He feared that if he made it a habit he would not be left in peace, as the villagers would always have a reason to call him out. He asked Velan's brother, 'How did you yourself manage to remain intact?'

'Oh, I was also there, but they didn't hit me. If they had I would have laid ten of them low. But my brother, he was careless.'

'Thin as a broomstick, but talks like a giant,' thought Raju, and advised, 'Tell your brother to apply turmeric to his wounds.' From the casual tone with which this man was speaking, Raju wondered if it

THE GUIDE ▪ 201

was possible that he himself had dealt a blow to Velan from behind; anything seemed possible in this village. All the brothers in the place were involved in litigation against one another; and anyone might do anything in view of the present sensational developments. Velan's brother rose to go. Raju said, 'Tell Velan to rest in bed completely.'

'Oh, no, master. How can he rest? He is joining the party tonight and he will not rest till he burns their houses.'

'It is not right,' Raju said, somewhat irritated by all this pugnacity.

Velan's brother was one of the lesser intelligences of the village. He was about twenty-one, a semi-moron who had grown up as a dependent in Velan's house, yet another of Velan's trials in life. He spent his days taking the village cattle out to the mountains for grazing: he collected them from various houses early in the day, and drove them to the mountainside, watched over them, and brought them back in the evening. All day he lounged under a tree's shade, eating a ball of boiled millet when the sun came overhead, and watching for the sun to slant westward to drive the cattle homeward. He had hardly anyone to speak to except his cattle the whole day and he spoke to them on equal terms and abused them and their genealogy unreservedly. Any afternoon in the stillness of the forest, if one had the occasion to observe, one could hear the hills echoing to the choice, abusive words that he hurled at the animals as he followed them with his stick. He was considered well equipped for this single task, and from each house was given four annas a month. They did not trust him with any more responsible tasks. He was one of those rare men in the village who never visited the Swamiji, but preferred to sleep at home at the end of the day. But now he had come, almost for the first time. The others were preoccupied and busy with their preparations for the coming fight, and he was one of those whose employment was affected by the drought; no one saw any sense in sending the cattle out to nose about the dry sand and paying the idiot four annas a month.

He had come here this morning, not because anyone had sent him to carry a message for the Swamiji, but because he was at a loose end and had suddenly felt that he might as well pay a visit to the temple and receive the Swami's blessing. The fight was the last thing the villagers would have liked to bring to the Swami's attention, although after finishing it they might have given him a mild version. But this boy brought the news on his own initiative and defended their action. 'But, Swami, why did they cut my brother's face?' He added sullenly, 'Should they be left free to do all this?'

Raju argued with him patiently. 'You beat the shopman first, didn't you?'

The boy took it literally and said, 'I didn't beat the shopman. The man who beat him was...' He gave a number of local names.

Raju felt too weary to correct him and improve his understanding. He simply said, 'It is no good; nobody should fight.' He felt it impossible to lecture him on the ethics of peace, and so merely said, 'No one should fight.'

'But they fight!' the boy argued. 'They come and beat us.' He paused, ruminating upon the words, and added, 'And they will kill us soon.'

Raju felt bothered. He did not like the idea of so much commotion. It might affect the isolation of the place and bring the police on the scene. He did not want anyone to come to the village. Raju suddenly began to think positively on these matters. He gripped the other's arm above his elbow and said, 'Go and tell Velan and the rest that I don't want them to fight like this. I'll tell them what to do later.' The boy prepared himself to repeat his usual arguments. But Raju said impatiently, 'Don't talk. Listen to what I say.'

'Yes, master,' the boy said, rather frightened at this sudden vehemence.

'Tell your brother, immediately, wherever he may be, that unless they are good I'll never eat.'

'Eat what?' asked the boy, rather puzzled.

'Say that I'll not eat. Don't ask what. I'll not eat till they are good.'

'Good? Where?'

This was frankly beyond the comprehension of the boy. He wanted to ask again, 'Eat what?' but refrained out of fear. His eyes opened wide. He could not connect the fight and this man's food. He wanted only to be released from the terrific grip over his left elbow. He felt he had made a mistake in coming to this man all alone—the bearded face, pushed so close to him, frightened him. This man might perhaps eat him up. He became desperately anxious to get out of the place. He said, 'All right, sir. I'll do it,' and the moment Raju let his hold go he shot out of the place, was across the sands and out of sight in a moment.

He was panting when he ran into the assembly of his village elders. They were sitting solemnly around a platform in the centre of the village, discussing the rains. There was a brick platform built around an ancient peepul tree, at whose root a number of stone figures were embedded, which were often anointed with oil and worshipped. This was a sort of town hall platform for Mangala. It was shady and cool and spacious; there was always a gathering of men on one side conferring on local problems, and on the other women who carried loaded baskets on their heads and rested; children chased each other; and the village dogs slumbered.

Here were sitting the elders of the village, discussing the rain, the fight tonight, and all the strategies connected with it. They had still many misgivings about the expedition. How the Swami would view the whole thing was a thing that could be understood only later. He might not approve. It would be best not to go to him until they themselves were clear in their heads about what to do. That the other group deserved punishment was beyond question. Among those talking were quite a number with bruises and cuts. But they had a fear of the police; they remembered a former occasion when there had been a faction fight, and the government posted a police force almost permanently and made the villagers feed them and pay for their keep.

Into this council of war burst Velan's brother. The atmosphere became tense. 'What is it, brother?' asked Velan.

The boy stopped to recover breath before speaking. They took him by the shoulder and shook him, at which he became more confused and blabbered and finally said, 'The Swami, the Swami, doesn't want food any more. Don't take any food to him.'

'Why? Why?'

'Because, because—it doesn't rain.' He added also, suddenly, recollecting the fight, 'No fight, he says.'

'Who asked you to go there?' asked his brother authoritatively.

'I—I didn't, but when I—found myself there he asked me and I told him—'

'What did you tell him?'

The boy became suddenly wary. He knew he would be thrashed if he said he had mentioned the fight. He didn't like to be gripped by the shoulder—in fact, he was averse to being gripped in any manner at all; but there the Swami squeezed his elbow and brushed his beard on his face, and here these men were tearing at his shoulder. He felt sorry he had ever got involved. It was best not to have anything to do with them.

They would wrench his shoulder off if they knew he had been telling the master about the fight. So he covered up the entire business in the best manner he could think of. He blinked. They demanded of him again, 'What did you tell him?'

'That there is no rain,' he said, mentioning the easiest subject that occurred to him.

They patted him on the head and said contemptuously, 'Big prophet to carry the news! He didn't know about it till then, I suppose.' A laugh followed. The boy also simpered and tried to get over it.

Then he remembered the message he had been entrusted with, and thought it safer to say something about it, otherwise the great man might come to know of it and lay a curse on him. And so he said, coming back to the original starting point, 'He wants no food until it is all right.'

He uttered it with such solemnity and emphasis that they asked, 'What did he say? Tell us exactly.'

The boy deliberated for a moment and said, 'Tell your brother not to bring me any more food. I won't eat. If I don't eat, it'll be all right; and then everything will be all right.' They stared at him, puzzled. He smiled, rather pleased at the importance he was receiving. They remained in thought for a moment.

And then one of them said, 'This Mangala is a blessed country to have a man like the Swami in our midst. No bad thing will come to us as long as he is with us. He is like a Mahatma. When Mahatma

Gandhi went without food, how many things happened in India! This is a man like that. If he fasts there will be rain. Out of his love for us he is undertaking it. This will surely bring rain and help us. Once upon a time a man fasted for twenty-one days and brought down the deluge. Only great souls that take upon themselves tasks such as this—' The atmosphere became electrified. They forgot the fight and all their troubles and bickerings.

The village was astir. Everything else seemed inconsequential now. Someone brought the news that upstream a crocodile had been found dead on the sand, having no watery shelter and being scorched by the sun. Someone else came with the news that the fast-drying lake bed in a nearby village was showing up an old temple which had been submerged a century ago, when the lake was formed. The image of the god was still intact in the inner shrine, none the worse for having lain under water so long; the four coconut trees around the temple were still there... And so on and so forth. More and more details were coming in every hour. Hundreds of people were now walking across the lake bed to visit the temple, and some careless ones lost their lives, sucked in by loose mud. All this now produced a lot of public interest, but no fear. They were now even able to take a more lenient view of the shopman who had assaulted his customer. 'After all, so and so should not have called him a whoreson; not a proper word.'

'Of course, one's kith and kin are bound to support one. What are they worth otherwise?' Velan brooded over the cut on his forehead, and a few others suddenly recollected their various injuries. They could not decide how far this could be forgiven. They consoled themselves with the thought that a good number in the other group must also be nursing injuries at that moment; it was a very satisfying thought. They suddenly decided that they should have a third party to come and arbitrate, so that the fight could be forgotten, provided the other group paid for the burned-down haystacks and entertained the chief men of this group at a feast. And they spent their time discussing the conditions of peace and rose in a body, declaring, 'Let us all go and pay our respects to Swami, our saviour.'

Raju was waiting for his usual gifts and food. He had, no doubt, fruits and other edible stuff left in his hamper, but he hoped they would bring him other fare. He had suggested to them that they should try to get him wheat flour, and rice flour, and spices. He wanted to try some new recipes, for a change. He had a subtle way of mentioning his special requirements. He generally began by taking Velan aside and saying, 'You see, if a little rice flour and chili powder could be got, along with some other things, I can do something new. On Wednesdays...' He enunciated some principle of living such as that on a special Wednesday he always liked to make his food with rice flour and such-and-such spice, and he mentioned it with an air of seriousness so that his listeners took it as a spiritual need, something of the man's inner discipline to keep his soul in shape and his understanding with the heavens in order. He had a craving for *bonda*, which he used to eat in the railway station stall when a man came there to vend his edibles on a wooden tray to the travellers. It was composed of flour, potato, a slice of onion, a coriander leaf, and a green chili—and oh! how it tasted—although he probably fried it in anything; he was the sort of vendor who would not hesitate to fry a thing in kerosene, if it worked out cheaper. With all that, he made delicious stuff, and when Raju used to ask the vendor how he made it, he gave him a recipe starting with, 'Just a small piece of ginger, and then it went on to this and that. While discoursing on the *Bhagavad Gita* to his audience the other evening, Raju had had a sudden craving to try this out himself—he was now equipped with a charcoal stove and frying pan, and what could be more musical than well-kneaded dough dropping into boiling oil? He had enumerated his wants to Velan as delicately as possible.

When he heard voices beyond the mound, he felt relieved. He composed his features for his professional role and smoothed out his beard and hair, and sat down in his seat with a book in his hand. As the voices approached, he looked up and found that a bigger crowd than usual was crossing the sands. He was puzzled for a second, but felt that perhaps they were jubilant over the fact that he had prevented a fight. He felt happy that he had after all achieved something, and saved the village. That idiot brother of Velan did not seem so bad after all. He hoped that they had the flour in a bag. It'd be improper to ask for it at once; they were bound to leave it in the kitchen.

They softened their steps and voices as they came nearer the pillared hall. Even the children hushed their voices when they approached the august presence.

They sat around in a silent semicircle as before, each in his place. The women got busy at once sweeping the floor and filling the mud lamps with oil. For ten minutes Raju neither looked at them nor spoke, but turned the leaves of his book. He felt curious to see how much of Velan's person was intact. He stole a glance across, and saw the scars on his forehead, and threw a swift look around and found that actually there was less damage than he had pictured in his mind. He resumed his studies, and only after he had gone through ten minutes of reading did he look up as usual and survey the gathering. He looked at his flock, fixed his eyes on Velan in particular, and said, 'Lord Krishna says here—' He adjusted his page to the light and read a passage. 'Do you know what it means?' He entered into a semi-philosophical discourse on a set of rambling themes, starting with the eating of good food and going on to absolute trust in god's goodness.

They listened to him without interrupting him, and only when he paused for breath at the end of nearly an hour did Velan say, 'Your prayers will surely be answered and save our village. Every one of us in the village prays night and day that you come through it safely.'

Raju was puzzled by what he heard. But he thought that such high and bombastic well-wishing was their habit and idiom and that they were only thanking him for putting enough sense into their heads not to go on with their fight. The assembly grew very loquacious and showered praise on him from all directions. A woman came up and touched his feet. Another followed. Raju cried, 'Have I not told you that I'll never permit this? No human being should ever prostrate before another human being.'

Two or three men came up, one of them saying, 'You are not another human being. You are a Mahatma. We should consider ourselves blessed indeed to be able to touch the dust of your feet.'

'Oh, no. Don't say that—' Raju tried to withdraw his feet. But they crowded round him. He tried to cover his feet. He felt ridiculous playing this hide-and-seek with his feet. He could find no place to put them. They tugged at various sides and they seemed ready to tickle his sides, if it would only give them his feet. He realized that there was really no escape from this demonstration and that it would be best to let them do what they liked. Almost everyone in the crowd had touched his feet and withdrawn, but not too far away; they surrounded him and showed no signs of moving. They gazed on his face and kept looking up in a new manner; there was a greater solemnity in the air than he had ever known before.

Velan said, 'Your penance is similar to Mahatma Gandhi's. He has left us a disciple in you to save us.' In their own rugged idiom, in the best words they could muster, they were thanking him. Sometimes they all spoke together and made a confused noise. Sometimes they began a sentence and could not get through with it. He understood that they spoke with feeling. They spoke gratefully, although their speech sounded bombastic. The babble was confusing. But their devotion to him was unquestionable. There was so much warmth in their approach that he began to feel it was but right they should touch his feet; as a matter of fact, it seemed possible that he himself might bow low, take the dust of his own feet, and press it to his eyes. He began to think that his personality radiated a glory... The crowd did not leave at the usual hour, but lingered on.

Velan had assumed that he was on a fast today and for the first time these months had failed to bring in any food. Just as well. When they attached so much value to his fasting he could not very well ask, 'Where is the stuff for my *bonda*?' It would be unseemly. No harm in attending to it later. They had assumed that he was fasting in order to stop their fight, and he was not going to announce to them that he had already had two meals during the day. He would just leave it at that, and even if his eyes should droop a little out of seeming fatigue, it would be quite in order. Now that it was all over, why couldn't they go away? He signalled to Velan to come nearer, 'Why not send away the women and children? Isn't it getting late?'

The crowd left at nearly midnight, but Velan remained where he had sat all the evening, leaning against a pillar. 'Don't you feel sleepy?' Raju asked.

'No, sir. Keeping awake is no big sacrifice, considering what you are doing for us.'

'Don't attach too much value to it. It's just a duty, that is all, and I'm not doing anything more than I ought to do. You can go home if you like.'

'No, sir. I'll go home tomorrow when the headman comes to relieve me. He will come here at five o'clock and stay on till the afternoon. I'll go home, attend to my work, and come back, sir.'

'Oh, it's not at all necessary that someone should always be here. I can manage quite well.'

'You will graciously leave that to us, sir. We are only doing our duty. You are undertaking a great sacrifice, sir, and the least we can do is to be at your side. We derive merit from watching your face, sir.'

Raju felt really touched by this attitude. But he decided that the time had come to get to the bottom of it. So he said, 'You are right. "One who serves the performer of a sacrifice derives the same merit", says our scripture, and you are not wrong. I thank god that my effort has succeeded, and you are all at peace with one another; that's my main concern. Now that's over, things are all right. You may go home. Tomorrow I'll take my usual food, and then I shall be all right. You will remember to fetch me rice flour, green chili, and—'

Velan was too respectful to express his surprise loudly. But he couldn't check himself any more. 'Do you expect it to rain tomorrow, sir?'

'Well...' Raju thought for a moment. What was this new subject that had crept into the agenda? 'Who can say? It's god's will. It may.' It was then that Velan moved nearer and gave an account of what his brother had told them, and its effect on the population around. Velan gave a very clear account of what the saviour was expected to do—stand in knee-deep water, look to the skies, and utter the prayer lines for two weeks, completely fasting during the period—and lo, the rains would come down, provided the man who performed it was a pure soul, was a great soul. The whole countryside was now in a happy ferment, because a great soul had agreed to go through the trial.

The earnestness with which he spoke brought tears to Raju's eyes. He remembered that not long ago he had spoken to them of such a penance, its value and technique. He had described it partly out of his head and partly out of traditional accounts he had heard his mother narrate. It had filled an evening's programme and helped him divert his audience's mind from the drought. He had told them, 'When the time comes, everything will be all right. Even the man who would bring you the rain will appear, all of a sudden.' They interpreted his words and applied them now to the present situation. He felt that he had worked himself into a position from which he could not get out. He could not betray his surprise. He felt that after all the time had come for him to be serious—to attach value to his own words. He needed time—and solitude to think over the whole matter. He got down from his pedestal; that was the first step to take. That seat had acquired a glamour, and as long as he occupied it people would not listen to him as to an ordinary mortal. He now saw the enormity of his own creation. He had created a giant with his puny self, a throne of authority with that slab of stone. He left his seat abruptly, as if he had been stung by a wasp, and approached Velan. His tone hushed with real humility and fear; his manner was earnest. Velan sat still as if he were a petrified sentry.

'Listen to me, Velan; it is essential that I should be alone tonight. It is essential that I should be alone through the day tomorrow too. And then come and see me tomorrow night. I'll speak to you tomorrow night. Until then neither you nor anyone else should see me.'

This sounded so mysterious and important that Velan got up without a word. 'I'll see you tomorrow night, sir. Alone?'

'Yes, yes; absolutely alone.'

'Very well, master; you have your own reasons. It is not for us to ask why or what. Big crowds will be arriving. I'll have men along the river to turn them back. It'll be difficult, but if it is your order it must be carried out.' He made a deep obeisance and went away. Raju stood looking after him for a while. He went into an inner room which he was using as a bedroom, and laid himself down. His body was aching from too much sitting up the whole day; and he felt exhausted by the numerous encounters. In that dark chamber, as the bats whirred about and the far-off sounds of the village ceased, a great silence descended. His mind was filled with tormenting problems. He tried to sleep. He had a fitful, nightmare-ridden, thought-choked three hours.

Did they expect him to starve for fifteen days and stand in knee-deep water eight hours? He sat up. He regretted having given them the idea. It had sounded picturesque. But if he had known that it would be applied to him, he might probably have given a different formula: that all villages should combine to help him eat *bonda* for fifteen days without a break. Up to them to see that the supply was kept up. And then the saintly man would stand in the river for two minutes a day, and it should bring down the rain sooner or later. His mother used to say, 'If there is one good man anywhere, the rains would descend for his sake and benefit the whole world,' quoting from a Tamil poem. It occurred to him that the best course for him would be to run away from the whole thing. He could walk across, catch a bus somewhere, and be off to the city, where they would not bother too much about him—just another bearded *sadhu* about, that was all. Velan and the rest would look for him and conclude that he had vanished to the Himalayas. But how to do it? How far could he go? Anyone might spot him within half an hour. It was not a practical solution. They might drag him back to the spot and punish him for fooling them. It was not even this fear; he was perhaps ready to take the risk, if there was half a chance of getting away. But he felt moved by the recollection of the big crowd of women and children touching his feet. He felt moved by the thought of their gratitude. He lit a fire and cooked his food, bathed in the river (at a spot where he had to scoop the sand and wait five minutes for the spring to fill his vessel), and gulped down a meal before anyone should arrive even accidentally. He kept a reserve of food, concealed in an inner sanctum, for a second meal at night. He thought suddenly that if they would at least leave him alone at night, he could make some arrangement and survive the ordeal. The ordeal then would be only standing knee-deep in water (if they could find it), muttering the litany for eight hours. (This he could suitably modify, in actual practice.) It might give him cramps, but he'd have to bear it for a few days, and then be believed the rains would descend in their natural course sooner or later. He would not like to cheat them altogether about the fast if he could help it.

When Velan arrived at night, he took him into his confidence. He said, 'Velan, you have been a friend to me. You must listen to me now. What makes you think that I can bring the rain?'

'That boy told us so. Did you not tell him so?'

Raju hesitated without giving a direct reply. Perhaps even at this point he might have rectified the whole thing with a frank statement. Raju hesitated for a moment. By habit, his nature avoided the direct and bald truth even now. He replied dodgingly, 'It's not that that I am asking. I want to know what has made you think so about me.'

Velan blinked helplessly. He did not quite understand what the great man was implying. He felt that it must mean something very noble, of course, but he was unable to answer the question. He said, 'What else should we do?'

'Come nearer. Sit down and listen to me. You may sleep here. I'm prepared to fast for the sake of your people and do anything if I can help this country—but it is a task to be taken on only by a saint. I am no saint.' Velan uttered many sounds of protest. Raju felt really sorry to be shattering his faith; but it was the only way in which he could hope to escape the ordeal. It was a cool night. Raju asked Velan to go up with him to the river step. He took his seat on it, and Velan sat on a step below. Raju moved down to his side. 'You have to listen to me, and so don't go so far away, Velan. I must speak into your ears. You must pay attention to what I am going to say. I am not a saint, Velan, I'm just an ordinary human being like anyone else. Listen to my story. You will know it yourself.' The river trickling away in minute driblets made no noise. The dry leaves of the peepul tree rustled. Somewhere a jackal howled. And Raju's voice filled the night. Velan listened to him without uttering a word of surprise or interjection, in all humility. Only he looked a little more serious than usual, and there were lines of care on his face.

7

I was accepted by Marco as a member of the family. From guiding tourists I seemed to have come to a sort of concentrated guiding of a single family. Marco was just impractical, an absolutely helpless man. All that he could do was to copy ancient things and write about them. His mind was completely in it. All practical affairs of life seemed impossible to him; such a simple matter as finding food or shelter or buying a railway ticket seemed to him a monumental job. Perhaps he married out of a desire to have someone care for his practical life, but unfortunately his choice was wrong—this girl herself was a dreamer if ever there was one. She would have greatly benefited by a husband who could care for her career; it was here that a handy man like me proved invaluable. I nearly gave up all my routine jobs in order to be of service to them.

He stayed for over a month at Peak House and I was in entire charge of all his affairs. He never stinted any expense as long as a voucher was available. They still kept their room in the hotel. Gaffur's car was permanently engaged, almost as if Marco owned it. The car did at least one trip a day between the Peak House and the town. Joseph looked after Marco so well that it was unnecessary for anyone else to bother about him. It was understood that I should devote a lot of time to looking after him and his wife, without sacrificing any other job I might have. He paid me my daily rate and also let me look after my 'routine jobs'. My so-called routine jobs now sounded big, but actually reduced themselves to keeping Rosie company and amusing her. Once in two days she went up to see her husband. She was showing extra solicitude for him nowadays. She fussed a great deal over him. It was all the same to him. His table was littered with notes and dates, and he said, 'Rosie, don't go near it. I don't want you to mess it up. It is just coming to a little order.' I never cared to know what exactly he was doing. It was not my business. Nor did his wife seem to care for the task he was undertaking. She asked, 'How is your food?' She was trying a new technique on him, after the inauguration of our own intimacy. She arranged his room.

She spoke to Joseph about his food. Sometimes she said, 'I'll stay on here and keep you company.' And Marco acknowledged it in an absentminded, casual manner. 'All right. If you like. Well, Raju, are you staying on or going back?'

I resisted my impulse to stay on, because I knew I was having her company fully downhill. It would be polite to leave her alone with him. So I said, without looking at him, 'I must go back. I have some others coming in today. You don't mind, I hope.'

'Not at all. You are a man of business. I should not monopolize you so much.'

'What time will you need the car tomorrow?'

He looked at his wife and she just said, 'Tomorrow, as early as you can.' He generally said, 'Bring me a few sheets of carbon, will you?'

As the car sped downhill, Gaffur kept throwing glances at me through the looking-glass. I was cultivating a lot of reserve with him nowadays. I didn't like him to gossip too much about anything. I was afraid of gossip. I was still sensitive to such things and I was nervous at being alone with Gaffur and felt relieved as long as his remarks were confined to automobiles; but it was not in his nature to stick to this subject. He would begin with automobiles but soon get mixed up. 'You must give me an hour for brake adjustments tomorrow. After all, mechanical brakes, you know; I still maintain they are better than hydraulic. Just as an old, uneducated wife is better than the new type of girl. Oh, modern girls are very bold. I wouldn't let my wife live in a hotel room all by herself if I had to remain on duty on a hilltop.'

It made me uncomfortable and I turned the topic deftly. 'Do you think car designers have less experience than you?'

'Oh, you think these engineers know more? A man like me who has to kick and prod a car to keep it on the road has, you may be sure...' I was safe; I had turned his mind from Rosie. I sat in suspense. I was in an abnormal state of mind. Even this did not escape Gaffur's attention. He mumbled often as he was driving me downhill, 'You are becoming rather stuck-up nowadays, Raju. You are not the old friend you used to be.' It was a fact. I was losing a great deal of my mental relaxation. I was obsessed with thoughts of Rosie. I revelled in memories of the hours I had spent with her last or in anticipation of what I'd be doing next. I had several problems to contend with. Her husband was the least of them. He was a good man, completely preoccupied, probably a man with an abnormal capacity for trust. But I was becoming nervous and sensitive and full of anxieties in various ways. Suppose, suppose—suppose? What? I myself could not specify. I was becoming fear-ridden. I couldn't even sort out my worries properly. I was in a jumble. I was suddenly seized with fears, sometimes with a feeling that I didn't look well enough for my sweetheart. I was obsessed with the thought that I hadn't perhaps shaved my chin smoothly enough, and that she would run her fingers over my upper lip and throw me out. Sometimes I felt I was in rags. The silk *jibba* and the lace-edged *dhoti* were being overdone or were old-fashioned. She was about to shut the door on me because I was not modern enough for her. This made me run to the tailor to have him make a few dashing bush-shirts and corduroys, and invest in hair- and face-lotions and perfumes of all kinds. My expenses were mounting. The shop was my main source of income, together with what Marco gave me as my daily wage. I knew that I ought to look into the accounts of the shop a little more closely. I was leaving it too much to the boy to manage. My mother often told me, whenever she was able to get at me, 'You will have to keep an eye on that boy. I see a lot of hangers-on there. Have you any idea what cash he is collecting and what is happening generally?'

I usually told her, 'I should certainly know how to manage these things. Don't think I'm so careless.' And she left me alone. And then I went over to the shop, assumed a tone of great aggressiveness, and checked the accounts. The boy produced some accounts, some cash, a statement of stock, something else that he needed for running the show, and some of his problems. I was in no mood to listen to his problems. I was busy and preoccupied, so I told him not to bother me with petty details and gave an impression (just an impression and nothing more) of being a devil for accounts.

He always said, 'Two passengers came asking for you, sir.'

Oh, bores, who wanted them, anyway? 'What did they want?' I asked with semi-interest.

'Three days' sightseeing, sir. They went away disappointed.'

They were always there. My reputation had survived my interest in the job. Railway Raju was an established name, and still pilgrims and travellers sought his help. The boy persisted. 'They wanted to know where you were.' This gave me food for thought. I didn't want this fool of a fellow to send them up to my Room 28 at the hotel. Fortunately, he did not know. Otherwise he might have done so. 'What shall I tell them, Raju-sir?' He always called me 'Raju-sir'. It was his idea of combining deference with familiarity.

I merely replied, 'Tell them I'm busy; that is all. I have no time. I'm very busy.'

'May I act as their guide, sir?' he asked eagerly. This fellow was acting as a successor in my jobs one by one. Next, probably, he would ask permission to keep the girl company! I felt annoyed with his question and asked him, 'Who will look after the shop?'

'I have a cousin. He can watch the shop for an hour or two, while I am away.'

I could not think of a reply. I could not decide. The whole thing was too bothersome. My old life, in which I was not in the least interested, was dogging my steps; my mother facing me with numerous problems: municipal tax, the kitchen tiles needing attention, the shop, accounts, letters from the village, my health, and so on and so forth; to me she was a figure out of a dream, mumbling vague sounds; and this boy had his own way of cornering and attacking me. Then Gaffur with his sly remarks and looks, ever on the brink of gossip—oh, I was tired of it all. I was in no mood for anything. My mind was on other matters. Even my finances were unreal to me, although if I cared to look at my savings-book I could know at a glance how the level of the reservoir was going down. But I did not want to examine it too closely as long as the man at the counter was able to give me the cash I wanted. Thanks to my father's parsimonious habits, I had a bank account. The only reality in my life and consciousness was Rosie. All my mental powers were now turned to keep her within my reach, and keep her smiling all the time, neither of which was at all easy. I would willingly have kept at her side all the time, as a sort of parasite; but in that hotel it was not easy, I was always racked with the thought that the man at the desk and the boys at the hotel were keeping an eye on me and were commenting behind my back.

I did not want to be observed going to Room 28. I was becoming self-conscious about it. I very much wished that the architecture of the place could be altered so that I might go up without having the desk-man watch me. I was sure he was noting down the hour of my arrival with Rosie, and of my departure. His morbid, inquisitive mind, I was sure, must have been working on all the details of my life behind the closed doors of Room 28. I didn't like the way he looked at me whenever I passed: I didn't like the curve of his lip—I knew he was smiling at an inward joke at my expense. I wished I could ignore him, but he was an early associate of mine, and I owed him a general remark or two. While passing him, I tried to look casual, and stopped to say, 'Did you see that Nehru is going to London?' or 'The new taxes will kill all initiative,' and he agreed with me and explained something, and that was enough. Or we discussed the Government of India's tourist plans or hotel arrangements, and I had to let him talk—the poor fellow never suspected how little I cared for tourism or taxes or anything now. I sometimes toyed with the thought of changing the hotel. But it was not easy. Both Rosie and her husband seemed to be deeply devoted to this hotel. He was somehow averse to changing, although he never came down from his heights, and the girl seemed to have got used to this room with its view of a coconut grove outside, and people irrigating it from a well. It was a fascination that I could not easily understand or explain.

In other ways too I found it difficult to understand the girl. I found as I went on that she was gradually losing the free and easy manner of her former days. She allowed me to make love to her, of course, but she was also beginning to show excessive consideration for her husband on the hill. In the midst of my caresses, she would suddenly free herself and say, 'Tell Gaffur to bring the car. I want to go and see him.'

I had not yet reached the stage of losing my temper or speaking sharply to her. So I calmly answered, 'Gaffur will not come till this time tomorrow. You were up only yesterday. Why do you want to go again? He expects you there only tomorrow.'

'Yes,' she would say and remain thoughtful. I didn't like to see her sit up like that on her bed and brood, her hair unattended, her dress all crinkled. She clasped her knees with her hands.

'What is troubling you?' I had to ask her. 'Won't you tell me? I will always help you.'

She would shake her head and say, 'After all, he is my husband. I have to respect him. I cannot leave him there.'

My knowledge of women being poor and restricted to one, I could not decide how to view her statements. I could not understand whether she was pretending, whether her present pose was pretence or whether her account of all her husband's shortcomings was false, just to entice me. It was complex and obscure. I had to tell her, 'Rosie, you know very well that even if Gaffur came, he couldn't drive uphill at this hour.'

'Yes, yes, I understand,' she would reply and lapse into a mysterious silence again.

'What is troubling you?'

She started crying. 'After all… after all… is this right what I am doing? After all, he has been so good to me, given me comfort and freedom. What husband in the world would let his wife go and live in a hotel room by herself, a hundred miles away?'

'It is not a hundred miles, but fifty-eight only,' I corrected. 'Shall I order you coffee or anything to eat?'

'No,' she would say point blank, but continue the train of her own thoughts. 'As a good man he may not mind, but is it not a wife's duty to guard and help, her husband, whatever the way in which he deals with her?' This last phrase was to offset in advance any reminder I might make about his indifference to her.

It was a confusing situation. Naturally, I could take no part in this subject: there was nothing I could add to or subtract from what she was saying. Distance seemed to lend enchantment to her view now. But I knew that she would have to spend only a few hours with him to come downhill raging against him, saying the worst possible things.

Sometimes I heartily wished that the man would descend from his heights, take her, and clear out of the place. That would at least end this whole uncertain business once and for all and help me to return to my platform duties. I could possibly try to do that even now. What prevented me from leaving the girl alone? The longer Marco went on with his work, the longer this agony was stretched. But he seemed to flourish in his solitude; that's probably what he had looked for all his life. But why could he not do something about his wife? A blind fellow. Sometimes I felt angry at the thought of him. He had placed me in a hopeless predicament. I was compelled to ask her, 'Why don't you stay up with him, then?'

She merely replied, 'He sits up all night writing, and—'

'If he sits up all night writing, during the day you should talk to him,' I would say with a look of innocence.

'But all day he is in the cave!'

'Well, you may go and see it too. Why not? It ought to interest you.'

'While he is copying, no one may talk to him.'

'Don't talk to him, but study the objects yourself. A good wife ought to be interested in all her husband's activities.'

'True,' she said, and merely sighed. This was a thoroughly inexperienced and wrong line for me to take; it led us nowhere, but only made her morose.

Her eyes lit up with a new hope when I spoke about the dance. It was after all her art that I first admired; of late, in our effort to live the lovers' life, that all-important question was pushed to the background. Her joy at finding shops, cinemas, and caresses made her forget for a while her primary obsession. But not for long. She asked me one evening, point blank, 'Are you also like him?'

'In what way?'

'Do you also hate to see me dance?'

'Not at all. What makes you think so?'

'At one time you spoke like a big lover of art, but now you never give it a thought.'

It was true. I said something in excuse, clasped her hands in mine, and swore earnestly, 'I will do anything for you. I will give my life to see you dance. Tell me what to do. I will do it for you.'

She brightened up. Her eyes lit up with a new fervour at the mention of dancing. So I sat up with her, helping her to day-dream. I found out the clue to her affection and utilized it to the utmost. Her art and her husband could not find a place in her thoughts at the same time; one drove the other out.

She was full of plans. At five in the morning she'd start her practice and continue for three hours. She would have a separate hall, long enough and wide enough for her to move in. It must have a heavy carpet, which would be neither too smooth under the feet nor too rough, and which would not fold while she practised her steps on it. At one corner of the room she'd have a bronze figure of Nataraja, the god of dancers, the god whose primal dance created the vibrations that set the worlds in motion. She would have incense sticks burning. After her morning practice, she would call up the chauffeur.

'Are you going to have a car?' I asked.

'Naturally, otherwise how can I move about? When I have so many engagements, it will be necessary for me to have a car. It'll be indispensable, don't you think?'

'Surely I'll remember it.'

She would then spend an hour or two in the forenoon studying the ancient works of the art, *Natya Shastra* of Bharat Muni, a thousand years old, and various other books, because without a proper study of the ancient methods it would be impossible to keep the purity of the classical forms. All the books were in her uncle's house, and she would write to him to send them on to her by and by. She would also want a pundit to come to her to help her to understand the texts, as they were all written in an old, terse style. 'Can you get me a Sanskrit pundit?' she asked.

'Of course I can. There are dozens of them.'

'I shall also want him to read for me episodes from *Ramayana* and *Mahabharata*, because they are a treasure house, and we can pick up so many ideas for new compositions from them.'

A little rest after lunch; and at three o'clock she would go out and do shopping, go for a drive and return home in evening or see a picture, unless, of course, there was a performance in the evening. If there was a performance, she would like to rest till three in the afternoon and reach the hall only half an hour before the show. 'That would be enough, because I shall do all the make-up and dressing before I leave the house.'

She thought of every detail, and dreamed of it night and day. Her immediate need would be a party of drummers and musicians to assist her morning practice. When she was ready to appear before the public, she would tell me and then I could fix her public engagements. I felt rather baffled by her fervour. I wished I could keep pace at least with her idiom. I felt that I ought immediately to pick up and cultivate the necessary jargon. I felt silly to be watching her and listening to her, absolutely tongue-tied. There were, of course, two ways open: to bluff one's way through and trust to luck, or to make a clean breast of it all. I listened to her talk for two days and finally confessed to her, 'I am a layman, not knowing much of the technicalities of the dance; I'd like you to teach me something of it.'

I didn't want her to interpret it as an aversion on my part to the art. That might drive her back into the arms of her husband, and so I took care to maintain the emphasis on my passion for the art. It gave us a fresh intimacy. This common interest brought us close together. Wherever we were she kept talking to me on the various subleties of the art, its technicalities, and explaining as to a child its idioms. She seemed to notice our surroundings less and less. In Gaffur's car as we sat she said, 'You know what a *pallavi* is? The time-scheme is all-important in it. It does not always run in the simple style of one-two, one-two; it gets various odds thrown in, and at a different tempo.' She uttered its syllables, 'Ta-ka-ta-ki-ta, ta-ka.' It amused me. 'You know, to get the footwork right within those five or seven beats requires real practice, and when the tempo is varied…' This was something that Gaffur could safely overhear, as we went up the hill, as we came out of a shop, as we sat in a cinema. While seeing a picture, she would suddenly exclaim, 'My uncle has with him a very old song written on a palm leaf. No one has seen it. My mother was the only person in the whole country who knew the song and could dance to it. I'll get that song too from my uncle. I'll show you how it goes. Shall we go back to our room? I don't want to see more of this picture. It looks silly,'

We immediately adjourned to Room 28, where she asked me to remain seated, and went into the ante-room and came back with her dress tucked in and tightened up for the performance. She said, 'I'll show you how it goes. Of course, I'm not doing it under the best of conditions. I need at least a drummer... Move off that chair, and sit on the bed. I want some space here.'

She stood at one end of the hall and sang the song lightly, in a soft undertone, a song from an ancient Sanskrit composition of a lover and lass on the banks of the Jamuna; and it began with such a verve, when she lightly raised her foot and let it down, allowing her anklets to jingle, I felt thrilled. Though I was an ignoramus, I felt moved by the movements, rhythm, and time, although I did not quite follow the meaning of the words. She stopped now and then to explain: '*Nari* means girl—and *mani* is a jewel... The whole line means: "It is impossible for me to bear this burden of love you have cast on me."' She panted while she explained. There were beads of perspiration on her forehead and lip. She danced a few steps, paused for a moment, and explained, 'Lover always means god,' and she took the trouble to explain further to me the intricacies of its rhythm. The floor resounded with the stamping of her feet. I felt nervous that those on the floor below might ask us to stop, but she never cared, never bothered about anything. I could see, through her effort, the magnificence of the composition, its symbolism, the boyhood of a very young god, and his fulfilment in marriage, the passage of years from youth to decay, but the heart remaining ever fresh like a lotus on a pond. When she indicated the lotus with her fingers, you could almost hear the ripple of water around it. She held the performance for nearly an hour; it filled me with the greatest pleasure on earth. I could honestly declare that, while I watched her perform, my mind was free, for once, from all carnal thoughts; I viewed her as a pure abstraction. She could make me forget my surroundings. I sat with open-mouthed wonder watching her. Suddenly she stopped and flung her whole weight on me with: 'What a darling. You are giving me a new lease of life.'

Next time we went up the hill our strategy was ready. I would drop her there and come back to town. She would stay behind for two days, bearing all the possible loneliness and irritation, and speak to her husband. It was imperative that before we proceeded any further we should clear up the entire matter with her husband. She would do the talking for two days. And then I would go up and meet them, and then we would plan further stages of work for her career. She had suddenly become very optimistic about her husband, and often leaned over to whisper, 'I think he will agree to our proposal,' so that Gaffur should not know, or revelled in further wishful thoughts. 'He is not bad. It's all a show, you know. He is merely posing to be uninterested. You don't talk to him at all. I'll do all the talking. I know how to tackle him. Leave him to me.' And so she spoke until we reached the top. 'Oh, see those birds! What colours! You know, there is a small piece about a parrot on a maiden's arm. I'll dance it for you sometime.'

He was in an unbelievably cheerful mood. He greeted his wife with greater warmth than ever before. 'Do you know there is a third cave; a sort of vault leads into it. I scraped the lime, and there you have a complete fresco of musical notations, in symbolic figures. The style is of the fifth century. I am puzzled how such a wide period-difference has come about,' he said, greeting us on the veranda itself. He had pulled up a chair and was watching the valley, with papers on his lap. He held up his latest discovery. His wife looked at it with due ecstasy and cried, 'Musical notations! What wonderful things! Do take me to see them, will you?'

'Yes; come with me tomorrow morning. I'll explain it to you.'

'Oh, wonderful!' And she cried, in a highly affected voice, 'I'll try and sing them to you.'

'I doubt if you can. It's more difficult than you imagine.'

She looked fevered and anxious about pleasing him. It seemed to bode no good. This all-round cheeriness somehow did not please me. He turned and asked, 'What about you, Raju? Would you like to see my discovery?'

'Of course, but I have to get back to town as soon as possible, I just came to leave the lady here, because she was so anxious; and to know if you want anything and if things are quite satisfactory.'

'Oh, perfect, perfect!' he cried. 'That Joseph is a wonderful man. I don't see him, I don't hear him, but he does everything for me at the right time. That's how I want things to be, you know. He moves on ball-bearings, I think.'

That's what I thought when I saw Rosie demonstrate to me in her hotel room, her whole movement being so much against the fixed factors of bone and muscle, walls and floor.

Marco continued his rhapsody on Joseph. 'I can never thank you enough for finding me a place like this and a man like Joseph. He's really a wonder. What a pity he should be wasting his talent on this hilltop!'

'You are very appreciative,' I said. 'I'm sure he'll be elated to know your opinion.'

'Oh, I have told him that without any reserve. I have also invited him to join my household any time he wishes to come and settle in the plains.'

He was unusually loquacious and warm. His nature flourished on solitude, and cave-frescoes. How happy he'd have been, I thought, to have had Joseph for a wife! My mind was busy with these thoughts as he was talking. Rosie went on like a good wife, saying, 'I hope there is food to eat, and everything is okay. If there is milk may I give you all coffee?' She ran in and returned to say, 'Yes, there is milk. I'll make coffee for all of you. I won't take more than five minutes.'

I was somehow feeling not quite at ease today. There was a lot of suspense and anxiety at the back of my mind. I was nervous of what he would say to Rosie and really anxious that he should not hurt her. Also, at the same time, a fear that if he became too nice to her, she might not care for me. I wanted him to be good to her, listen to her proposals, and yet leave her to my care! What an impossible, fantastic combination of circumstances to expect!

While Rosie was fussing with the coffee inside, he brought out another chair for me. 'I always do my work here,' he said. I felt that he honoured the valley with his patronage. He took out a bundle of sheets in an album, and a few photographs. He had made voluminous notes on all the cave-paintings. He had filled sheet after sheet with their description, transcription, and what not. They were obscure, but still I went through them with a show of interest. I wished I could ask questions on their value, but again I found myself tongue-tied, because I lacked the idiom. I wished I had been schooled in a jargon-picking institution; that would have enabled me to move with various persons on equal terms. No one would listen to my plea of ignorance and take the trouble to teach me as Rosie did. I listened to him. He was flinging at me dates, evidence, generalizations, and descriptions of a variety of paintings and carvings. I dared not ask what was the earthly use of all that he was doing. When coffee arrived, brought on a tray by Rosie (she had glided in softly, as if to show that she could rival Joseph's steps I was startled when she held the cups under my nose), he said to me, 'When this is published, it'll change all our present ideas of the history of civilization. I shall surely mention in the book my debt to you in discovering this place.'

Two days later I was back there. I went there at noon, at a time when I was sure that Marco would have gone down to the cave so that I might possibly get Rosie alone for a few moments. They were not in the bungalow. Joseph was there, arranging their midday meal in the back room. He said, 'They have gone down and are not back yet.'

I looked up at Joseph's face as if to get a sign of how things were. But he seemed evasive. I asked cheerily, 'How is everything Joseph?'

'Very well, sir.'

'That man thinks so well of you!' I said to flatter him.

But he took it indifferently. 'What if he does! I only do my duty. In my profession, some may curse, and some may bless, but I don't care who says what. Last month there was a group who wanted to assault me because I said I could not procure girls for them, but was I afraid? I ordered them to quit next morning. This is a spot for people to live in. I give them all the comforts ungrudgingly. It costs eight annas sometimes to get a pot of water, and I have to send cans and pots with any bus or truck going downhill, and wait for its return— but the guests will never know the difficulty. They are not expected to. It's my business to provide, and it's their business to pay the bill. Let there be no confusion about it. I do my duty and others must do theirs. But if they think I'm a procurer, I get very angry.'

'Naturally, no one would like it,' I said just to cut his monologue. 'I hope this man does not bother you in any way?'

'Oh, no, he is a gem. A good man; would be even better if his wife left him alone. He was so happy without her. Why did you bring her back? She seems to be a horrible nagger.'

'Very well, I'll take her downhill and leave the man in peace,' I said, starting for the cave. The pathway on the grass had become smooth and white with Marco's tread. I passed through the thicket and was crossing the sandy stretch when I found him coming from the opposite direction. He was dressed heavily as usual, the portfolio swung in his grip. A few yards behind him followed Rosie. I could not read anything from their faces.

'Hello!' I cried cheerily, facing him. He looked up, paused, opened his mouth to say something, swallowed his words, stepped aside to avoid encountering me, and resumed his forward march. Rosie followed as if she were walking in her sleep. She never even turned to give me a look. A few yards behind Rosie I brought up the rear, and we entered the bungalow gate as a sort of caravan. I felt it would be best to follow their example of silence, and to look just as moody and morose as they. It matched the company very well.

From the top of the veranda he turned to address us. He said, 'It'll not be necessary for either of you to come in.' He went straight into his room and shut the door.

Joseph emerged from the kitchen door, wiping a plate. 'I'm waiting to take instructions for dinner.'

Rosie passed up the steps without a word, moved down the veranda, opened the door of his room, passed in, and shut the door. This utter quietness was getting on my nerves. It was entirely unexpected and I did not know how to respond to it. I thought he would either fight us or argue or do something. But this behaviour completely baffled me.

Gaffur came round, biting a straw between his teeth, to ask, 'What time are we going down?'

I knew this was not his real intention in coming, but to see the drama. He must have whiled away his time gossiping with Joseph; and they must have pooled their information about the girl. I said, 'Why are you in a hurry, Gaffur?' and added with bitterness, 'When you can stay on and see a nice show.'

He came close to me and said, 'Raju, this is not at all good. Let us get away. Leave them alone. After all, they are husband and wife; they'll know how to make it up. Come on. Go back to your normal work. You were so interested and carefree and happy then.'

I had nothing to say to this. It was very reasonable advice he was giving me. Even at that moment, it would have been all different if god had given me the sense to follow Gaffur's advice. I should have gone quietly back, leaving Rosie to solve her problems with her husband. That would have saved many sharp turns and twists in my life's course. I told Gaffur, 'Wait near the car, I'll tell you,' keeping irritation out of my voice.

Gaffur went away, grumbling. Presently I heard him sounding the horn—as irate bus-drivers do when their passengers get down at a wayside teashop. I decided to ignore it. I saw the door on the other side open. Marco showed himself outside the front veranda, and said, 'Driver, are you ready to go?'

'Yes, sir,' said Gaffur.

'Very well then,' said the man. He picked up his bundle and started walking to the car. I saw him through the glass shutters of the hall window. It puzzled me. I tried to cross the hall and go out through the door, but it was bolted. I quickly turned, ran down the steps, and went round to Gaffur's car. Marco had already taken his seat. Gaffur had not started the engine yet. He was afraid to ask about the others, but marked time by fumbling with the switch-key. He must have been surprised at the effect of sounding the horn. God knows why he did it; perhaps he was testing it or idling or wanted to remind everyone concerned that time was passing.

'Where are you going?' I asked Marco, taking courage and putting my head into the car.

'I'm going down to the hotel to close my account there.'

'What do you mean?' I asked.

He looked me up and down with a fierce glance. 'I do not have to explain. I took the room and I am closing the account; that is all. Driver, you may present me your bill direct. Have a receipt ready when you want payment.'

'Is no one else coming?' ventured Gaffur, looking in the direction of the bungalow.

The man merely said, 'No,' and added, 'if anyone else is coming, I'll get out.'

'Driver,' I said with a sudden tone of authority. Gaffur was startled at being called 'driver' by me. 'Take that man wherever he may want to go and bring me back the car tomorrow—and you will make complete settlement of all your bills with him. Keep a separate account for my own trips.' I could have made a further demonstration of arrogance by saying I had brought the car for my own business and so forth, but I saw no point in all that. As I stood watching Marco, a sudden impulse moved me even without my knowledge. I opened the door of the car and pulled him out of it.

For all the heavy helmet and glasses that he wore, he was frail— too much frieze-gazing and cave-visiting had emaciated him. 'What? Are you attempting to manhandle me?' he shouted.

'I want to talk to you. I want you to talk. You can't just go away like this.' I found his breath coming and going sharply. I calmed down and said, softening my style, 'Come in and have your food and speak out. Let us talk, discuss things, and then do what you like. You can't abandon a wife in this place and go away.' I looked at Gaffur and said, 'You are not in a hurry, are you?'

'No, no. Have your food and come, sir. Plenty of time still.'

'I'll ask Joseph to give you food,' I added. I felt sorry that I had not taken charge of the situation earlier.

'Who are you?' Marco asked suddenly. 'What is your business with me?'

'A great deal. I have helped you. I have given a lot of time to your business. I undertook a lot of responsibility for you, these several weeks.'

'And I dispense with your service from this minute,' he cried. 'Give me your bill and be done with it.' Even in his most excited, emotional state, he would not forget his vouchers.

I said, 'Had we better not go into it calmly, sitting down and calculating? I have with me some money that you left with me before.'

'Very well,' he grunted. 'Let us be done with everything, and then you get out of my sight.'

'Easily done,' I said. 'But look here, this bungalow has two suites of rooms, and I can engage one perfectly legitimately.'

Joseph appeared on the steps. 'Will you be wanting a dinner tonight?'

'No,' he said.

'Yes, I may,' I said. 'You may leave, Joseph, if you are in a hurry. If I am staying, I'll send for you. Open the other suite and account it to me.'

'Yes, sir.' He unlocked another door and I strode into it with the air of a proprietor. I left the door open. It was my room and I was free to leave the door ajar if I chose.

I looked out of the window. The sun's rays from the west were touching the tops of trees with gold. It was a breathtaking sight. I wished Rosie could see it. She was inside. I had lost the privilege of walking into their room. I sat down in the wooden chair in my suite and wondered what to do. What was it that I had done now? I had no clear programme. I had no doubt successfully pulled him out of the car. But that took us nowhere. He had gone and bolted himself in his room, and I was in mine. If I had let him go, I might at least have had a chance to bring Rosie round and get her to talk about herself. Now I had made a mess. Could I go out and ask Gaffur to sound the horn again so that the man might emerge from his room?

Half an hour passed thus. There was absolutely no sign of any speech or movement. I tiptoed out of my room. I went to the kitchen.

Joseph was gone. I lifted the lids of the vessels. Food was there. No one seemed to have touched it. Heaven knew they were both starving. I felt a sudden pity for the man. Rosie must have completely faded out. It was her habit to ask for something to eat every two hours. At the hotel I constantly ordered a tray for her, if we were out I would stop all along the way to buy fruit or refreshment. Now the poor girl must be exhausted—and add to it the walk up and down to the cave. I felt suddenly angry at the thought of her. Why couldn't she eat or tell me what was what instead of behaving like a deaf-mute? Had the monster cut off her tongue? I wondered in genuine horror. I put the food on plates, put them on a tray, walked to their door. I hesitated for a second—only for a second; if I hesitated longer, I knew I would never go in. I pushed the door open with my feet. Rosie was lying on her bed with eyes shut. (Was she in a faint, I wondered for a second.) I had never seen her in such a miserable condition before. He was sitting in his chair, elbow on the table, his chin on his fist. I had never seen him so vacant before. I felt pity for him. I held myself responsible for it. Why couldn't I have kept out of all this? I placed the tray before him.

'People have evidently forgotten their food today. If you have a burden on your mind it's no reason why you should waste your food.'

Rosie opened her eyes. They were swollen. She had large, vivacious eyes, but they looked as if they had grown one round larger now, and were bulging and fearsome, dull and red. She was a sorry sight in every way. She sat up and told me, 'Don't waste any more of your time with us. You go back. That's all I have to say,' in a thick gruff, crackling voice. Her voice shook a little as she spoke. 'I mean it. Leave us now.'

What had come over this woman? Was she in league with her husband? She had every authority to ask me to get out. Probably she repeated her folly in encouraging me all along. All I could say in reply was, 'First, you must have your food. For what reason are you fasting?'

She merely repeated, 'I want you to go.'

'Aren't you coming down?' I persisted to Marco. The man behaved as if he were a deaf-mute. He never showed any sign of hearing us.

She merely repeated, 'I am asking you to leave us. Do you hear?'

I grew weak and cowardly at her tone. I muttered, 'I mean, you are—or he may want to go down, if it is so—'

She clicked her tongue in disgust. 'Do you not understand? We want you to leave.'

I grew angry. This woman who had been in my arms forty-eight hours ago was showing off. Many insulting and incriminating remarks welled up in my throat. But even in that stress I had the sense to swallow back my words, and, feeling that it would be dangerous to let myself stand there any longer, turned on my heel and went in a stride to the car. 'Gaffur, let us go.'

'Only one passenger?'

'Yes.' I banged the door and took my seat.

'What about them?'

'I don't know. You had better settle with them later.'

'If I have to come again to talk to them, who pays the fare for the trip?'

I beat my brow. 'Begone, man. You can settle all that later.'

Gaffur sat in his seat with the look of a philosopher, started the car, and was off. I had a hope, as I turned to look, that she might watch me from the window. But no such luck. The car sped downward. Gaffur said, 'It's time your elders found a bride for you.' I said nothing in reply, and he said, through the gathering darkness, 'Raju, I'm senior in years. I think this is the best thing you have done. You will be more happy hereafter.'

Gaffur's prophecy was not fulfilled in the coming days. I cannot remember a more miserable period of my life. The usual symptoms were present, of course: no taste for food, no sound sleep, no stability (I couldn't stay put in any one place), no peace of mind, no sweetness of temper or speech—no, no, no, a number of no's. With all seriousness I returned to my normal avocation. But everything looked so unreal. I relieved the boy at the shop, sat there and handed out things and received cash, but always with a feeling that it was a silly occupation. I walked up and down the platform when the train arrived. Sure as anything, I could always get someone to take round. 'Are you Railway Raju?'

'Yes,' and then the fat paterfamilias, wife, and two children.

'You see, we are coming from...and So-and-so mentioned your name to us as a man who would surely help us... You see, my wife is keen on a holy bath at the source of the Sarayu, and then I'd like to see an elephant camp, and anything else you suggest will be most welcome. But remember, only three days. I couldn't get even an hour of extra leave; I'll have to be in my office on...'

I hardly paid attention to what they said. I knew all their lines in advance; all that I paid attention to was the time at their disposal, and the extent of their financial outlay. Even the latter did not really interest me. It was more mechanical than intentional. I called up Gaffur, sat in the front seat, took the party about. While passing the New Extension, I pointed without even turning my head, 'Sir Frederick Lawley...' when we passed the statue. I knew exactly when the question would come, 'Whose is this statue?' and I knew when the next question was coming and had my answer ready, 'The man left behind by Robert Clive to administer the district. He built all the tanks and dams and developed this district. Good man. Hence the statue.' At the tenth-century Iswara temple at Vinayak Street, I reeled off the description of the frieze along the wall: 'If you look closely, you will see the entire epic *Ramayana* carved along the wall,' and so forth. I took them to the source of the Sarayu on the misty heights of Mempi Peak, watched the lady first plunge in the basin, the man avowing that he did not care and then following her example. I then took them into the inner shrine, showed them the ancient stone image on the pillar, with Shiva absorbing the Ganges River in his matted locks...

I collected my fee, and my commission from Gaffur and the rest, and saw them off next day. I did it all mechanically, without zest. I was, of course, thinking of Rosie all the time. 'That man has probably starved her to death, driven her mad, or left her in the open to be eaten by tigers,' I told myself. I looked forlorn and uninterested and my mother tried to find out why. She asked, 'What has gone wrong with you?'

'Nothing,' I replied. My mother had been so little used to seeing me about the house that she felt surprised and uneasy. But she left me alone. I ate, slept, hung about the railway platform, conducted visitors about, but I was never at peace with myself. My mind was troubled all the while. It was a natural obsession. I didn't even know what had happened, what all the silence and unnatural calm meant. This was a most unexpected development. As I had visualized, I had thought in my dreamy-happy way that he'd present me with his wife and say, 'I'm happy you are going to look after her and her art; I'd like to be left alone to pursue my cave studies; you are such a fine fellow to do this for us.' Or, on the other hand, he might have rolled up his sleeve to throw me out—one or the other, but I never bargained for this kind of inexplicable stalemate. And what was more, for the girl to support him with such ferocity. I was appalled at the duplicity of her heart. I agonized over and over again, piecing together the data and reading their meaning. I deliberately refrained from opening the subject with Gaffur. He respected my sentiment and never mentioned it again, although I was hoping desperately each day that he would say something about them. On certain days when I wanted him, he was not available. I knew then that he must have gone to the Peak House. I refrained from going near the Anand Bhavan. If any of my customers wanted a hotel I sent them nowadays to the Taj. I did not have to bother myself about them unduly. Marco had said he'd settle their accounts direct—well, you could depend upon him to do it. I came into the picture only to collect a commission from them, as from Gaffur himself. But I was prepared to forgo it all. I was in no mood to make money. In the world of gloom in which I was plunged there was no place for money. There must have been some money, I suppose, somewhere. My mother was able to carry on the household as before, and the shop continued to exist. I knew Gaffur's account must also have been settled. But he never said a word about it. So much the better. I didn't want to be reminded of the life that was gone.

I felt bored and terrified by the boredom of normal life, so much had I got used to a glamorous, romantic existence. Gradually I found taking tourists around a big nuisance. I began to avoid the railway station. I let the porter's son meet the tourists. He had already attempted his hand at it before. Of course, the tourists might miss my own speeches and descriptions, but lately I had become dull-witted, and they probably preferred the boy, as he was at least as curious and interested as they in seeing places. Perhaps he was beginning to answer to the name of Railway Raju too.

How many days passed thus? Only thirty, though they looked to me like years. I was lying asleep on the floor of my house one afternoon. I was half awake and had noted the departure of the Madras Mail at four-thirty. When the chug-chug of the train died away, I tried to sleep again, having been disturbed by its noisy arrival. My mother came and said, 'Someone is asking for you.' She didn't wait for questions, but went into the kitchen.

I got up and went to the door. There stood Rosie on the threshold, with a trunk at her feet and a bag under her arm. 'Rosie, why didn't you say you were coming? Come in, come in. Why stand there? That was only my mother.' I carried her trunk in. I could guess a great many things about her. I didn't want to ask her any questions. I didn't feel like knowing anything. I fussed about her, lost my head completely. 'Mother!' I cried. 'Here is Rosie! She is going to be a guest in our house.'

My mother came out of the kitchen formally, smiled a welcome, and said, 'Be seated on that mat. What's your name?' she asked kindly, and was rather taken aback to hear the name 'Rosie'. She expected a more orthodox name. She looked anguished for a moment, wondering how she was going to accommodate a 'Rosie' in her home.

I stood about awkwardly. I had not shaved since the morning; I had not combed my hair; my *dhoti* was discoloured and rumpled; the vest I wore had several holes on the back and chest. I folded my arms across my chest to cover the holes. I could not have made a worse impression if I had tried hard. I was ashamed of the torn mat—it had been there since we built the house—the dark hall with the smoky walls and tiles. All the trouble I used to take to create an impression on her was gone in a moment. If she realized that this was my normal setting, god knew how she would react. I was glad at least I was wearing my torn vest instead of being barebodied as was my habit at home. My mother hardly ever noticed the hairiness of my chest, but Rosie, oh—

My mother was busy in the kitchen, but she managed to come out for a moment to observe the formality of receiving a guest. A guest was a guest, even though she might be a Rosie. So my mother came up and sat down on the mat with an air of settling down to a chat. The very first question she asked was, 'Who has come with you, Rosie?' Rosie blushed, hesitated, and looked at me. I moved a couple of steps backward in order that she might see me only dimly, and not in all my raggedness.

I replied, 'I think she has come alone, Mother.'

My mother was amazed. 'Girls today! How courageous you are! In our day we wouldn't go to the street corner without an escort. And I have been to the market only once in my life, when Raju's father was alive.'

Rosie blinked and listened in silence, not knowing how to react to these statements. She simply opened her eyes wide and raised her brows. I watched her. She looked a little paler and slightly careworn—not the swollen-eyed, gruff-toned monster she had seemed the other day. Her tone was sweet as ever. She looked slightly weak, but as if she hadn't a care in the world. My mother said, 'Water is boiling; I'll give you coffee. Do you like coffee?' I was relieved that the conversation was coming down to this level. I hoped my mother would continue to talk about herself rather than ask questions. But it was not to be. She asked next, 'Where do you come from?'

'From Madras,' I answered promptly.

'What brings you here?'

'She has come to see some friends.'

'Are you married?'

'No,' I answered promptly.

My mother shot a look at me. It seemed to be meaningful. She withdrew her glance swiftly from me, and, looking at her guest kindly, asked, 'Don't you understand Tamil?'

I knew I should shut up now. I let Rosie answer in Tamil, 'Yes. It's what we speak at home.'

'Who else have you in your house?'

'My uncle, my aunt, and—' She was trailing away, and my mother shot at her the next terrible question, 'What is your father's name?'

It was a dreadful question for the girl. She knew only her mother and always spoke of her. I had never questioned her about it. The girl remained silent for a moment and said, 'I have…no father.'

My mother was at once filled with the greatest sympathy and cried, 'Poor one, without father or mother. I am sure your uncle must be looking after you well. Are you a BA?'

'Yes,' I corrected. 'She is an MA.'

'Good, good, brave girl. Then you lack nothing in the world. You are not like us uneducated women. You will get on anywhere. You can ask for your railway ticket, call a policeman if somebody worries you, and keep your money. What are you going to do? Are you going to join government service and earn? Brave girl.' My mother was full of admiration for her. She got up, went in, and brought her a tumbler of coffee. The girl drank it off gratefully. I was wondering how best I could sneak out and groom myself properly. But there was no chance. My father's architectural sense had not gone beyond building a single large hall and a kitchen. Of course, there was the front *pyol* on which visitors and menfolk generally sat. But how could I ask Rosie to move there? It was too public—the shop-boy and all his visitors would come round, gaze at her and ask if she was married. This was a slightly difficult situation for me. We had got used to common living in that hall. It had never occurred to us to be otherwise. We never wanted anything more than this. My father lived in his shop, I played under the tree, and have received male visitors on the outside *pyol* and left the inner room for mother or any lady that might come. When we slept we went in. If it was warm, we slept on the *pyol*. The hall was a passage, a dressing-room, drawing-room, study, everything combined. My shaving mirror was on a nail; my finest clothes hung on a peg; for a bath I dashed to a chamber in the back yard, half open to the sky, and poured over my head water drawn straight from the well. I ran up and down and conducted my toilet while my mother came into or out of the kitchen or slept or sat moping in the hall. We had got used to each other's presence and did not mind it in the least. But now with Rosie there?

My mother, as if understanding my predicament, said to the girl, 'I'm going to the well. Will you come with me? You are a city girl. You must know something of our village life too.' The girl quietly rose and followed her; I hoped she'd not be subjected to an inquisition at the well. The minute their backs were turned I got busy, ran hither and thither, scraped my chin in a hurry, cut myself a little, bathed, groomed myself, and changed into better clothes, and by the time they were back from the well I was in a condition to be viewed by the Princess of the Earth. I went over to the shop and sent the boy to fetch Gaffur.

'Rosie, if you would like to wash and dress, go ahead. I'll wait outside. We'll go out after that.'

It was perhaps an unwarranted luxury to engage Gaffur for an outing. But I saw no other way. I could not talk to her in our home, and I could not make her walk through the streets. Although I had done it before, today it seemed different. I felt a little abashed to be seen with her.

I told Gaffur, 'She is back.'

He said, 'I know it. They were here at the hotel, and he went by the Madras train.'

'You never told me anything.'

'Why should I? You were going to know anyway.'

'What, what has happened?'

'Ask the lady herself, now that you have her in your pocket.' He sounded resentful.

I told him placatingly, 'Oh, don't be sour, Gaffur... I want the car for the evening.'

'I'm at your service, sir. What do I have the taxi for unless it is to drive you where you command?' He winked and I was relieved to see him back in his old cheerful mood. When Rosie appeared at the door I went and told my mother, 'We will come back, Mother, after a little outing.'

'Where?' asked Gaffur, looking at us through the glass. As we hesitated he asked puckishly, 'Shall I drive to the Peak House?'

'No, no,' Rosie cried, becoming very alert at the mention of it. 'I have had enough of it.' I didn't pursue the subject.

As we passed the Taj I asked, 'Would you like to eat there?'

'Your mother gave me coffee; that is enough. What a fine mother you have!'

'The only trouble is she asks you about marriage!' We laughed nervously at this joke.

'Gaffur, drive on to the river,' I said. He drove through the market road, honking his horn impatiently through the crowd. It was a crowded hour. Lots of people were moving around. The lights were up. Shop lights sparkled and lit up the throughfare. He took a sharp turn at Ellaman Street—that narrow street in which oil-merchants lived, the oldest street in the city, with children playing in it, cows lounging, and donkeys and dogs blocking the passage so narrow that any passing car almost touched the walls of the houses. Gaffur always chose this way to the river, although there was a better approach. It gave him some sort of thrill to honk his car horn and scatter the creatures in the road in a fright. Ellaman Street ended with the last lamp on the road, and the road imperceptibly merged into the sand. He applied the brake under the last lamp, with a jerk sufficient to shake us out of the car. He was in an unusually jovial mood today; he was given to his own temperaments and moods, and no one could predict how he would behave at a given moment. We left him under the lamp. I said, 'We want to walk about.' He winked at me mischievously in reply.

The evening had darkened. There were still a few groups sitting here and there on the sand. Some students were promenading. Children were playing and running in circles and shouting. On the river step, some men were having their evening dip. Far off at Nallappa's Grove cattle were crossing the river with their bells tinkling. The stars were out. The Taluk office gong sounded seven. A perfect evening—as it had been for years and years. I had seen the same scene at the same hour for years and years. Did those children never grow up? I became a little sentimental and poetic, probably because of the companion at my side. My feelings and understanding seemed to have become suddenly heightened. I said, 'It's a beautiful evening,' to start a conversation. She briefly said, 'Yes.' We sought a secluded place, away from the route of promenading students.

I spread out my handkerchief, and said, 'Sit down, Rosie.' She picked away the kerchief and sat down. The gathering darkness was congenial. I sat close to her and said, 'Now tell me everything from beginning to end.'

She remained in thought for a while and said, 'He left by the train this evening, and that is all.'

'Why did you not go with him?'

'I don't know. It is what I came for. But it didn't happen that way. Well, it is just as well. We were not meant to be in each other's company.'

'Tell me what happened. Why were you so rude to me that day?'

'I thought it best that we forget each other, and that I go back to him.'

I did not know how to pursue this inquiry. I had no method of eliciting information—of all that had gone before. I fumbled and hummed and hawed in questioning, till I suddenly felt that I was getting nowhere at all. I wanted a chronological narration, but she seemed unable to provide it. She was swinging forwards and backwards and talking in scraps. I was getting it all in a knot. I felt exasperated. I said, 'Answer me now, step by step. Give an answer to each question. I left you with him to speak about the proposal we had discussed. What did you tell him?'

'What we had agreed—that he should permit me to dance. He was quite happy till I mentioned it. I never spoke about it that whole day or till late next day. I led him on to tell me about his own activity. He showed me the pictures he had copied, the notes he had made, and spoke far into the night about their significance. He was going to be responsible for rewriting of history, he said. He was talking about his plans for publishing his work. He said later he would go to Mexico, and to some of the Far Eastern countries to study similar subjects and add them on to his work. I was full of enthusiasm although I did not follow everything he said. I felt after all an understanding was coming between us—there in that lonely house, with trees rustling and foxes and animals prowling around, some light glimmering in the far-off valley. Next morning I went with him to the cave to have a look at the musical notations he had discovered. We had to pass through the main cave and beyond it into a vault by a crumbling ladder. A fierce, terrifying place. Nothing on earth would have induced me to go to a spot like that, stuffy, fierce, and dark. "There may be cobras here," I said. He ignored my fears. "You should feel at home, then," he said and we laughed. And then he lit up a lantern and showed me the wall on which he had scraped off the lime and discovered new pictures. They were the usual grotesque, ancient paintings of various figures, but he managed to spell out the letters around them, and take them down as musical notations. It was nothing I could make out or make use of. They were abstract verse about some theories of an ancient musical system or some such thing. I said, "If these were about dancing, I could perhaps have tried—" He looked up sharply. The word "dance" always stung him. I was afraid to go on with the subject. But there, squatting on the ancient floor, amidst cobwebs and bats, in that dim lantern light, I felt courage coming back. "Will you permit me to dance?"

'Promptly came his reply, with a scowl, the old face was coming back. "Why?"

"'I think I'd be very happy if I could do that. I have so many ideas. I'd like to try. Just as you are trying to—"

"'Oh, you want to rival me, is that it? This is a branch of learning, not street acrobatics."

"'You think dancing is street acrobatics?"

"'I'm not prepared to discuss all that with you. An acrobat on a trapeze goes on doing the same thing all his life; well, your dance is like that. What is there intelligent or creative in it? You repeat your tricks all your life. We watch a monkey perform, not because it is artistic but because it is a monkey that is doing it." I swallowed all the insults; I still had hopes of converting him. I lapsed into silence and let him do his work. I turned the subject to other things, and he was normal again. After dinner that night he went back to his studies and I to my game-watching on the veranda. As usual, there was nothing to watch, but I sat there turning over in my head all that he had said and all that I had said, and wondering how to get through the business. I ignored all insults and troubles in the hope that if we reached an agreement in the end, it'd all be forgotten. As I sat there, he came behind me, and, putting his hand on my shoulder, said, "I thought we had come to a final understanding about that subject. Did you or did you not promise that you'd never mention it again?"'

The Taluk office gong sounded eight and all the crowd had vanished. We were alone on the sand. Still I'd not learned anything about Rosie. Gaffur sounded the horn. It was no doubt late, but if I went home she would not he able to speak. I said, 'Shall we spend the night at the hotel?'

'No. I'd like to go back to your house. I have told your mother that I'll be back.'

'All right,' I said, remembering my cash position. 'Let us stay here for half an hour more. Now tell me.'

'His tone,' she resumed, 'was now so kind that I felt I need not bother even if I had to abandon my own plans once and for all: if he was going to be so nice, I wanted nothing more—I'd almost made up my mind that I would ask nothing of him. Yet as a last trick I said, encouraged by his tone, "I want you to see just one small bit, which I generally do as a memento of my mother. It was her piece, you know." I got up and pulled him by his hand to our room. I pushed aside the chair and other things. I adjusted my dress. I pushed him down to sit on the bed, as I had done with you. I sang that song about the lover and his girl on the banks of the Jamuna and danced the piece for him He sat watching me coldly. I had not completed the fifth line when he said, "Stop, I have seen enough."

'I stopped, abashed. I had been certain that he was going to be captivated by it and tell me to go ahead and dance all my life. But he said, "Rosie, you must understand, this is not art. You have not sufficient training. Leave the thing alone."

'But here I committed a blunder. I said haughtily, "Everyone except you likes it."

"'For instance?'"

"'Well, Raju saw me do it, and he was transported. Do you know what he said?'"

"'Raju! Where did you do it for him?'"

"'At the hotel.' And then he said, "Come and sit here," pointing at the chair, like an examining doctor. He subjected me to a close questioning. I think it went on all night. He asked details of our various movements ever since we came here, what time you came to the hotel each day, when you left, where you kept yourself in the room, and how long, and so on, all of which I had to answer. I broke down and cried. He got from my answers enough indication of what we had been doing. Finally he said, "I didn't know that that hotel catered to such fervid art-lovers! I was a fool to have taken too much decency for granted." Till dawn we sat there. He on the bed, and I on the chair. I was overcome with sleep and put my head on the table, and when I awoke he was gone to the caves.

'Joseph had left some coffee for me. I tidied myself up and went down in search of him. I felt I had made the capital blunder of my life. I had been indiscreet in talking to him as I had been indiscreet and wrong in all my actions. I realized I had committed an enormous sin. I walked as in a dream down to the cave. My mind was greatly troubled. I didn't want anything more in life than to make my peace with him. I did not want to dance. I felt lost… I was in terror. I was filled with some sort of pity for him too, as I remembered how he had sat up unmoving on the bed all night while I sat in the chair. The look of despair and shock on his face haunted me. I walked down the valley, hardly noticing my surroundings. If a tiger had crossed my path I'd hardly have noticed it… I found him sitting in his cave on his usual folding stool, sketching out his copies. His back was turned to the entrance when I went in. But as I got into the narrower entrance the light was blocked and he turned. He looked at me coldly. I stood like a prisoner at the bar. "I have come to apologize sincerely. I want to say I will do whatever you ask me to do. I committed a blunder…"

'He returned to his work without a word. He went on as if he had been alone. I waited there. Finally, when he had finished his day's work, he picked up his portfolio and papers and started out. He put on his helmet and spectacles and went past me as if I had not existed. I had stood there for nearly three hours, I think. He had measured, copied, noted down, and examined with a torch, but without paying the slightest attention to me. When he went back to the bungalow, I followed him. That's where you saw us. I went to his room. He sat in his chair and I on the bed. No word or speech. You came into the room again. I sincerely hoped you would leave us and go away, and that we could be peaceful between ourselves... Day after day it went on. I stayed on hopefully. I found that he would not eat the food I touched. So I let Joseph serve him. I ate my food alone in the kitchen. If I lay on the bed, he slept on the floor. So I took to sleeping on the floor, and he went and lay on the bed. He never looked at me or spoke. He arranged with Joseph and went down a couple of times, leaving me alone in the bungalow. He returned and went about his business without worrying about me. But I followed him, day after day, like a dog—waiting on his grace. He ignored me totally. I could never have imagined that one human being could ignore the presence of another human being so completely. I followed him like a shadow, leaving aside all my own pride and self-respect; I hoped that ultimately he'd come round. I never left his side even for a moment, whether in his room or in the cave. It was a strain to remain speechless in that vast lonely place. I thought I had gone dumb. Joseph was the only one to whom I could say a word whenever he appeared, but he was a reserved man and did not encourage me. I had spent three weeks thus, in a vow of silence. I could not stand it any more. So one night as he sat at his table I said, "Have you not punished me enough?" My voice sounded strange, and like someone else's to me after so many weeks. It had a booming quality in that silent place that startled me. He started at the sound, turned, looked at me, and said, "This is my last word to you. Don't talk to me. You can go where you please or do what you please."

"'I want to be with you. I want you to forget everything. I want you to forgive me—' I said. Somehow I began to like him very much. It seemed enough if he forgave me and took me back.

'But he said, "Yes, I'm trying to forget—even the earlier fact that I ever took a wife. I want to get out of here too—but I have to complete my work; and I'm here for that. You are free to get out and do what you please."

'"I'm your wife and I'm with you."

'"You are here because I'm not a ruffian. But you are not my wife. You are a woman who will go to bed with anyone that flatters your antics. That's all. I don't want you here, but if you are going to be here, don't talk. That is all."

'I felt too hurt. I thought that Othello was kindlier to Desdemona. But I bore everything. I had a wild hope that in the end he'd relent, that when we left this place he might change. Once we were back in our home, everything would be all right.

'One day he started packing up. I tried to help him, but he would not let me; and then I packed up my things too, and followed him. Gaffur's car arrived. Both of us came down to the hotel. Back in Twenty-eight. The room looked poisonous to me now. He stayed for a day settling accounts; and at train time he went with the baggage to the railway station. I followed him mutely. I waited patiently. I knew he was going back to our home at Madras. I wanted very much to go back home. The porter carried our trunks. He pointed at my portion of the baggage and told the porter, "I don't know about these—not mine." So the porter looked at me for a second and separated my box. When the train arrived the porter carried only his baggage, and he took his seat in a compartment. I didn't know what to do. I picked up my trunk and followed. When I tried to step into the compartment he said, "I have no ticket for you," and he flourished a single ticket and shut the door on me. The train moved. I came to your home.'

She sat sobbing for a while. I comforted her. 'You are in the right place. Forget all your past. We will teach that cad a lesson by and by.' I made a grandiose announcement, 'First, I'll make the world recognize you as the greatest artist of the time.'

Within a short time my mother understood everything. When Rosie had gone in for a bath, she said, cornering me, 'This cannot go on

THE GUIDE ■ 245

long, Raju—you must put an end to it.'

'Don't interfere, Mother. I am an adult. I know what I am doing.'

'You can't have a dancing girl in your house. Every morning with all that dancing and everything going on! What is the home coming to?'

Encouraged by me, Rosie had begun to practise. She got up at five in the morning, bathed, and prayed before the picture of a god in my mother's niche, and began a practice session which went on for nearly three hours. The house rang with the jingling of her anklets. She ignored her surroundings completely, her attention being concentrated upon her movements and steps. After that she helped my mother, scrubbed, washed, swept, and tidied up everything in the house. My mother was pleased with her and seemed kind to her. I never thought that my mother would create a problem for me now, but here she was. I said, 'What has come over you all of a sudden?'

My mother paused. 'I was hoping you would have the sense to do something about it. It can't go on like this for ever. What will people say?'

'Who are "people"?' I asked.

'Well, my brother and your cousins and others known to us.'

'I don't care for their opinion. Just don't bother about such things.'

'Oh! That's a strange order you are giving me, my boy. I can't accept it.'

The gentle singing in the bathroom ceased; my mother dropped the subject and went away as Rosie emerged from her bath fresh and blooming. Looking at her, one would have thought that she had not a care in the world. She was quite happy to be doing what she was doing at the moment, was not in the least bothered about the past, and looked forward tremendously to the future. She was completely devoted to my mother.

But unfortunately my mother, for all her show of tenderness, was beginning to stiffen inside. She had been listening to gossip, and she could not accommodate the idea of living with a tainted woman. I was afraid to be cornered by her, and took care not to face her alone. But whenever she could get at me, she hissed a whisper into my ear. 'She is a real snake-woman, I tell you. I never liked her from the first day you mentioned her.'

I was getting annoyed with my mother's judgement and duplicity. The girl, in all innocence, looked happy and carefree and felt completely devoted to my mother. I grew anxious lest my mother should suddenly turn round and openly tell her to quit. I changed my tactics and said, 'You are right, Mother. But you see, she is a refugee, and we can't do anything. We have to be hospitable.'

'Why can't she go to her husband and fall at his feet? You know, living with a husband is no joke, as these modern girls imagine. No husband worth the name was ever conquered by powder and lipstick alone. You know, your father more than once...' She narrated an anecdote about the trouble created by my father's unreasonable, obstinate attitude in some family matter and how she met it. I listened to her anecdote patiently and with admiration, and that diverted her for a while. After a few days she began to allude to the problems of husband and wife whenever she spoke to Rosie, and filled the time with anecdotes about husbands: good husbands, bad husbands, reasonable husbands, unreasonable ones, savage ones, slightly deranged ones, moody ones, and so on and so forth; but it was always the wife, who by her doggedness, perseverance and patience, that brought him round. She quoted numerous mythological stories of Savitri, Sita, and all the well-known heroines. Apparently it was a general talk, apropos of nothing, but my mother's motives were naively clear. She was so clumsily roundabout that anyone could see what she was driving at. She was still supposed to be ignorant of Rosie's affairs, but she talked pointedly. I knew how Rosie smarted under these lessons, but I was helpless. I was afraid of my mother. I could have kept Rosie in a hotel, perhaps, but I was forced to take a more realistic view of my finances now. I was helpless as I saw Rosie suffer, and my only solace was that I suffered with her.

My worries were increasing. The boy at the shop was becoming more clamorous. My sales were poor, as the railways were admitting more pedlars on the platforms. My cash receipts were going down and my credit sales alone flourished. The wholesale merchants who supplied me with goods stopped credit to me. The boy's method of account-keeping was so chaotic that I did not know whether I was moving forward or backward. He produced cash from the counter in a haphazard manner, and there were immense gaps on the shelves all over the shop. The boy was probably pocketing money and eating off the stuff. With my credit at the wholesalers' gone, the public complained that nothing one wanted was ever available. Suddenly the railways gave me notice to quit. I pleaded with the old station master and porter, but they could do nothing; the order had come from high up. The shop was given to a new contractor.

I could not contemplate the prospect of being cut off from the railways. I grew desperate and angry. I shed tears at seeing a new man in the place where I and my father had sat. I slapped the boy on the cheek and he cried, and his father, the porter, came down on me and said, 'This is what he gets for helping you! I had always told the boy—he was not your paid servant, anyway.'

'Payment for him? He has swallowed all the cash, credit, and every consumable article in the shop. Fattened himself on it! He must pay me for all his gluttony, which has ruined my business.'

'It's not he who has ruined you, but the *saithan* inside, which makes you talk like this.' He meant Rosie, I'm sure; she was peeping out of the doorway of our house. My mother watched from the *pyol* in great pain. It was a most unedifying spectacle.

I did not like the porter's reference, and so said something violent and tried to attack him. The station master appeared on the scene and said, 'If you create a disturbance here, I'll have to prohibit your entry.'

The new shopman watched the scene with detachment. A whiskered fellow—I did not like his leering look. I turned on him fiercely, leaving the porter, and cried, 'Well, you'll also face the same situation, remember, some day. Don't be too sure.'

He twirled his whiskers and said, 'How can everyone hope for the same luck as yours?' He winked mischievously, at which I completely lost my temper and flew at him. He repelled me with a back-stroke of his left hand as if swatting a fly, and I fell back, and knocked against my mother, who had come running onto the platform, a thing she had never done in her life. Luckily, I didn't knock her down.

She clung to my arm and screamed, 'Come away. Are you coming or not?' And the porter, the whiskered man, and everyone swore, 'You are saved today, because of that venerable old lady.' She dragged me back to the house; a few batches of paper, a register, and one or two odd personal belongings which I had kept in the shop were under my arm; with these I entered my house, and I knew my railway association was now definitely ended. It made my heart heavy. I felt so gloomy that I did not turn to see Rosie standing aside, staring at me. I flung myself in a corner of the hall and shut my eyes.

8

My creditor was the Sait, a wholesale merchant in Market Road. He called on me the next day. There was a knock on the door, and there he was. I was watching Rosie at her practice, leaning against the wall and lounging on the mat. I felt abashed at the sight of the Sait at my door. I knew why he had come. He had brought a fat ledger wrapped up in a blue cloth. He seemed pleased at the sight of me, as if he had feared that I had run away from my post. I was at a loss to say anything for a moment. I didn't want to show confusion. After the railway station episode, I was recovering my sense of perspective again. While watching Rosie do her practice, I seemed to get a clearer notion of what I should be doing. The sound of her anklets, and the whispered music she sang, her rhythm and movement, helped. I felt that I was once again becoming a man of importance. My mother, fortunately for me, had not spoken a word to me since the previous evening, and that saved me a great deal of embarrassment and strain. My mother could not help speaking to Rosie; in spite of all her prejudice, she liked the girl really and could not help treating her kindly. She had not the heart to starve her or offend her in any way. She attended on her enough to give her food and shelter, and left her alone. Only she could not trust herself to speak to me after the scene at the railway station. I am sure she felt that I had ruined, by my erratic ways, what her husband had so laboriously built up. But fortunately she did not take it out on the poor girl, but let her alone—after her usual dose of homilies and parables, all of which Rosie took in good humour.

The Sait was a thin man with a multi-coloured turban on his head. He was a prosperous businessman, very helpful with credit, but, of course, expected proper settlement of debts. He was at my door. I knew why. I fussed over him, and said, 'Come in, come in. Be seated. What a rare pleasure!' I dragged him and seated him on the *pyol.*

He was a good friend of mine, and he hesitated to talk about the dues. There was an awkward silence for a moment. Only Rosie's anklet-jingles could be heard for a while. He listened to it and asked, 'What is it?'

'Oh!' I said casually. 'A dance practice is going on.'

'Dance practice!' He was astounded. It was the last thing he expected in a home like mine. He sat thinking for a while, as if putting two and two together. He shook his head lightly. The story of the '*saithan* inside' had evidently reached him. He suppressed any inquiry regarding it as not his business, and said, 'What has come over you, Raju? You have not paid my dues for months and months, and you used to be so regular!'

'Business conditions have not been good, old man,' I said with a sort of affected resignation and cheer.

'No, it's not that. One must—'

'Oh, and that boy whom I trusted cheated completely.'

'What is the use of blaming others?' he asked. He seemed to be a ruthless man, who was bent upon harassing me. He took out his notebook, opened it out, and pointed at the bottom of a column. 'Eight thousand rupees! I can't let this go on very long. You will have to do something about it.'

I was tired of being told to do 'something about something'. My mother started it with regard to the girl, someone else about something else. The girl had started to say, 'We must do something,' and now this man; I felt irritated by his advice and said curtly, 'I know it.'

'What do you propose to do about it?'

'Of course you are going to be paid—'

'When?'

'How can I say…? You must wait.'

'All right. You want another week?' he asked.

'Week!' I laughed at the joke. He looked hurt. Everyone seemed hurt by me at this time.

He became very serious and said, 'Do you think it is a laughing matter? Do you think I have come to amuse you?'

'Why do you raise your voice, Sait? Let us be friends.'

'Friendship has nothing to do with this,' he said, lowering his voice. When he raised it the jingling inside could not be heard. But when he lowered it we could hear Rosie's steps in the background. A smile, perhaps, played over my lips as I visualized her figure on the other side of the wall. He felt irritated at this again. 'What, sir, you laugh when I say I want money, you smile as if you were dreaming. Are you in this world or in paradise? I came to talk to you in a businesslike manner today, but it is not possible. All right, don't blame me.' He bundled up his account book and rose to go.

'Don't go, Sait. Why are you upset?' I asked. Everything I said unfortunately seemed to have a ring of levity about it. He stiffened and grew more serious. The more he scowled, the more I found it impossible to restrain myself. I don't know what devil was provoking so much mirth in me at this most inappropriate moment. I was bubbling with laughter. I suppressed a tremendous urge to giggle. Somehow his seriousness affected me in this way. Finally, when he turned away from me in utter wrath, the profound solemnity of this puny man with his ledger clutched under his arm and his multicoloured turban struck me as so absurd that I was convulsed with laughter. He turned his head, threw a brief glance at me, and was off.

With a smiling face, I re-entered the house and took up my position on the mat. Rosie paused for a second to ask, 'Something very amusing? I heard your laughter.'

'Yes, yes, something that made me laugh.'

'Who was he?' she asked.

'A friend,' I said. I did not want her to know these troubles. I didn't want anyone to be bothered with these things. I did not like to be bothered by anything. Living with Rosie under the same roof was enough for me. I wanted nothing more in life. I was slipping into a fool's paradise. By not talking about money, I felt I had dismissed the subject—a stupid assumption. The world outside Rosie seemed so unreal that it was possible for me to live on such an assumption. But not for long.

Within a week or ten days I found myself involved in court affairs. My sense of humour had completely ruined my relations with the Sait, and he had proceeded directly to get satisfaction through a court. My mother was distraught. I had not a friend in the world except Gaffur. I sought him out one day at the fountain parapet and told him where I stood. I was returning from the court. He was all sympathy, and said, 'Have you a lawyer?'

'Yes. The one there over the cotton godown.'

'Oh—he is the adjournment expert. He can keep the case going for years. So don't worry. Is it a civil suit or criminal suit?'

'Criminal! They have made out a case against me that, when he came to ask for his dues, I threatened to beat him. I wish I had done so!'

'What a pity! If it were a civil case, it could go on for years, and you would be none the worse for it while it lasted. Have you got *that* in your house?' he asked slyly. I gave him a fierce look. And he said, 'How can I blame a woman for what you are...? Why don't you look after tourists again?'

'I can't go near the railway station now. The railway staff are going to depose against me, to prove that I beat people up.'

'Is it true?'

'Hm. If I catch the porter's son, I'm going to wring his neck.'

'Don't do such things, Raju; you will not help yourself. You have brought sufficient confusion on yourself. Do pull yourself together. Why don't you do sensible things?'

I thought this over. I said, 'If I had five hundred rupees, I could start a new life.' I outlined to him a plan to utilize Rosie's services and make money. The thought of her warmed me up. 'She is a gold mine,' I cried. 'If I had money to start her with—oh!' My visions soared. I said to him, 'You know Bharat Natyam is really the greatest art business today. There is such a craze for it that people will pay anything to see the best. I cannot do anything about it because I have no money. Can't you help me, Gaffur?' He was amused at my request. It was now my turn to feel upset at laughter. I said, 'I have done so much for your business.'

He was essentially a man of heart. He appealed to my reason. 'I'm not a rich man, Raju. You know how I borrow money for even the upkeep of the car. If I had five hundred, I'd let my passengers ride on better tyres. No, no, Raju...listen to my advice. Send her away and try to get back to ordinary, real life. Don't talk all this art business. It's not for us.'

On hearing this, I grew so upset that I said something to hurt him. He got back into his driving seat with a serious face. 'If you like a drive any time, call me; that's all I can do to help you. And, remember, I'm not asking for the old dues from you—'

'Set it off against the commission due to me for all your Peak House trips,' I said haughtily.

'Very well,' he said, and started his car. 'Call me any time you want the car; it's always there. I pray that god may give you better sense.' He was off. I knew here was another friend passing out of my life.

Unfortunately, he was not the last. My mother's turn came soon. I was rapt, watching Rosie do a piece called 'The Dancing Feet'. Rosie said she had introduced a couple of variations, and wanted me to give my opinion. I was becoming a sort of expert on these matters nowadays. I watched her critically, but what I watched were the curves that tempted me to hug her on the spot. But my mother was passing in and out, and nowadays we had to seize our romantic moments and get through with it at odd times—for instance, when my mother went to fetch water. We knew exactly how long she would be away and utilized it. It was all irksome, but very novel, and made me forget my troubles. Whenever I watched her sway her figure, if there was no one about I constantly interrupted her performance, although I was supposed to watch her from an art critic's point of view. She pushed me away with, 'What has come over you?' She was a devoted artist;

her passion for physical love was falling into place and had ceased to be a primary obsession with her.

I had a little money still left in the savings, although I gave no hint of it to anyone. A couple of days after the Sait's coming, I drew the entire amount from the bank. I did not want it to be seized. This was keeping us. I had a small lawyer handling my case in the court. I had to give him part of my money for court fees and such things. He had his office in the attic of a cotton shop in Market Road—a choking place with one shelf of books, one table, one chair, and one bench for clients. He had spotted me on the very first day while I was loitering with terror in my eyes, obeying the first summons. He had ingratiated himself into my favour while I waited in the corridor. He asked, 'Did you hit the Sait, really? Speak the truth to me.'

'No, sir. It's a lie.'

'Evidently they want to bring in a criminal motive to quicken the procedure. We will dispute that first, and then the civil; we have a lot of time. Don't worry. I'll deal with all that. How much money have you in your pocket?'

'Only five rupees.'

'Give it here.' If I had said 'two' he'd probably have been content to take that. He pocketed it, held up a sheet of paper for my signature, and said, 'That's right. It fixes all your affairs up nicely.'

At the court I was asked to go behind an enclosure while the judge looked at me. The Sait was there with his notebook, and he had his lawyer, of course; we glared at each other. His lawyer said something; my five-rupee lawyer said something, gesticulating in my direction; and the court-servant patted my back and told me to go. My lawyer nodded to me. It was all over before I could understand anything. My lawyer met me outside. 'Managed to get an adjournment. I'll tell you the next date later. Meet me at my office, over the cotton godown—come by the staircase on the side lane.' He was off. If this was all the bother there was, I felt I could get through it easily. I was in excellent hands.

I told my mother on returning from the court, 'There is nothing to worry about, Mother; it's going nicely.'

'He may throw us out of this house. Where will you go after that?'

'Oh, all that will take a long time. Don't unduly burden your mind,' I cried.

She gave me up in despair. 'I don't know what is coming over you. You don't take anything seriously nowadays.'

'It's because I know what to worry about; that's all,' I said grandly.

Nowadays our domestic discussions were carried on in the presence of Rosie. No privacy was needed; we had got used to her. Rosie behaved as if she did not hear these domestic matters. She looked fixedly at the floor or at the pages of a book (the only things I managed to salvage from our shop), and moved off to a corner of the hall, as if to be out of earshot. She did not, even when she was alone with me, embarrass me by asking any questions about our affairs.

My mother had adjusted herself to my ways as an unmitigated loafer, and I thought she had resigned herself to them. But she had her own scheme of tackling me. One morning as I was watching Rosie's footwork with the greatest concentration, my uncle dropped in like a bolt from the blue. He was my mother's elder brother, an energetic landowner in my mother's village who had inherited her parents' home and was a sort of general adviser and director of all our family matters. Marriages, finances, funerals, litigation, for everything he was consulted by all the members of the family—my mother and her three sisters, scattered in various parts of the district. He seldom left his village, as he conducted most of his leadership by correspondence. I knew my mother was in touch with him—a postcard a month from him, closely written, would fill her with peace and happiness for weeks and she would ceaselessly talk about it. It was his daughter that she wanted me to marry—a proposal which she fortunately pushed into the background, in view of recent developments.

Here entered the man himself, standing at the door and calling in his booming voice, 'Sister!' I scrambled to my feet and ran to the door. My mother came hurrying from the kitchen. Rosie stopped her practice. The man was six feet tall, darkened by the sun from working in the fields, and had a small knotted tuft on his skull; he wore a shirt with an upper cloth, his *dhoti* was brown, not white like a townsman's.

He carried a bag of jute material in his hand (with a green print of Mahatma Gandhi on it), and a small trunk. He went straight to the kitchen, took out of the bag a cucumber, a few limes, and plantains and greens, saying, 'These are for my sister, grown in our gardens.' He placed them on the floor of the kitchen for his sister. He gave a few instructions as to how to cook them.

My mother became very happy at the sight of him. She said, 'Wait, I'll give you coffee.'

He stood there explaining how he came, by a bus; what he had been doing when he received my mother's letter, and so on and so forth. It was a surprise to me to know that she had written to him to come. She had not told me. 'You never told me you wrote to Uncle!' I said.

'Why should she tell you?' snapped my uncle. 'As if you were her master!' I knew he was trying to pick a quarrel with me. He lowered his voice to a whisper, pulled me down by the collar of my shirt, and asked, 'What is all this one hears about you? Very creditable development you are showing, my boy. Anybody would be proud of you!' I wriggled myself free and frowned. He said, 'What has come over you? You think yourself a big man? I can't be frightened of scapegraces like you. Do you know what we do when we get an intractable bull calf? We castrate it. We will do that to you, if you don't behave.'

My mother went on minding the boiling water as if she didn't notice what went on between us. I had thought she would come to my support, but she seemed to enjoy my predicament, having designed it herself. I felt confused and angry. As I moved out I could overhear my mother speaking to him in whispers. I could guess what she was saying. I went back to my mat, rather shaken.

Rosie was standing where I had left her with her hip slightly out, her arm akimbo. She was like one of those pillar-carvings in the temples. The sight of her filled me with a sudden nostalgia for the days when I took people to see the old temples and I sighed for the variety of life and contacts and experiences I used to have. Rosie looked a little scared. 'Who is he?' she asked in a low tone.

'Don't bother about him. He must be crazy. You don't have to worry.'

That was enough for her. My guidance was enough. She accepted it in absolutely unquestioning faith and ignored everything else completely. It gave me a tremendous confidence in myself and seemed to enhance my own dimensions. I told her, 'You need not stop your dance. You may go on with it.'

'But, but—' she indicated my uncle.

'Forget his existence completely,' I said. I was in a very challenging mood, but inside me I trembled still to think what my uncle might have to say. 'You don't have to bother about anyone except me,' I said with sudden authority. (My uncle used to be called in to frighten me when I was a boy.) 'This is my house. I do as I please here. If people don't like me, they need not visit me; that is all.' I laughed weakly.

What was the use of pouring out all these challenging statements to this girl? She resumed her song and dance, and I sat observing her, with extra attention as if I were her teacher. I observed my uncle peep out of the kitchen, and so I made myself more deliberately teacher-like. I issued commands and directions to Rosie. My uncle watched my antics from the kitchen. Rosie went on with her practice as if she were in her private room. My uncle presently came over to watch, his eyes bulging with contempt and cynicism. I ignored him completely. He watched for a moment, and let out a loud: 'Hm! So this is what is keeping you busy! Hm! Hm! Never dreamed that anyone in our family would turn out to be a dancer's backstage-boy!'

I remained silent for a while before mustering courage and resolution to attack him. He mistook my silence for fear and brought out another of his broadsides. 'Your father's spirit will be happy to see you now, literally grovelling at the feet of a dancing girl.'

He was out to provoke me. I turned round and said, 'If you have come to see your sister, you had better go in and stay with her. Why do you come where I am?'

'Aha!' he cried, delighted. 'Good to see some spirit in you. There is still hope for you, although you need not try it on your uncle first. Did I not mention a moment ago what we do to recalcitrant bull calves?' He was squatting on the floor now, sipping his coffee.

'Don't be vulgar,' I said. 'At your age too!'

'Hey, wench!' he cried to Rosie, addressing her in the singular, or something even lower than singular. 'Now stop your music and all those gesticulations and listen to me. Are you of our family?' He waited for an answer. She stopped her dance and simply stared at him. He said, 'You are not of our family? Are you of our clan?' He again waited for her to answer and answered himself. 'No. Are you of our caste? No. Our class? No. Do we know you? No. Do you belong to this house? No. In that case, why are you here? After all, you are a dancing girl. We do not admit them in our families. Understand? You seem to be a good, sensible girl. You should not walk into a house like this and stay on. Did anyone invite you? No. Even if you are invited you should go on staying where you belong, and not too long here. You cannot stay like this in our house. It is very inconvenient. You should not be seducing young fools, deserting your husband. Do you follow?' She sank down at this onslaught, covering her face with her hands. My uncle was evidently gratified at the success of his efforts, and proceeded to drive home his point. 'You see, you should not pretend to cry at these things. You must understand why we say such things. You must clear out by the next train. You must promise to go. We will give you money for your railway ticket.'

At this a big sob burst from her. I was completely maddened by it. I flew at my uncle and knocked the cup out of his hand, shouting, 'Get out of this house.'

He picked himself up, saying, 'You tell me to get out. Has it come to this? Who are you, puppy, to ask me to get out? I'll make you get out. This is my sister's house. You go out if you want enjoyment with dancing girls—'

My mother came running out of the kitchen with tears in her eyes. She flew straight at the sobbing Rosie, crying, 'Are you now satisfied with your handiwork, you she-devil, you demon? Where have you dropped on us from? Everything was so good and quiet—until you came; you came in like a viper. Bah! I have never seen anyone work such havoc on a young fool! What a fine boy he used to be! The moment he set his eyes on you, he was gone. On the very day I heard him mention the "serpent girl" my heart sank. I knew nothing good could come out of it.' I didn't interrupt my mother; I allowed her all the speech she wanted to work off feelings she had bottled up all these weeks. She then catalogued all my misdeeds down to my latest appearance in the court, and how I was going to lose even this house, so laboriously built by my father.

The girl looked up with her tear-drenched face and said amidst sobs, 'I will go away, Mother. Don't speak so harshly. You were so good to me all these days.'

My uncle now interrupted to tell his sister, 'This is your mistake, Sister. That wench is right in a way. Why should you have been so good to her? You should have told her at the beginning what was what.'

I seemed powerless to suppress this man or send him away. He said what he liked and stayed where he liked. Unless I physically pushed him out, there was no way of saving poor Rosie; but he could knock me flat if I laid hands on him. I was appalled at the somersault in my mother's nature the moment she got support in the shape of a brother. I went over to Rosie, put my arm around her to the shock of the two (my uncle cried, 'The fellow has lost all shame!'), and whispered to her, 'Shut your ears to all that they say. Let them say what they like. Let them exhaust themselves. But you are not leaving. I'm going to be here, and you are going to be here. Others who don't like the arrangement are welcome to leave.'

They went on a little longer, and when they could say nothing more they retired to the kitchen. I never spoke a word more. I learned a great secret, that of shutting my ears, and I felt happy that Rosie too could put herself through this hardening process, absolutely relying on my support. She lifted her head and sat up, watching the household coldly. My mother called me in to eat when food was ready. I took care to see that Rosie was also fed. My mother didn't call us until she had fed my uncle on the vegetables he had brought and had cooked them according to his specifications. After food he went over to the *pyol*, spread out his upper cloth, sat on it munching paan, and then lay down on the cool floor to sleep. I felt relieved to hear his snores. The calm after the storm was absolute. My mother served us food without looking at us. A great silence reigned in the house. It continued until three-thirty in the afternoon.

My uncle renewed the fight by coming in to announce to all whom it might concern, 'An hour more for the train. Is the passenger ready?' He looked at Rosie sitting below a window and reading. She looked up, disturbed. I never left her side that whole afternoon. Whatever people might say, I wanted to be near at hand to support her. As long as my uncle remained in town there could be no relaxation of the vigil. I would have given anything to know when my uncle would be leaving. But he was a man of independent notions and was not affected by my genuine desire to have him go.

Rosie looked up, slightly scared. I held a hand up to give her courage. My mother came out of her corner and, looking kindly at Rosie, said, 'Well, young woman, it has been nice having you, but you know, it is time for you to go.' She was trying new tactics now, of kindliness and a make-believe that Rosie had agreed to leave. 'Rosie, girl, you know the train is at four-thirty. Have you packed up all your things? I found your clothes scattered here and there.'

Rosie blinked unhappily. She did not know how to answer. I intervened to say, 'Mother, she is not going anywhere.'

My mother appealed to me. 'Have some sense, Raju. She is another man's wife. She must go back to him.'

There was such calm logic in what she said, I had nothing more to do but repeat blindly, 'She can't go anywhere, Mother. She has got to stay here.'

And then my mother brought out her trump card. 'If she is not going, I have to leave the house,' she said.

My uncle said, 'Did you think she was helpless, and only a dependant on you?' He thumped his chest and cried, 'As long as I am breathing, I will never let down a sister.'

I appealed to my mother, 'You don't have to go, Mother.'

'Then throw that wench's trunk out and give her a push towards the railway, and your mother will stay. What do you take her for? You think she is the sort that can keep company with all kinds of dancing—'

'Shut up, Uncle,' I said, and I was taken aback by my own temerity.

I feared he might repeat his threat to recalcitrant bulls. Fortunately, he said, 'Who are you, puppy, to say if I am to shut up or speak? You think I notice you? Are you sending that...that...out or not? That's all we want to know.'

'No; she is not going,' I said very calmly.

He heaved a sigh, glared at the girl, looked at my mother.

'Well, Sister, you must start packing, then. We will go by the evening bus.'

My mother said, 'All right. I can pack in a minute.'

'Don't go, Mother,' I pleaded.

'See that girl's obstinacy. She watches it all so calmly,' said my uncle.

Rosie pleaded, 'Mother, don't go.'

'Oho!' said my uncle. 'She has reached the stage of addressing you as Mother. Next she will be calling me Uncle-in-law, I suppose.' He turned to me with a horrible grin and said, 'Your mother needn't quit really. This house is hers for her lifetime. If I had had her cooperation, I'd have shown you a few nice tricks today. She would have stayed on till the end. My brother-in-law was no fool. He made you master of only one half of the home...' All of a sudden he entered into legal complexities, arising from my father's will, and described how he would have tackled the whole situation if he had been in my mother's position, and how he would have disputed every inch of the ground and taken the matter to the Supreme Court, and how he would have shown the world what to do with scapegraces who had no respect for family traditions but yet tried to enjoy their ancestors' hard-earned wealth. I was relieved as long as he waxed eloquent over legalities, as it helped him forget Rosie for the time being. True to the tradition of the landed gentry, he found litigation an engrossing subject. But the spell was broken when my mother came in to say, 'I'm ready.' She had picked up a few clothes here and there. Her large steel trunk, which had never been moved from its place in a corner for decades and decades, was packed and ready to be lifted out. She had a basket with a handle into which she had thrown a few copper and brass vessels. My uncle announced, 'These belong to our house, given by my father when this girl, my dear sister, married and was going to set up her own family.

It's our gift to her, and so don't gaze on it with such a look.'

I looked away and said, 'She certainly can take what she likes. Nobody will say anything.'

'Aha, you are proud of that, are you?' he said. 'You are showing a lot of liberality to your mother, aren't you?'

I had never in my life seen him so unpleasant. We had always been in terror of him when we were children, but this was the first occasion I had seen so much of him as an adult. My mother looked saddened rather than angry, and seemed almost ready to come to my rescue. She interrupted him sharply to say with extraordinary consideration in her voice, 'I need nothing more. This will do.' She picked up several small prayer books, which she read every day of her life before her midday meal, sitting before the pictures of the god in meditation. I had seen her for years at the same time sitting with closed eyes in front of the niche in the wall, and it now filled me with sadness that I would not see her there any more. I followed her about the house as she picked out her articles and packed. My uncle, as if to keep an eye on me, followed my steps. Apparently he feared I might induce my mother to stay on.

In spite of his supervision, I asked, 'Mother, when will you be back?'

She hesitated to answer, and said finally, 'I'll—I'll—let us see.'

'The moment she gets a telegram that the line is clear,' said Uncle and added, 'We are not the sort to let down our sisters, remember. That house in the village is always hers to return to; so that she has not got to be at anybody's mercy. Our house belongs to our sister as much as to us,' he added boastfully.

'Don't fail to light the lamps in the god's niche,' said my mother, going down the steps. 'Be careful with your health.' Uncle carried the trunks and she carried the basket. Soon they were at the end of the street and turned the corner. I stood on the step watching. At the threshold stood Rosie. I was afraid to turn round and face her, because I was crying.

We were a married couple to all appearances. Rosie cooked the food, and kept the house. I seldom went out except to do a little shopping.

All day long she danced and sang. I made love to her constantly and was steeped in an all-absorbing romanticism, until I woke up to the fact that she was really getting tired of it all. Some months passed before she asked me, 'What are your plans?'

'Plans!' said the sleeper, awakening. 'What plans?'

She smiled at this and said, 'There you are, always lying on the mat watching me or holding me in your arms. I have now had good practice—I can manage a show of four hours, although with accompaniments it would have been much more helpful—'

'I'm here, accompanying and marking time for you. What other accompaniment do you want?'

'I need a full orchestra. We have stayed indoors long enough,' she said. I found her so earnest that I had not the courage to joke any more.

I said, 'I'm also thinking. Very soon we must do something.'

'Rosie is a silly name,' I said as a first step after two days of hard thinking. 'The trouble with you is that although your people are a traditional dance family, they didn't know how to call you. For our public purposes, your name must be changed. What about "Meena Kumari"?'

She shook her head. 'It's no better. I see no reason to change my name.'

'You don't understand, my dear girl. It's not a sober or sensible name. If you are going to appear before the public with that name, they will think it's someone with cheap tricks, such as those we see in gambling side-shows. For a classical dancer, you should call yourself something that is poetic and appealing.'

She realized that there was a point in what I said, and she picked up a pad and pencil and noted down all the names that came into her head. I added my own. We wanted to see how they sounded and also how they looked on paper. Sheet after sheet was filled up and discarded. It became a sort of joke. We seemed to be forgetting our main job in enjoying the fun. Each name had something ridiculous about it, comic-sounding or an impossible association. At dead of night she sat up to ask, 'What about...?'

'The name of the wife of a demon-king—people will be frightened,' I said. Eventually, after four days of hard thinking and elimination (a labour which gave us the satisfaction of being engaged in professional duties), we arrived at 'Nalini', a name that could have significance, poetry, and universality, and yet be short and easily remembered.

With the attainment of a new name, Rosie entered a new phase of life. Under the new name, Rosie and all she had suffered in her earlier life were buried from public view. I was the only one who knew her as Rosie and called her so. The rest of the world knew her as Nalini. I bestirred myself, began to go out and meet people in the town. I attended meetings of various groups—at the University, the town hall, and the Club, and watched for a chance. When the Albert Mission boys had their annual social, I mixed in their affairs through the slender link of the clerk in the Union, who had once read with me at the old *pyol* school, and I suggested, 'Why not a dance recital instead of the usual Shakespeare tragedy?' I held forth on the revival of art in India so vehemently that they could not easily brush me aside, but had to listen. Heaven knew where I had found all this eloquence. I delivered such a lecture on the importance of our culture and the place of the dance in it that they simply had to accept what I said. Someone doubted if a classical dance would be suitable for a student assembly. I proved that the classical dance could be viewed as the lightest of entertainments, considering its versatility. I was a man with a mission. I dressed myself soberly for the part in a sort of rough-spun silk shirt and an upper cloth and a hand-spun and hand-woven *dhoti*, and I wore rimless glasses—a present from Marco at one of our first meetings. I wore a wristwatch; all this in my view lent such weight to what I said that they had to listen to me respectfully. I too felt changed; I had ceased to be the old Railway Raju and I earnestly wished that I too could bury myself, as Rosie had done, under a new name. Fortunately it didn't make much difference. No one seemed to bother about my affairs as those in the immediate railway colony did, and even if they knew they seemed to have other things to remember than my career and its ups and downs. I never knew I could speak so fluently on cultural matters. I had picked up a little terminology from Rosie and put it to the best use. I described 'The Dancing Feet' and explained its significance word by word and almost performed the dance act myself. They watched me in open-mouthed wonder. I threw a further bait to the committee: if they liked, they could go with me and see a sample of the show. They enthusiastically agreed. I mentioned her as a cousin who was on a visit, and who was famous in her own place.

The next morning Rosie had tidied up the hall so that it did not look too bad. She had decorated the place with flowers from a gold mohur tree. She had stuck the bunch in a bronze tumbler, and kept it in a corner; it touched up our little home with some sort of beauty. She had also pushed away our rolls of bedding and other boxes, stools, and odds and ends to the farthest corner, thrown a *dhoti* over the heap, and covered it again cunningly with a striped carpet pulled from under a bed. This gave it a mysterious look. She had shaken the old mat and rolled it up so that the tattered portions were invisible. She managed to have ready cups of brown, steaming coffee. All this was an excellent preparation, calculated to win a public for her. The men, two of them, came and knocked on the door. When I opened it there they stood. Rosie had hung a printed sheet over the kitchen doorway and was behind it. I opened the door, saw the men there, and said, 'Oh, you have come!' as if I had thought they wouldn't. Somehow I felt it would be good to give it all a casual air. They smirked foolishly, realizing they had come on an agreeable errand to watch a possible beauty.

I seated them on the mat, spoke to them of world politics for a moment, and said, 'You can spare a little time, I suppose? I'll ask my cousin if she is free.'

I walked through the kitchen curtain and she was standing there. I grinned and winked at her. She stood stock-still and grinned back at me. We were enjoying this piece of stage-management; we felt we had already begun to put on a show. She had tied her hair into a knot, decorated her forehead with a small vermilion dot, lightly sprinkled a little powder on her face, and clad herself in a blue cotton saree—

an effect of simplicity produced with a lot of preparation. After five minutes of silent waiting, I nodded, and she followed me out.

The Secretary and the Treasurer gaped. I said, 'These are my friends. Sit down.' She smiled, and seated herself on a small mat—modestly away. I knew at that moment that her smile was an 'open sesame' to her future. There was an awkward pause for a moment and then I said, 'These are my friends. They are having a variety show in the College Union, and were wondering if you would do anything for them.'

She asked, 'Variety? What other items are you having?' and puckered her brow in a superior way.

They said apologetically, 'A few fancy-dress items, mimicry and such things.'

She said, 'How can you fit my programme into that? How much time do you want to give me?' She was taking charge of their programme.

They said, greatly flustered, 'One hour, an hour and a half—anything you like.'

Now she delivered them a homily. 'You see, a dance programme is not like variety, it needs time to be built up. It's something that has to develop even as one is performing and one is watching.'

They agreed with her sentiments absolutely. I interrupted to say, 'Their main idea in coming now is to see you, and to see whatever bit of your art you can show them. Would you oblige us?'

She made a wry face and grumbled, looked hesitant, and gave us no reply.

'What is it? They are waiting for a reply from you. They are busy men.'

'Oh, no. No need to hustle the lady. We can wait.'

'How, how to—manage now—no accompaniments—without accompaniments I never like—' she was saying, and I said, 'Oh, this is not a full-dress show. Just a little— When there is a full-dress show we shall have accompaniments. After all, you are the most important item.' I cajoled her and the other two happily joined me; and Rosie agreed hesitantly, saying, 'If you are so keen, I can't refuse. But don't blame me if it is not good.' She went behind the curtain once again, returned bearing coffee on a plate, and set it down.

Out of formal politeness the gentlemen said, 'Why bother about coffee?' I pressed them to accept it.

As they sipped their coffee, Rosie began her dance, to the accompaniment of a song that she lightly sang. I ventured to beat time with my hands, like a very knowing one. They watched in fascination. She suddenly paused, wiped the perspiration from her brow, took a deep breath, and, before resuming again, said to me, 'Don't beat time; it misleads me.'

'All right,' I said, awkwardly grinning, trying not to look snubbed. I whispered, 'Oh, she is so precise, you know.' They shook their heads.

She finished her piece and asked, 'Shall I go on? Shall I do "The Dancing Feet"?'

'Yes, yes,' I cried, glad to be consulted. 'Go on. They will like it.'

When they recovered from the enchantment, one of them said, 'I must admit I have never cared for Bharat Natyam, but watching this lady is an education. I now know why people are in raptures over it.'

The other said, 'My only fear is that she may be too good for our function. But it doesn't matter. I'll reduce the other items to give her all the time she wants.'

'We must make it our mission to educate the public taste,' I said. 'We must not estimate the public taste and play down to it. We must try to raise it by giving only the best.'

'I think up to the interval we shall have the variety and all such tomfoolery. After the interval this lady can take up the entire show.'

I looked up at her for a second as if waiting for her approval, and said, 'She'll, of course, be pleased to help you. But you must provide the drummer and accompanists,' and thus acquired at last the accompanists Rosie had been clamouring for all along.

9

My activities suddenly multiplied. The Union function was the start. Rocket-like, she soared. Her name became public property. It was not necessary for me to elaborate or introduce her to the public now. The

very idea would be laughed at. I became known because I went about
with her, not the other way round. She became known because she had
the genius in her, and the public had to take notice of it. I am able
to speak soberly about it now—only now. At that time I was puffed
up with the thought of how I had made her. I am now disposed to
think that even Marco could not have suppressed her permanently;
sometime she was bound to break out and make her way. Don't be
misled by my present show of humility; at the time there was no limit
to my self-congratulation. When I watched her in a large hall with a
thousand eyes focused on her, I had no doubt that people were telling
themselves and each other, 'There he is, the man but for whom—' And
I imagined all this adulation lapping around my ears like wavelets. In
every show I took, as a matter of right, the middle sofa in the first
row. I gave it out that that was my seat wherever I might go, and
unless I sat there Nalini would be unable to perform. She needed my
inspiring presence. I shook my head discreetly; sometimes I lightly
tapped my fingers together in timing. When I met her eyes, I smiled
familiarly at her on the stage. Sometimes I signalled her a message
with my eyes and fingers, suggesting a modification or a criticism of
her performance. I liked the way the president of the occasion sat
next to me, and leaned over to say something to me. They all liked
to be seen talking to me. They felt almost as gratified as if they spoke
to Nalini herself. I shook my head, laughed with restraint, and said
something in reply, leaving the watching audience at our back to guess
the import of our exchanges, although actually it was never anything
more than, 'The hall seems to have filled.'

I threw a glance back to the farthest corner of the hall, as if to
judge the crowd, and said, 'Yes, it's full,' and swiftly turned round, since
dignity required that I look ahead. No show started until I nodded
to the man peeping from the wings, and then the curtain went up. I
never gave the signal until I satisfied myself that everything was set.
I inquired about the lighting, microphone arrangements, and looked
about as if I were calculating the velocity of the air, the strength of
the ceiling, and as if I wondered if the pillars would support the
roof under the circumstances. By all this I created a tenseness which

helped Nalini's career. When they satisfied all the conditions and a performance began, the organizers felt they had achieved a difficult object. Of course, they paid for the dance, and the public was there, after paying for their seats, but all the same I gave the inescapable impression that I was conferring on them a favour by permitting the dance. I was a strict man. When I thought that the programme had gone on long enough I looked at the watch on my wrist and gave a slight nod of the head, and Nalini would understand that she must end the show with the next item. If anyone made further suggestions, I simply laughed them off. Sometimes slips of paper travelled down from the back of the hall, with requests for this item or that, but I frowned so much when a slip was brought near me that people became nervous to pass on such things. They generally apologized, 'I don't know. Someone from the back bench—it just came to me—' I took it with a frown, read it with bored tolerance, and pushed it away over the arm of the sofa; it fell on the carpet, into oblivion. I made it look as if such tricks should be addressed to lesser beings and that they would not work here.

One minute before the curtain came down, I looked for the Secretary and nodded to him to come over. I asked him, 'Is the car ready? Please have it at the other door away from the crowd. I'd like to take her out quietly.' It was a false statement. I really liked to parade her through the gaping crowds. After the show, there were still people hanging around to catch a glimpse of the star. I walked ahead of her or beside her without much concern. At the end of the performance they presented her with a large garland of flowers, and they gave me one too. I accepted mine with protest. 'There is really no reason why you should waste money on a garland for me,' I said; I slung it carelessly on my arm or in the thick of the crowd dramatically handed it over to Nalini with 'Well, you really deserve two,' and made her carry it for me.

It was a world of showmanship till we reached the privacy of our house, when she would throw off the restraint and formality of hours and give me a passionate hug with 'Even if I have seven rebirths I won't be able to repay my debt to you.' I swelled with pride when

I heard her, and accepted it all as my literal due. Methodically she started wrapping the flowers in a wet towel so that they might remain fresh in the morning.

On programme days she cooked our supper in the afternoon. We could easily have afforded to engage a cook, but she always said, 'After all, for two people, we don't need a cook moping around the house. I must not lose touch with my womanly duties.' She spoke of the evening show all through dinner, criticizing some arrangement or the background accompaniment, how so-and-so just failed to catch up. She lived entirely in the memory of her evening show. Sometimes after food she demonstrated a piece. And then she picked up a book and read on till we went to bed.

In a few months I had to move out of my old house. The Sait managed to score a point of law and secured an attachment of the property before judgement. My lawyer came to me and said, 'Don't worry about it; it only means he will have to pay the house tax, with arrears, if any. Of course, your mother's signature may be required too, but I'll get it. It is just like mortgaging the house to him. You may have to give him rent—a nominal one if you stay here.'

'Paying rent for my own house!' I said. 'If I have to pay rent I prefer a better house.' For our growing stature the house was inadequate. No visitor could be entertained. No privacy. No place for my furniture. My father had designed this house for a shopkeeper, not for a man of consequence and status who had charge of a growing celebrity. 'Moreover, where is the place for you to practise in?' I asked Nalini when she demurred at the notion of moving out. Somehow she was deeply attached to the house, the place which first gave her asylum.

The lawyer went to the village and returned with my mother's signature on the document. 'How did she take it?' I could not help asking.

'Not badly, not badly,' said the adjournment expert. 'Well, of course, we cannot expect elderly people to take the same view as we do. I had to argue and persuade her, though your uncle proved a difficult man.'

Four days later my mother's letter came; she had written on a yellow paper with a pencil: '...I gave my signature not because I was happy about it but because otherwise the lawyer would not go from here, and your uncle would not let him stay in peace. It is all confusing to me. I'm sick of everything. I signed without your uncle's knowledge, when he was away in the garden, so that the lawyer might leave this place without any damage to his person. Anyway, what does it all mean? Your lawyer mentioned that you are looking for a new house for that woman. If it is so, I'll come back to live in my old house. After all, I wish to spend the rest of my days in my own house.' It was good of my mother to have set aside her own anger and written to me. I felt touched by her solicitude. I was troubled by her desire to come back. I could understand it, but I resisted the idea. It seemed best to let the Sait take the home and be done with it once and for all. Who wanted this ramshackle house anyway? To have Mother live in the house, I should have to pay a rent to the Sait. Who would look after her? I was so busy. I rationalized in all possible ways and put away her letter without a reply. I moved to another house and became very busy, and in all the rush quietened my conscience. I felt sorry, but I rationalized: 'After all her brother is dear to her, and he will look after her. Why should she come here and live all alone?'

The stylish house at New Extension was more in keeping with our status. It was two-storied, with a large compound, lawns, garden, and garage. On the upper floor we had our bedrooms and a large hall where Nalini practised her dance. It was carpeted with a thick, deep blue, spun-silk carpet at one end, leaving a space of marble tiles for her to dance on. I had managed to fix up a pedestal and a bronze image of dancing Nataraja in one corner. It was her office. I had now a permanent group of musicians—five of them: a flautist, a drummer, etc. She had a 'dance master' whom I discovered in Koppal, a man who had steeped himself in the traditional dance for half a century and lived in his village home. I ferreted him out and brought him over to Malgudi and gave him an outhouse in our compound to live in. All kinds of people were always passing in and out of our house. I had a large staff of servants—a driver for our car, two gardeners for the garden, a Gurkha sentry at the gate with a dagger at his waist, and two cooks because our entertainments were beginning to grow. As I have said, a miscellaneous population was always passing in and out of the compound: musicians, their friends, those that came to see me by appointment, the servants, their friends, and so on. On the ground floor I had an office with a secretary-in-waiting, a young graduate from the local college, who dealt with my correspondence.

I had three or four grades of visitors. Some I received on the veranda; these were musicians or aspiring musicians who wanted a chance to accompany Nalini. I was offhand with them. About ten such asked for an interview with me every day. They were always waiting on the outer veranda to have a chance to speak to me. I went in and out, hardly noticing them. They respectfully rose at the sight of me and saluted, and if they intercepted me I kept up a show of giving them a hearing, and then said, 'Leave your address with my clerk there. If there is anything that can be done, I'll ask him to call you up.' When they flourished a batch of testimonials I snatched a brief look at them and said, 'Good, good. But there is nothing I can do now. Leave your name in the office'—and I passed on. My outer veranda was cluttered with benches on which people sat and waited all day to have a chance to speak to me. I treated them with the scantiest attention. I left them to guess when I would come to my table. Sometimes obscure composers turned up with new songs especially created for Nalini's benefit. Sometimes when I sat at the office table I did not mind if they peeped in and took their chance to speak to me. I never offered this class of visitor a chair, but did not mind if he pulled one up and sat down. When I wanted to dispose of him, I pushed my chair back and went in abruptly, leaving it to my secretary to see him off. Sometimes I observed through the glass window in the hall how big a crowd waited for me outside, and I made a strategic exit through a side door, straight on to the garage, and from there dashed to the gate, while the visitors looked on helplessly. I felt vastly superior to everyone.

Apart from those that came as supplicants, there were others who approached me with genuine offers of engagement. They were the higher grade of visitors. I received them on the hall sofa and rang the bell for coffee. I offered my inner circle of visitors coffee day and night. Our coffee bill alone amounted to three hundred a month, enough to maintain a middle-class family in comfort. The appointments in the hall were all expensive—brass-inlaid trays, ivory knick-knacks, group photographs with Nalini in the middle. Sitting in that hall and looking round, I had the satisfaction of feeling that I had arrived.

Where was Nalini in all this? Away and out of sight. She spent a great part of the day in her rehearsal hall with her musicians. One could hear the stamping of feet and the jingle of anklets on the upper floor. After all, she was living the life she had visualized. Visitors had always a hope that they might get a glimpse of her passing in or out of the house. I knew what they were looking for, with their shifty looks darting at the inner doorway. But I took care to see that no one saw her. I had a monopoly of her and nobody had anything to do with her. If anyone ventured to ask for her I said, 'She is busy,' or 'No need to trouble her. You have told me; that is enough.' I resented anyone's wanting to make a direct approach to her. She was my property. This idea was beginning to take root in my mind.

There were, however, a few friends of the inner circle whom I took upstairs to her room. It was a very eclectic group. They had to be my intimates; I had had no friends at all formerly; my friendship was now sought after by others. I was on back-slapping terms with two judges, four eminent politicians of the district whose ward could bring ten thousand votes at any moment for any cause, and two big textile-mill owners, a banker, a municipal councillor, and the editor of *The Truth*, a weekly, in which an appreciation of Nalini appeared from time to time. These men could come into my hall without appointment, demand coffee, and ask loudly, 'Where is Nalini? Upstairs? Well, I think I'll see her for a moment and go.' They could go up, talk to her, order coffee, and stay on as long as they pleased. They addressed me as 'Raj', familiarly. I liked to hobnob with them because they were men of money or influence.

Apart from them, sometimes musicians or actors or other dancers called on Nalini and spent hours and hours with her. Nalini enjoyed

their company immensely, and I often saw them in her hall, some lying
on carpets, some sitting up, all talking and laughing, while coffee and
food were being carried to them. I occasionally went up and chatted
with them—always with a feeling that I was an interloper in that
artistic group. Sometimes it irritated me to see them all so happy and
abandoned. I signalled to Nalini to come over to the bedroom, as if
for a big, important aside, and when she closed the door I whispered,
'How long are they going to stay?'

'Why?'

'They have been here the whole day and may go on till night.'

'Well, I like their company. It's good of them to visit us.'

'Oh, as if we had no one else to visit us.'

'It's all right. How can I tell them to go? And it makes me happy
to be with them.'

'Surely; I'm not denying it. But remember, you have to rest and
we have a train journey ahead. You will have to pack up, and also
practise. Remember you have promised new items for the Trichy show.'

'That's easy to manage!' she said, turning round and going back
to her friends, shutting the door on me. I silently fretted. I liked her
to be happy, but only in my company. This group of miscellaneous
art folk I didn't quite approve of. They talked too much shop and
Nalini was likely to tell them all our business secrets. She never missed
a chance to get a gathering of such friends, wherever she might be.
She said, 'They are people with the blessing of Goddess Saraswathi on
them, and they are good people. I like to talk to them.'

'You don't know the world—they'll be a jealous lot. Don't you
know that the real artists never come together? These people come to
you because they are your inferiors.'

'I'm tired of all talk of superior and inferior. What is so superior
about us?' she asked in real indignation.

'Well, you know, you have more engagements than a hundred of
them put together,' I said.

'That's more money,' she said. 'I don't care much for that sort
of superiority.'

Gradually arguments began to crop up between us, and that, I said, put the final husband-wife touch on our relationship. Her circle was widening. Artists of the first and second rank, music teachers, dilettantes of the town, schoolgirls who wanted ideas for their school functions, all kinds of people asked to see her. Wherever possible I turned them back, but if they managed to slip through and get upstairs, I could do nothing about it. Nalini kept them for hours and would hardly let them go back.

We had calls from hundreds of miles away. Our trunks were always packed and ready. Sometimes when we left Malgudi we did not return home for nearly a fortnight. Our engagements took us to all corners of south India, with Cape Comorin at one end and the border of Bombay at the other, and from coast to coast. I kept a map and a calendar and tried to plan out our engagements. I studied the invitations and suggested alternative dates, so that a single journey might combine several engagements. Arranging an itinerary for each period took up a lot of my energy. We were out of town for about twenty days in the month, and during the ten days we were in Malgudi we had one or two dates nearer home, and whatever was left over could be counted as rest. It was a strenuous programme, and, wherever I might be, my secretary kept me informed of the mail arriving each day and received instructions by phone. I was committed three months ahead. I had a large calendar on which I marked in red the dates of engagements, and hung it up at first in her rehearsal hall, but she protested, 'It's ugly. Take it away!'

'I want you to keep an idea before you of where you are going next.'

'Not necessary,' she cried. 'What am I going to do, looking at those dates?' She rolled it up and put it in my hand. 'Don't show it to me. It only frightens me to see so many engagements,' she said. When I told her to get ready for the train, she got ready; when I asked her to come down, she came down; she got in and out of trains at my bidding. I don't know if she ever noticed what town we were in or what *sabha* or under whose auspices a show was being held. It was all the same, I think, whether it was Madras city or Madurai, or a remote hill town like Ootacamund. Where there was no railway, a car came to fetch us from the railhead. Someone met us at the platform, led us to a limousine waiting outside, and drove us to a hotel or a bungalow. Our circus of accompanying musicians was taken away in a bunch and berthed comfortably somewhere. I kept this lot in good humour by fussing about their comfort. 'They are our accompanists. I hope you have made proper arrangements for them too.'

'Yes, yes, sir. We've reserved two large rooms for them.'

'You must send them a car later to bring them over to our place.' I always made it a point to collect them and keep them handy two hours ahead of a show. They were a timeless lot, those instrumental players; they slept, or went shopping, or sat around playing cards— never looking at a clock. Handling them was an art—they had to be kept in good humour; otherwise they could ruin a whole evening and blame it on mood or fate. I paid them well. I kept up a show of looking after them, but I kept aloof. I was careful to see that they assumed no familiarity with Nalini.

If the show was at six, I generally insisted upon Nalini's resting until four o'clock in the afternoon. If we were guests in a house, she generally liked to sit around with the womenfolk and chat endlessly with them. But I went up to her and said with a good deal of firm kindness, 'I think you had better rest a while; the train journey last night was not very comfortable,' and she finished the sentence she was uttering or hearing and came up to our guest-room.

She felt annoyed at my interference. 'Why should you come and pull me out of company? Am I a baby?' I expostulated with her that it was for her own good that I did so. I knew it was only a partial truth. If I examined my heart I knew I had pulled her out because I did not like to see her enjoy other people's company. I liked to keep her in a citadel.

If there was a train to catch after the show, I managed to have a car waiting ready to take us to the station. I had food brought to us on the train in silver or stainless-steel vessels, and we had our supper in the privacy of our compartment. But it was a brief, short-lived relief, as it soon began all over again, getting down at another station, going through another performance, and off again. When we visited places of importance, she sometimes asked to be taken to see a famous temple or a shop or some local sight. I always replied, 'Yes, yes. Let us see if we can fit it in,' but it was never done, as I always had to catch another train so as to fulfil another engagement. We were going through a set of mechanical actions day in and day out—the same receptions at the station, fussy organizers, encounters, and warnings, the same middle sofa in the first row, speeches and remarks and smiles, polite conversation, garlands and flash photos, congratulations, and off to catch the train—pocketing the most important thing, the cheque. Gradually I began to say, not 'I am going to Trichy for a performance by Nalini', but 'I am performing at Trichy on Sunday, on Monday I have a programme...', and then, 'I can dance in your place only on...' I demanded the highest fee, and got it, of anyone in India. I treated those that came to ask for a show as supplicants, I had an enormous monthly income, I spent an enormous amount on servants and style, and I paid an enormous amount of income tax. Yet I found Nalini accepting it all with a touch of resignation rather than bouncing contentment. She had seemed such a happy creature in our old house, even when my uncle was bullying her.

Nalini cherished every garland that she got at the end of a performance. Usually she cut it up, sprinkled water on it, and preserved it carefully, even when we were in a train. She said, holding up a piece of the garland and sniffing the air for its fragrance, 'To me this is the only worthwhile part of our whole activity.'

We were in a train when she said it. I asked her, 'What makes you say so?'

'I love jasmine.'

'Not the cheque that comes with it?'

'What is one to do with so much? All day long and all through the week you are collecting cheques, and more and more often. But when is the time coming when we can enjoy the use of those cheques?'

'Well, you have a big household, a big car and what not—is that not enjoyment of life?'

'I don't know,' she said, remaining moody. 'How I wish I could go into a crowd, walk about, take a seat in the auditorium, and start out for an evening without having to make up or dress for the stage!'

Some dangerous weariness seemed to be coming over her. I thought it best not to prod too much. Perhaps she wanted fewer engagements, but that was not possible. I asked, 'You are not saying that your legs are aching, are you?'

It had the desired effect. It pricked her pride and she said, 'Certainly not. I can dance for several hours at each show. Only you want me to stop.'

'Yes, yes; true,' I cried. 'Otherwise you would be fatiguing yourself.'

'Not only that; you also want to catch the train—though what will be lost if we catch the next day's, I don't know—'

I didn't allow her to finish her sentence. I flatteringly called her a shrewd girl, laughed and enjoyed it as a joke, fondled her, and made her forget the subject. I thought it was a dangerous line of thought. It seemed absurd that we should earn less than the maximum we could manage. My philosophy was that while it lasted the maximum money had to be squeezed out. We needed all the money in the world. If I were less prosperous, who would care for me? Where would be the smiles which greeted me now wherever I turned, and the respectful agreement shown to my remarks when I said something to the man in the next chair? It filled me with dread that I should be expected to do with less. 'If we don't work and earn when the time is good, we commit a sin. When we have a bad time no one will help us.' I was planning big investments as soon as possible—as soon as we could count on a little more margin. As it was, the style of living and entertaining which I had evolved was eating up all our resources.

Sometimes she said, 'Spending two thousand a month on just the two of us. Is there no way of living more simply?'

'Leave that to me; we spend two thousand because we have to. We have to maintain our status.' After a good deal of thought, I ran the bank account in her name. I didn't want my creditors to get at me again. My adjournment lawyer was proceeding at his own pace, sometimes coming to me for a signature or funds, and managing things without bothering me. Nalini signed any cheque I asked her to sign. One thing I must add: whenever I was in town I gathered a big circle of friends and we played cards practically twenty-four hours at a stretch. I had set apart a room for the purpose and I had two personal servants serving tea and coffee and even food on the spot; and we had surreptitious drinks too, although there was prohibition in force—well, the prohibition law was not for a man of my influence. I had managed to get a medical certificate to say that I needed alcohol for my welfare. Although I myself cared very little for drink, I hugged a glass of whisky for hours. 'Permit-holder' became a social title in our land and attracted men of importance around me, because the permit was a difficult thing to acquire. I showed respect for the law by keeping the street-window shut when serving drink to non-permit folk. All kinds of men called me 'Raj' and slapped my back. We played Three Cards sometimes for two days at a stretch; I changed a two-thousand-rupee cheque for the purpose, and expected those who came there to meet me on equal terms. Through my intimacy with all sorts of people, I knew what was going on behind the scenes in the government, at the market, at Delhi, on the race course, and who was going to be who in the coming week. I could get a train reservation at a moment's notice, relieve a man summoned to jury work, reinstate a dismissed official, get a vote for a co-operative election, nominate a committee man, get a man employed, get a boy admitted to a school, and get an unpopular official shifted elsewhere, all of which seemed to me important social services, an influence worth buying at the current market price.

In the glow of this radiant existence, I had practically overlooked the fact that Marco still existed. We hardly mentioned his name. I never took note of the fact that he still inhabited the globe, and I took the only precaution needed—I avoided any engagement near his house. I didn't want to run the risk of facing him again. I had no idea what Nalini had in mind. I believed she still felt embittered at the thought of him, and would rather not be reminded of him. I supposed that all associations with him were dim, fossilized, or had ceased to exist.

I also thought that under her new name Nalini she was safely out of range, but I was mistaken. We played for a whole week at Malgudi. The post one day brought us a book. Generally I received a miscellaneous collection of mail—catalogues, programmes, verse, and what not, all of which was seen and disposed of by my secretary. Some Tamil and English illustrated journals meant for Nalini were sent up. I hardly looked at anything except letters offering engagements, and certainly never at books and journals. I was a man of many preoccupations, and I found it impossible nowadays to sit down with any book and had instructed my secretary not to bother me with them. But one day he brought a packet, saying, 'Would you look at this, sir. I thought it might be of special interest.'

He held the book open. I snatched it from him. It was a book by Marco, a book full of illustrations and comments. 'See page 158' said a pencilled message. I turned it over, and there it was, the heading 'Mempi Cave Pictures'. At the head of the chapter was a brief line to say, 'The author is obliged to acknowledge his debt to Sri Raju of Malgudi Railway Station for his help.' The book was from a firm of publishers in Bombay, with their compliments, sent by instructions of the author. It was a gorgeous book costing twenty rupees, full of art plates, a monograph on *The Cultural History of South India.* It was probably an eminent work on the subject, but beyond me.

I told the secretary, 'I'll keep it. It's all right.' I turned the pages. Why did the boy bring it up as a special matter? Did he know who was who? Or—? I dismissed the idea. It must have been because he was rather taken by the blue and gold of the binding and the richness of the material. He must have feared that if he didn't draw my attention to it, I might probably demand an explanation. That was all. So I said, 'Thank you, I'll read it.' And then I sat wondering what I should do about it. Should I take it upstairs to Nalini or—? I told myself, 'Why should she be bothered with this? After all, it is a piece of academic work, which has bored her sufficiently.' I turned it over again, to see if there was any letter enclosed. No. It was impersonal, like the electricity bill. I turned to page 158 and re-read his note. It was thrilling to see my name in print. But why did he do it? I lost myself in speculating on his motives. Was it just to keep his word because he had promised, or could it be to show that he had not forgotten me so lightly? Anyway, I thought it would be best to put the book away. I carried it to my most secret, guarded place in the house—the liquor chest adjoining the card room, the key of which I carried next to my heart—stuffed the volume out of sight, and locked it up. Nalini never went near it. I did not mention the book to her. After all, I told myself, 'What has she to do with it? The book is sent to me, and the acknowledgement is of my services.' But it was like hiding a corpse. I've come to the conclusion that nothing in this world can be hidden or suppressed. All such attempts are like holding an umbrella to conceal the sun.

Three days later Marco's photograph appeared in the *Illustrated Weekly of Bombay*, on the middle page. The *Illustrated Weekly* was one of the papers Nalini always read—it was full of wedding pictures, stories, and essays she enjoyed. The photograph was published along with a review of his book, which was called 'An epoch-making discovery in Indian cultural history'. I was looking through my accounts in the hall, free from all visitors. I heard footsteps clattering down in a great run. I turned and saw her coming with the magazine in her hand, all excitement. She thrust the page before me and asked, 'Did you see that?'

I showed appropriate surprise and told her, 'Calm yourself. Sit down.'

'This is really great. He worked for it all his life. I wonder what the book is like!'

'Oh, it's academic. We won't understand it. For those who care for such things, it must seem interesting.'

'I want so much to see the book! Can't we get it somewhere?' She suddenly called my secretary, an unprecedented act on her part. 'Mani,' she said and held the picture up to him, 'you must get me this book.'

He came nearer, read the passage, brooded for a moment, looked at me, and said, 'All right, madam.'

I hurriedly told him, 'Hurry up with that letter, and go in person to the post office and remember to add a late fee.' He was gone. She still sat there. Unless she was called to meet visitors, she never came downstairs. What was this agitation that made her do these things? I wondered for a moment whether I ought not to bring the book out to her. But she would ask me for so many explanations. I simply suppressed the whole thing. She returned upstairs to her room. I noticed later that she had cut out the photo of her husband and placed it on her dressing mirror. I was rather shocked. I wanted to treat it as a joke, but could not find the right words, and so left it alone. I only averted my eyes when I passed the dressing mirror.

It was a long week in town; otherwise we should have been fully occupied in moving about, and probably would have missed that particular issue of the *Illustrated Weekly*. On the third day, while we were in bed, the very first question she asked me was, 'Where have you kept the book?'

'Who told you about it?"

'Why bother? I know it has come to you. I want to see it.'

'All right, I'll show it to you tomorrow.' Evidently Mani must be responsible. I had made it a convention in our establishment that the secretary should have no direct access to her, but the system was breaking down. I decided to punish him properly for his lapse.

She sat reclining on her pillow with a journal in her hand, to all appearances reading, but actually preparing herself for a fight. She pretended to read for a moment and suddenly asked, 'Why did you want to hide it from me?'

I was not ready for this, and so I said, 'Can't we discuss it all tomorrow? Now I'm too sleepy.'

She was out for a fight. She said, 'You can tell me in a word why you did it and go to sleep immediately.'

'I didn't know it would interest you.'

'Why not? After all—'

'You have told me that you never thought his work interesting.'

'Even now I'll probably be bored. But anything happening to him is bound to interest me. I'm pleased he has made a name now, although I don't know what it is all about.'

'You suddenly fancy yourself interested in him, that's all. But the book came to *me*, not to you, remember.'

'Is that sufficient reason why it should be hidden from me?'

'I can do what I please with my own book, I suppose? That's all. I'm going to sleep. If you are not reading, but are merely going to think, you can as well do it in the dark, and put out the light.'

I don't know why I spoke so recklessly. The light was put out, but I found that she was sitting up—and crying in the dark. I wondered for a second whether I should apologize and comfort her. But I decided otherwise. She had been bottling up a lot of gloom lately, it seemed to me. It would do her good to have it all out without my interference. I turned over and pretended to sleep. Half an hour passed. I switched on the light, and there she was, quietly crying still.

'What has come over you?'

'After all, after all, he is my husband.'

'Very well. Nothing has happened to make you cry. You should feel pleased with his reputation.'

'I am,' she said.

'Then stop crying and go to sleep.'

'Why does it irritate you when I speak of him?'

I realized it was no use trying to sleep. I might as well meet the challenge. I replied, 'Do you ask why? Don't you remember when and how he left you?'

'I do, and I deserved nothing less. Any other husband would have throttled me then and there. He tolerated my company for nearly a month, even after knowing what I had done.'

'You talk about a single incident in two different ways. I don't know which one I should take.'

'I don't know. I may be mistaken in my own judgement of him. After all, he had been kind to me.'

'He wouldn't even touch you.'

'Should you taunt me with that?' she asked with sudden submissiveness. I couldn't understand her. I had an appalling thought that for months and months I had eaten, slept, and lived with her without in the least understanding her mind. What were her moods? Was she sane or insane? Was she a liar? Did she bring all these charges against her husband at our first meeting just to seduce me? Would she be levelling various charges against me now that she seemed to be tiring of me—even to the extent of saying that I was a moron and an imbecile? I felt bewildered and unhappy. I didn't understand her sudden affection for her husband. What was this sudden mood that was coming over her? I did my best for her. Her career was at its height. What was it that still troubled her? Could I get at it and find a remedy? I had been taking too much for granted in our hectic professional existence.

'We must go on a holiday somewhere,' I said.

'Where?' she asked in a businesslike manner.

I was taken aback. 'Where? Anywhere! Somewhere.'

'We are always going somewhere. What difference is it going to make?'

'We'll go and enjoy ourselves on our own, without any engagement.'

'I don't think it's going to be possible until I fall sick or break my thighbone,' she said and giggled viciously. 'Do you know the bulls yoked to an oil-crusher—they keep going round and round and round, in a circle, without a beginning or an end?'

I sat up and told her, 'We'll go as soon as the present acceptances are finished.'

'In three months?'

'Yes. After they are finished we'll pause for a little breath.' She looked so unconvinced of this that I said, 'Well, if you don't like an engagement, you can always say no.'

'To whom?'

'Why, of course, to me.'

'Yes, if you would tell me before you accept and take an advance.'

There was something seriously wrong with her. I went over to her bed, sat on it, shook her by the shoulder a little just to make it look personal, and asked, 'What is the matter with you? Are you not happy?'

'No. I'm not happy. What will you do about it?'

I threw up my arms. I really could not say anything. 'Well, if you tell me what is wrong, I can help. As far as I can see, there is nothing for you to be sorry about—you are famous, you have made money, you do what you like. You wanted to dance; you have done it.'

'Till the thought of it makes me sick,' she added. 'I feel like one of those parrots in a cage taken around village fairs, or a performing monkey, as he used to say—'

I laughed. I thought the best solvent would be laughter rather than words. Words have a knack of breeding more words, whereas laughter, a deafening, roaring laughter, has the knack of swallowing everything up. I worked myself into a paroxysm of laughter. She could not remain morose very long in the face of it. Presently she caught the contagion, a smirk developed into a chuckle, and before she knew what was what her body rocked with laughter, all her gloom and misgivings exploded in laughter. We went to sleep in a happy frame of mind. The time was two hours past midnight.

Our life fell into a routine after this little disturbance. After a break of only three days, during which time I steeped myself in the card game, avoiding all discussions with her, our encounters were casual and slight. She was passing through a period of moodiness, and it was safest to keep out of her way and not to rouse her further. The engagements for the next three months were all-important, running, as they did, into the season of music and dance in south India, for which I had taken heavy advance payments. We had ahead of us a travel programme of nearly two thousand miles, from Malgudi back to Malgudi, and if we went through with it there was ample time for her to get over the mood, and then I could push her into another quarter-year of activity. I had no intention of slackening this programme. It seemed so unnecessary, so suicidal. My only technique was to keep her in good humour to the best of my ability from quarter to quarter.

We were getting through our engagements uneventfully. We were back in Malgudi. Mani was away for a couple of days and I was attending personally to an accumulation of correspondence on my table. Offers of engagements I piled up on one side. I had some misgivings about accepting any of them right away as I normally would. I felt I should do well to speak to her before replying. Of course she'd have to accept them, but I wanted to give her a feeling of being consulted. I sorted them out.

Suddenly I came upon a letter addressed to 'Rosie, alias Nalini'.

It had on it the address of a lawyer's firm in Madras. I wondered what to do with it for a while. She was upstairs, probably reading one of her inexhaustible journals. I felt nervous about opening the letter. I had half an impulse to take it to her: a sensible part of me said, 'It must, after all, be her business. She is an adult, with her own affairs. Let her tackle it, whatever it may be.' But this was only fleeting wisdom. The letter had arrived by registered post some days ago and Mani had received it and kept it on the table. It had a big seal on its flap. I looked at it with misgiving for a while, told myself that I was not to be frightened by a seal, and just cut it open. I knew she would not mind my seeing her letters. The letter came from a lawyer and said, 'Madam, under instruction from our client, we are enclosing an application for your signature, for the release of a box of jewellery left in safe custody at the Bank of... in the marked place. After this is received we shall proceed to obtain the other signature as well, since you are aware that the deposit is in your joint names, and obtain the release of the said box, and arrange to forward it to you under insurance cover in due course.'

I was delighted. So this was going to bring in more jewellery for her. Of course she would be elated. But how big was the box? What were the contents worth? These were questions that agitated my mind for a while. I looked through the letter for some clue; but the lawyer was sparing of words. I took the letter and turned to go and give it to her. But on the staircase I paused. I returned to my room and sat in my chair, thinking. 'Well, let me think it over. Where is the hurry?' I asked myself. 'She has waited for this box so long. Just a couple of days more is not going to matter. Anyway, she never mentioned it, perhaps she doesn't care.' I took the letter to my drink casket and locked it up. A good thing Mani was not there. Otherwise he might have created a mess.

I had some visitors after this. I talked to them and went out in the evening to see a few friends. I tried to distract my mind in various ways, but the packet bothered me. I returned home late. I avoided going upstairs. I heard her jingles upstairs, and knew that she was practising. I returned to my office table with the letter from the drink cabinet. I opened it carefully and read it again. I looked at the enclosed application. It was on a printed form; after her signature was going to be Marco's. What was the man's purpose in sending it now? Why this sudden generosity to return her an old box? Was he laying a trap for her, or what was it? Knowing the man as I did, I concluded that it might not be anything more than a correct disposal of his affairs, similar to his acknowledgement of my help in his book. He was capable of cold, machine-like rectitude; his vouchers were in order; he saw probably no sense in being responsible for Rosie's box any more. Rightly, too. The right place for Rosie's box was here. But how to release it? If Rosie saw this letter she would do god knew what. I had a fear that she would not view it calmly, in a businesslike manner. She would in all likelihood lose her head completely. She was likely to place the wildest interpretation on it and cry out, 'See how noble he is!' and make herself miserable and spoil for a fight with me. There was no knowing what would set off the trigger nowadays. His mere photo in the *Illustrated Weekly* drove her crazy: after that book incident I was very careful. I never showed her the book at all.

Next day I waited for her to ask for it, but she never mentioned it again. I thought it'd be safest to leave it there. I was very careful. I kept her in good humour and engaged, that was all; but I was aware that some sort of awkwardness had developed between us, and I kept myself aloof with extreme care. I knew that if I allowed more time she would be all right. But I felt that to show her this letter would be suicidal. She might refuse to do anything except talk about his nobility. Or (who could say?) she might insist on taking the next train to his place, throwing up everything. But what was to be done with the letter? 'Just let it rest in the company of whisky bottles till it is forgotten,' I told myself and laughed grimly.

During dinner, as usual, we sat side by side and spoke of things such as the weather, general politics, the price and condition of vegetables, and so on. I kept the subject rigorously to inconsequential affairs. If we held on for another day, it'd be perfect. On the third day we should be on the move again, and the bustle and activity of travel would shield us from troublesome personal topics.

After dinner she sat down on the hall sofa to chew betel leaves, turned over the pages of a journal on the hall table and then went upstairs. I felt relieved. The swing was coming back to normal. I spent a little time in my office, looking into accounts. The income-tax statement was due to be sent in a couple of weeks. I was poring over my very personal account-book just to see where we stood, and how to prepare our expense accounts. After brooding over this mystic matter for a while I went upstairs. I knew I had given her enough time either to be steeped in the pages of a book or to sleep. Anything to avoid talk. I was becoming uncertain of my own attitude nowadays. I feared I might blurt out about the letter. I laid my head on the pillow and turned over, with the formula, 'I'll sleep, I think. Will you switch off when you are done?' She grunted some reply.

How much jewellery might be in the box? Was it his present to her or her mother's or what? What a girl! She never gave it a thought! Perhaps they were antiquated and she did not care for them. If so they might be sold now and converted into cash, and no income-tax officer would ever dream of its existence. Must be a substantial lot if it had to be kept in safe custody. But who could say? Marco was eccentric enough to do strange things. He was the sort of fellow to keep even a worthless packet at the bank, because that was the right thing—to—do—the—r-right thing to—do... I fell asleep.

Soon after midnight I awoke. She was snoring. An idea bothered me. I wanted to see if there was any time limit mentioned. Suppose I kept the letter secret and some serious consequences arose? I wanted to go down and examine the document at once. But if I got up, she would also wake up and ask questions. Or if I took no notice at all of it, what would happen? The box would continue to remain in safe custody; or the lawyer might write a reminder, which might come in when I was out and slip its way through to her, and then questions, explanations, scenes. This was proving a greater bother than I had thought at first. Nothing that that man did was ever quiet or normal. It led to unbelievable complexities. As I kept thinking of it, it magnified itself until I felt that I had dynamite in my pocket. I slept fitfully till about five o'clock, and then left my bed. I lost no time in going to the drink cabinet, pulling out the document, and examining it. I carefully read through the document, line by line, several times over. The lawyers said, 'per return post', which seemed to my fevered mind an all-important instruction. I took it over to the office desk. I found a scrap of paper and made a careful trial of Rosie's signature. I had her sign so many cheques and receipts each day that I was very familiar with it. Then I carefully spread out the application form and wrote on the indicated line: 'Rose, Nalini'. I folded it and put it in an addressed cover which the lawyers had enclosed, sealed it, and I was the first to appear at the window when our extension branch post office opened at seven-thirty.

The postmaster said, 'So early! You have come yourself!'

'My clerk is sick. I was out for a morning walk. Please register this.' I had walked down for fear that opening the garage door might wake her up.

I had no clear idea as to when or how the jewel box might arrive, but I looked for it every day. 'Any parcel in the post, Mani?' I asked constantly. This almost threatened to become a habit. I expected it within the next two days. No signs of it. We had to go out of town for four days. Before leaving I instructed Mani, 'There may be an insured packet coming. Tell the postman to keep it in deposit till we are back on Tuesday. They keep such things, don't they?'

'Yes, sir. But if it is only a registered parcel, I can sign for you.'

'No, no. This is an insured parcel and it will have to be signed for by one of us. Tell the postman to bring it again on Tuesday.'

'Yes, sir,' said Mani, and I left him abruptly; otherwise he might have started expanding on the subject.

We were back on Tuesday. The moment Rosie went upstairs I asked Mani, 'Did the parcel arrive?'

'No, sir. I waited for the postman, but there was nothing.'

'Did you tell him that we were expecting an insured parcel?'

'Yes, sir, but there was nothing.'

'Strange!' I cried. 'Per return', the lawyers had written. They probably wanted the signature, that was all. Perhaps Marco planned to appropriate the box himself and had tried this ruse. But as long as that lawyer's letter was with me, I could hang them; none of their tricks was going to succeed. I went to my drink cabinet and re-read the letter. They had committed themselves clearly. 'We shall arrange to forward, under insurance cover....' If it meant nothing in a lawyer's letter, where was it going to mean anything? I felt somewhat puzzled, but told myself that it would ultimately arrive; banks and lawyers' offices could not be hustled; they had their own pace of work, their own slow red-tape methods. Slow-witted red-tapeists—no wonder the country was going to the dogs. I put the letter back and locked it up safely. I wished I didn't have to go to the drink cabinet every time I wanted to read the letter; the servants, knowing the contents, might begin to think that I took a swill of whisky every few minutes. My desk would be the right place for the letter, but I had a suspicion that Mani might see it; if he caught me studying the letter so often, he was sure to want to take a look at it by stealing up at my back and pretending to have some question to ask. He had worked for me for months and months without my noticing anything against him, but now he and everyone around appeared sinister, diabolical, and cunning.

That evening we had an engagement at Kalipet, a small town sixty miles away. The organizers were providing a van for the musicians, and a Plymouth for me and Nalini, so that we might fulfil the engagement and return home the same night. It was a benefit show for building a maternity home, and they had collected seventy thousand rupees. The price of tickets ranged from two hundred and fifty rupees in a kind of fancy scale, and officials persuaded businessmen and merchants to contribute. Businessmen ungrudgingly paid up on condition that they were given the nearest seats in the first row. They wanted to sit as near the performer as possible, with a chance of being noticed. In their thoughts, Nalini, while dancing, noted their presence and later inquired, 'Who were those important men in the front row?' Poor creatures, they hardly knew how Nalini viewed her audience. She often remarked, 'They might be logs of wood for all I care. When I dance I hardly notice any face. I just see a dark well in the auditorium, that's all.'

This was a very large-scale function because of official interest in it. The officials were interested because the chief man of the place, who was behind all the shows, was a minister of the state cabinet, and it had been his ambition in life to build a first-rate maternity centre in this area. Knowing the circumstances, I had moderated my demand to a thousand rupees for expenses, which meant it was free of income tax. After all, I too liked to contribute to a social cause, and certainly we would not come out of it too badly anyway. But it was all the same for Nalini. Instead of travelling by train, we were going by car, that was all. She was pleased that we should be returning home the same night.

The show was held in an immense pavilion specially constructed with bamboos and coconut matting and decorated with brilliant tapestry, bunting, flowers, and coloured lights. The stage itself was so beautifully designed that Nalini, who generally ignored everything except the flowers at the end, cried, 'What a lovely place. I feel so happy to dance here.' Over a thousand people were seated in the auditorium.

She began her first movement, as usual, after a signal from me. She entered, carrying a brass lamp, with a song in praise of Ganesha, the elephant-faced god, the remover of impediments.

Two hours passed. She was doing her fifth item—a snake dance, unusually enough. I liked to watch it. This item always interested me. As the musicians tuned their instruments and played the famous snake song, Nalini came gliding onto the stage. She fanned out her fingers slowly, and the yellow spotlight, playing on her white, upturned palms, gave them the appearance of a cobra hood; she wore a diadem for this act, and it sparkled. Lights changed, she gradually sank to the floor, the music became slower and slower, the refrain urged the snake to dance—the snake that resided on the locks of Shiva himself, on the wrist of his spouse, Parvathi, and in the ever-radiant home of the gods in Kailas. This was a song that elevated the serpent and brought out its mystic quality; the rhythm was hypnotic. It was her masterpiece. Every inch of her body from toe to head rippled and vibrated to the rhythm of this song which lifted the cobra out of its class of an underground reptile into a creature of grace and divinity and an ornament of the gods.

The dance took forty-five minutes in all; the audience watched in rapt silence. I was captivated by it... She rarely chose to do it indeed. She always said that a special mood was needed, and always joked that so much wriggling twisted her up too much and she could not stand upright again for days. I sat gazing as if I were seeing it for the first time. There came to my mind my mother's remark on the first day, 'A serpent girl! Be careful.' I felt sad at the thought of my mother. How much she could have enjoyed watching this. What would she have said if she could have seen Rosie now, in her shining costume and diadem? I felt a regret at the rift that had developed between me and my mother. She occasionally wrote me a postcard, and I sent her small sums of money now and then, dashing off a few lines to say I was well. She often asked when I'd get back the house for her—well, that involved a big sum and I told myself I'd attend to it as soon as I had some time. Anyway, what was the hurry? She was quite happy in the village; that brother of hers looked after her very well. Somehow I could never fully forgive her for her treatment of Rosie on that fateful day. Well, we were now on cordial terms, but far away from each other, the best possible arrangement. I was watching Nalini and at the same time thinking of my mother. At this moment, one of the men of the organization came up to me unobtrusively and said, 'You are wanted, sir.'

'Who wants me?'

'The District Superintendent of Police.'

'Tell him I'll be with him as soon as this act is over.'

He went away. The District Superintendent! He was one of my card-playing mates. What did he want to see me about now? Of course, the officials were all here, expecting the minister (a sofa was kept vacant for him), and extra police were posted to control the crowd and the traffic. After this act, when the curtain came down, thunderous applause broke out, and I went out. Yes, the District Superintendent was there. He was in plain dress.

'Hello, Superintendent, I didn't know you were coming; you could have come with us in the car,' I cried.

He plucked my sleeve and drew me aside because there were too many people watching us. We went to a lonely spot under a lamp outside, and he whispered, 'I'm awfully sorry to say this, but I've a warrant for your arrest. It has come from headquarters.'

I smiled awkwardly, partly disbelieving him. I thought he was joking. He pulled out a paper. Yes, it was a true and good warrant for my arrest on a complaint from Marco, the charge being forgery. When I stood ruminating, the Superintendent asked, 'Did you sign any recent document for—the lady?'

'Yes; she was busy. But how can you call that forgery?'

'Did you write "For" or just write her name?' He plied me with questions. 'It's a serious charge,' he said. 'I hope you will pull through, but for the moment I have to take you in custody.'

I realized the gravity of the situation. I whispered, 'Please don't create a scene now. Wait until the end of the show, and till we are back home.'

'I'll have to be with you in the car, and after the warrant is served you can arrange for a surety bond till the case is taken up. That will leave you free, but first I'm afraid you will have to go with me to the magistrate. He has to sanction it. I have no powers.'

I went back to my sofa in the hall. They brought me my garland. Somebody got up and made a speech thanking the dancer and Mr Raju for their help in getting the collection to over seventy thousand rupees. Incidentally he spun out a lot of verbiage around the theme of the dance in India, its status, philosophy, and purpose. He went on and on. He was a much-respected president of the local high school or some such thing. There was tremendous applause at the end of his speech. More speeches followed. I felt numb, hardly hearing anything. I didn't care what they said. I didn't care whether the speech was long or short. When it was over, I went to Nalini's dressing-room. I found her changing. A number of girls were standing around her, some waiting for autographs, and some just looking on. I said to Nalini, 'We will have to hurry.'

I went back to the Superintendent in the corridor, composing my looks, trying to look cheerful and unconcerned. A lot of the first-row men surrounded me to explain their appreciation in minute detail. 'She just towers above all others,' someone said. 'I have seen dancers for a half-century—I'm the sort of man who will forgo a meal and walk twenty miles to see a dance. But never have I seen,' etc. etc. 'This maternity home, you know, will be the first of its kind. We must have a wing named after Miss Nalini. I hope you will be able to come again. We would like to have you both for the opening ceremony. Could you give us a photograph of her...? We'd like to enlarge it and hang it in the hall... That'll be source of inspiration for many others, and, who knows, in this very building may be born a genius who may follow the footsteps of your distinguished wife.'

I didn't care what they said. I simply nodded and grunted till Nalini came out. I knew that the men surrounded and talked to me only in the hope of getting a close view of Nalini. As usual, she had her garland; I gave her mine. The Superintendent led the way unobtrusively to our Plymouth waiting outside. We had to walk through a crowd buzzing around us like flies. The driver held the door open.

'Get in. Get in,' I said impatiently to Nalini. I sat beside her. Her face was partially illuminated by a shaft of gaslight from a lamp hanging on a tree. Thick dust hung in the air, churned up by the traffic; all the vehicles, cars, bullock-carts, and *jutkas* were leaving in a mass, with a deafening honking of horns and rattle of wheels. A few policemen stood at a discreet distance and saluted the Superintendent as our car moved away. He occupied the front seat next to the driver. I told her, 'Our friend, the District Superintendent, is coming back with us to the city.'

It was about two hours' journey. She talked for a while about the evening. I gave her some comments on her performance. I told her something of what I had heard people say about her snake-dance. She said, 'You are never tired of it,' and then lapsed into silence and drowsiness, only waiting for our destination, as our car whizzed along the country highway, past long rows of bullock-carts with their jingling bells. 'They sound like your anklets,' I whispered to her clumsily.

The moment we reached our home, she threw a smile at the

Superintendent, murmured 'Good night', and vanished into the house.
The Superintendent said to me, 'Let us go now in my jeep.' It was
waiting at the gate.

I sent away the Plymouth. I said, 'I say, Superintendent, give me
a little time, please. I want to tell her about it.'

'All right. Don't delay. We must not get into trouble.'

I went up the staircase. He followed. He stood on the landing
while I went into her room. She listened to me as if I were addressing a
stone pillar. Even now I can recollect her bewildered, stunned expression
as she tried to comprehend the situation. I thought she would break
down. She often broke down on small issues, but this seemed to
leave her unperturbed. She merely said, 'I felt all along you were not
doing right things. This is *karma*. What can we do?' She came out
to the landing and asked the officer, 'What shall we do about it, sir?
Is there no way out?'

'At the moment I have no discretion, madam. It's a non-bailable
warrant. But perhaps tomorrow you may apply for reconsideration of
bond. But we can do nothing till tomorrow, till it's moved before the
magistrate.' He was no longer my friend, but a frightful technician.

10

I had to spend a couple of days in the lock-up, among low criminals.
The District Superintendent ceased to be friendly the moment we were
in the Central Police Station. He just abandoned me to the routine
care of the station officer.

Rosie came to see me in the police lock-up and wept. I sat for
the first time with my eyes averted, in the farthest corner of the cell.
After a while I recovered my composure and told her to go and see
our banker. All that she asked was, 'Oh, we had so much money!
Where is it all gone?'

I went back home three days later, but the old, normal life was
gone. Mani worked in a mechanical manner, with bowed head, in his
own room. There was no work for him to do. Fewer letters arrived
for me. There was a sepulchral quietness about the house. Nalini's feet

were silent upstairs. No visitors came. She had had to scrape up a bail bond for ten thousand rupees. If I had lived as a normal man of common sense, it would not have been difficult to find the amount. As it was, I had tied up whatever was left over in several foolish share certificates, on which the banks would not advance any money, and the rest I had spent in show living, including the advances taken for future engagements.

I suggested to Rosie, 'Why don't you go through with your engagements for the next quarter? We should receive the balance of the fees.' I caught her at dinner, because nowadays I spent all my time downstairs and left her alone. I lacked the confidence to face her alone in her room. I even spent my sleeping hours on the hall sofa.

She did not answer. I repeated my question, at which she muttered, when the cook went in to fetch something, 'Must we discuss it before the cook?' I accepted the snub meekly.

I was now a sort of hanger-on in the house; ever since she had released me from police custody, the mastery had passed to her I fretted inwardly at the thought of it. When the first shock of the affair had subsided, she became hardened. She never spoke to me except as to a tramp she had salvaged. It could not be helped. She had had to scrape together all her resources to help me. She went through her act of help m a sort of cold, businesslike manner. I ate my food in silence. She deigned to spend some time in the hall after food. She came and sat down there. She had a tray of betel leaves by her side on the sofa. I pushed it off and dared to seat myself by her side. Her lips were reddened with betel juice. Her face was flushed with the tingling effect of betel leaves. She looked at me imperiously and asked, 'Now, what is it?' Before I opened my mouth she added, 'Remember, you should speak nothing before the cook. The servants are gossiping too much. On the first of the month I'm going to send one of them away.'

'Wait, wait. Don't rush,' I began.

'What should I wait for?' Her eyes glistened with tears; she blew her nose. I could do nothing about it but just watch. After all the mastery had passed to her and if she thought fit to cry, it was her business. She had enough strength in her to overcome it if she thought it necessary. It was I who needed comforting. I was overwhelmed with a sudden self-pity. Why should she cry? She was not on the threshold of a prison. She had not been the one who had run hither and thither creating glamour and a public for a dancer; it was not she who had been fiendishly trapped by a half-forgotten man like Marco—an apparent gazer at cave-paintings, but actually venomous and vindictive, like the cobra lying in wait for its victim. I can now see that it was a very wrong line of thought to adopt. But how could I help it? It was only such perverse lines of thought and my excessive self-pity that enabled me to survive those moments; one needed all that amount of devilry to keep oneself afloat. I could give no time for others. I could not bother to think of her own troubles, of the mess she had been led into, of the financial emptiness after all those months of dancing and working, of the surprise sprung upon her by my lack of—what should we call it, judgement? No, it was something much lower than that. Lack of ordinary character! I see it all now clearly, but at that time I still clung to my own grievances, and could watch without much perturbation her emotional tantrums. I allowed her to have her cry as usual. She wiped her eyes and asked, 'You said something when we were eating?'

'Yes; but you wouldn't let me proceed,' I said petulantly. 'I was asking why you should not go through with the programmes, at least those for which we have received an advance.'

She remained in thought for a while and said, 'Why should I?'

'Because we received only an advance, while what we desperately need is the full fee in every case.'

'Where is all the money?'

'You should know. The account is all in your name, and you may see the bankbook if you like.' It was a cruel thing to say. Some devil was wagging his tongue within my skull. I was suddenly racked with the feeling that after all I had done for her she was not sufficiently sympathetic to my cause.

She spurned continuing this perverse discussion. She merely said, 'Please tell me what those engagements are and I'll return them all their money.'

I knew that this was just a brave statement. Where would she find the amount to refund? 'Why should you? Why should you not go through with them?'

'Is money your only consideration? Don't you see how I can't face the public again?'

'Why not? If I'm under arrest, I'm under arrest; that is all. Not you. Why should you not go about your business normally?'

'I can't; that is all. I can say nothing more.'

I asked coldly, 'What do you propose to do in future?'

'Perhaps I'll go back to him.'

'Do you think he will take you back?'

'Yes, if I stop dancing.'

I laughed in a sinister manner. 'Why do you laugh?' she asked.

'If it were only the question of dancing, he might.'

Why did I talk like this? It hurt her very much. 'Yes; you are in a position to say such a thing now. He may not admit me over the threshold, in which event it is far better to end one's life, on his doorstep.' She remained moody for a while. It gave me a profound satisfaction to see her imperiousness shattered after all. She added, 'I think the best solution for all concerned would be to be done with this business of living. I mean both of us. A dozen sleeping pills in a glass of milk, or two glasses of milk. One often hears of suicide pacts. It seems to me a wonderful solution, like going on a long holiday. We could sit and talk one night perhaps, and sip our glasses of milk, and maybe we should wake up in a trouble-free world. I'd propose it this very minute if I were sure you would keep the pact, but I fear that I may go ahead and you may change your mind at the last second.'

'And have the responsibility of disposing of your body?' I said, which was the worst thing I could have said. Why was I speaking like this again and again? I think I was piqued that she would not continue her dancing, was a free creature, while I was a jailbird.

I said, 'Is it not better to keep dancing than think these morbid thoughts?' I felt I must take charge of her again. 'Why won't you dance? Is it because you think I won't be there to look after you? I'm sure you can manage. And it may after all be only for a short time.

298 ■ TIMELESS MALGUDI

Oh, there is nothing in this case of ours. It'll just break down at the first hearing. You take my word for it. It's a false charge.'

'Is it?' she asked.

'How can they prove anything against me?'

She merely ignored this legal rambling and said, 'Even if you are free, I'll not dance in public any more. I am tired of all this circus existence.'

'It was your own choice,' I said.

'Not the circus life. I visualized it as something different. It's all gone with that old home of yours!'

'Oh!' I groaned. 'And you wouldn't let me rest then. You drove me hard to help you come before the public, and now you say this! I don't know, I don't know, you are very difficult to satisfy.'

'You don't understand!' she cried, and got up and went upstairs. She came down a few steps to say, 'It does not mean I'm not going to help. If I have to pawn my last possession, I'll do it to save you from jail. But once it's over, leave me once and for all; that's all I ask. Forget me. Leave me to live or die, as I choose; that's all.'

She was as good as her word. A sudden activity seized her. She ran about with Mani's help. She sold her diamonds. She gathered all the cash she could, selling all the shares under par. She kept Mani spinning around. She sent him to Madras to pick up a big lawyer for me. When the stress for cash became acute and she found we would have a lot to make up, she became somewhat more practical-minded. She swallowed her own words and went through her engagements, shepherding the musicians herself, with Mani's help, making all the railway arrangements, and so forth. I taunted her as I saw her moving around. 'You see, this is what I wanted you to do.'

There was no dearth of engagements. In fact, my present plight, after a temporary lull, seemed to create an extra interest. After all, people wanted to enjoy a show, and how could they care what happened to me? It hurt me to see her go through her work, practice, and engagements unconcernedly. Mani was very helpful to her, and those who invited her gave her all assistance. Everything went to prove that she could get on excellently without me. I felt like telling Mani, 'Be careful. She'll lead you on before you know where you are, and then you will find yourself in my shoes all of a sudden! Beware the snake-woman!' I knew my mind was not working either normally or fairly. I knew I was growing jealous of her self-reliance. But I forgot for the moment that she was doing it all for my sake. I feared that, in spite of her protestations to the contrary, she would never stop dancing. She would not be able to stop. She would go from strength to strength. I knew, looking at the way she was going about her business, that she would manage—whether I was inside the bars or outside, whether her husband approved of it or not. Neither Marco nor I had any place in her life, which had its own sustaining vitality and which she herself had underestimated all along.

Our lawyer had his own star value. His name spelled magic in all the court-halls of this part of the country. He had saved many a neck (sometimes more than once) from the noose; he had absolved many a public swindler in the public eye and in the eye of the law; he could prove a whole gang of lawless hooligans to be innocent victims of a police conspiracy. He set at naught all the laboriously built-up cases of the prosecution; he made their story laughable; he picked the most carefully packed evidence between his thumb and forefinger and with a squeeze reduced it to thin air; he was old-fashioned in appearance, with his long coat and an orthodox-style *dhoti* and turban and over it all his black gown. His eyes scintillated with mirth and confidence when he stood at the bar and addressed the court. When the judge's eyes were lowered over the papers on his desk, he inhaled a deep pinch of snuff with the utmost elegance. We feared at one stage that he might refuse to take our case, considering it too slight for his attention; but fortunately he undertook it as a concession from one star to another—for Nalini's sake. When the news came that he had accepted the brief (a thousand rupees it cost us to get this out of him), we felt as if the whole case against me had been dropped by the police with apologies for the inconvenience caused. But he was expensive—each consultation had to be bought for cash at the counter.

He was in his own way an 'adjournment lawyer'. A case in his hands was like dough; he could knead and draw it up and down. He split a case into minute bits and demanded as many days for microscopic examination. He would keep the court fidgeting without being able to rise for lunch, because he could talk without completing a sentence; he had a knack of telescoping sentence into sentence without pausing for breath.

He arrived by the morning train and left by the evening one, and until that time he neither moved off the court floor nor let the case progress even an inch for the day—so that a judge had to wonder how the day had spent itself. Thus he prolonged the lease of freedom for a criminal within the available time, whatever might be the final outcome. But this meant also for the poor case-stricken man more expense, as his charges per day were seven hundred and fifty rupees, and he had to be paid railway and other expenses as well, and he never came without juniors to assist him.

He presented my case as a sort of comedy in three acts, in which the chief villain was Marco, an enemy of civilized existence. Marco was the first prosecution witness for the day, and I could see him across the hall wincing at every assault mounted against him by my star lawyer. He must have wished that he had not been foolhardy enough to press charges. He had his own lawyer, of course, but he looked puny and frightened.

The first part of the comedy was that the villain wanted to drive his wife mad; the second part of the comedy was that the wife survived this onslaught, and on the point of privation and death was saved by a humble humanitarian called Raju, who sacrificed his time and profession for the protection of the lady and enabled her to rise so high in the world of the arts. Her life was a contribution to the prestige of our nation and our cultural traditions. When the whole world was thirsting for Bharat Natyam, here was this man slighting it, and when she made a big name for herself, someone's gorge rose. Someone wanted to devise a way of blowing up this whole edifice of a helpless lady's single-handed upward career, Your Honour. And then the schemer brought

THE GUIDE ■ 301

out the document—a document which had been forgotten and lain in concealment for so many years. There was some other motive in involving the lady by getting her to sign the document—he would go into it at a later part of the argument. (It was his favourite device to make something look sinister; he never found the opportunity to return to it later.) Why should anyone want to trot out a document which had been kept back for all those years? Why did he leave it alone so long? Our lawyer would leave the point for the present without a comment. He looked about like a hound scenting a fox. The document, Your Honour, was returned without signature. The idea was not to get involved, and the lady was not the type to get caught by jewellery; she cared little for it. And so the document was unsigned and returned, the good man Raju himself carrying it to the post office in order to make sure of its dispatch, as the postmaster would testify. So it was a big disappointment for the schemer when the document went back unsigned. So they thought of another trick: someone copied the lady's signature on it and took it to the police. It was not his business to indicate who could have done it; he was not interested in the question. He was only interested to the extent of saying categorically that it was not his client who had done it; and unhesitatingly he would recommend that he should be immediately discharged and exonerated.

But the prosecution case was strong, though unspectacular. They put Mani in the box and examined him till he blurted out that I was desperately looking for an insured parcel every day; the postmaster was cross-examined and had to admit that I had seemed unusual, and finally it was the handwriting expert who testified that it could reasonably be taken to be my handwriting: he had detailed proofs from my writings on the backs of cheques, on receipts and letters.

The judge sentenced me to two years' imprisonment. Our star lawyer looked gratified, I should properly have got seven years according to law books, but his fluency knocked five years off, though, if I had been a little careful...

The star lawyer did not achieve this end all at once, but over a period of many months, while Nalini worked harder than ever to keep the lawyer as well as our household going.

I was considered a model prisoner. Now I realized that people generally thought of me as being unsound and worthless, not because I deserved the label, but because they had been seeing me in the wrong place all along. To appreciate me, they should really have come to the Central Jail and watched me. No doubt my movements were somewhat restricted: I had to get out of bed at an hour when I'd rather stay in, and turn in when I'd rather stay out—that was morning five and evening five. But in between these hours I was the master of the show. I visited all departments of the prison as a sort of benevolent supervisor. I got on well with all the warders: I relieved them in their jobs when other prisoners had to be watched. I watched the weaving section and the carpentry sheds. Whether they were murderers or cut-throats or highwaymen, they all listened to me, and I could talk them out of their blackest moods. When there was a respite, I told them stories and philosophies and what not. They came to refer to me as *Vadhyar*—that is, Teacher. There were five hundred prisoners in that building and I could claim to have established a fairly widespread intimacy with most of them. I got on well with the officials too. When the jail superintendent went about his inspections, I was one of those privileged to walk behind and listen to his remarks; and I ran little errands for him, which endeared me to him. He had only to look ever so slightly to his left, and I knew what he wanted. I dashed up and called the warder he was thinking of calling; he had only to hesitate for a second, and I knew he wanted that pebble on the road to be picked up and thrown away. It pleased him tremendously. In addition, I was in a position to run ahead and warn warders and other subordinates of his arrival; and that gave them time to rouse themselves from brief naps and straighten out their turbans.

I worked incessantly on a vegetable patch in the back yard of the superintendent's home. I dug the earth and drew water from the well and tended it carefully. I put fences round, with brambles and thorns so that cattle did not destroy the plants. I grew huge brinjals and beans, and cabbages. When they appeared on their stalks as tiny buds, I was filled with excitement. I watched them develop, acquire shape, change colour, shed the early parts. When the harvest was ready, I plucked them off their stalks tenderly, washed them, wiped them clean to a polish with the end of my jail jacket, arranged them artistically on a tray of woven bamboo (I had arranged to get one from the weaving shed), and carried them in ceremoniously. When he saw the highly polished brinjals, greens, and cabbages, the superintendent nearly hugged me for joy. He was a lover of vegetables. He was a lover of good food, wherever it came from. I loved every piece of this work, the blue sky and sunshine, and the shade of the house in which I sat and worked, the feel of cold water; it produced in me a luxurious sensation. Oh, it seemed to be so good to be alive and feeling all this; the smell of freshly turned earth filled me with the greatest delight. If this was prison life, why didn't more people take to it? They thought of it with a shudder, as if it were a place where a man was branded, chained, and lashed from morning to night! Medieval notions! No place could be more agreeable; if you observed the rules you earned greater appreciation here than beyond the high walls. I got my food, I had my social life with the other inmates and the staff, I moved about freely within an area of fifty acres. Well, that's a great deal of space when you come to think of it; man generally manages with much less. 'Forget the walls, and you will be happy,' I told some of the newcomers, who became moody and sullen the first few days. I felt amused at the thought of the ignorant folk who were horrified at the idea of a jail. Maybe a man about to be hanged might not have the same view, nor one who had been insubordinate, or violent; but short of these, all others could be happy here. I felt choked with tears when I had to go out after two years, and I wished that we had not wasted all that money on our lawyer. I'd have been happy to stay in this prison permanently.

The superintendent transferred me to his office as his personal servant. I took charge of his desk, filled his inkwells, cleaned his pens, mended his pencil, and waited outside his door to see that no one disturbed him while he worked. If he so much as thought of me, I went in and stood before him, I was so alert. He gave me file-boxes to carry to his outer office; I brought in the file-boxes that they gave back to his table. When he was away, the newspapers arrived. I took charge of them and glanced through their pages before taking them to him. I don't think he ever minded; he really liked to read his paper in bed, after his lunch, in the process of snatching a siesta. I quietly glanced through the speeches of world statesmen, descriptions of the Five Year Plan, of ministers opening bridges or distributing prizes, nuclear explosions, and world crises. I gave them all a cursory look.

But on Friday and Saturday I turned the last page of *The Hindu* with trembling fingers—and the last column in its top portion always displayed the same block, Nalini's photograph, the name of the institution where she was performing, and the price of tickets. Now at this corner of south India, now there, next week in Ceylon, and another week in Bombay or Delhi. Her empire was expanding rather than shrinking. It filled me with gall that she should go on without me. Who sat now on that middle sofa? How could the performance start without my signal with the small finger? How could she know when to stop? She probably went on and on, while others just watched without the wit to stop her. I chuckled to myself at the thought of how she must have been missing her trains after every performance. I opened the pages of the paper only to study her engagements and to calculate how much she might be earning. Unless she wrote up her accounts with forethought, super-tax would swallow what she so laboriously piled up with all that twisting and writhing of her person! I would have suspected Mani of having stepped into my shoes, and that would have provided more gall for me to swallow, but for the fact that in the early months of my stay Mani came to see me on a visitor's day.

Mani was the only visitor I had in prison; all other friends and relatives seemed to have forgotten me. He came because he felt saddened by my career. He wore a look of appropriate gloom and seriousness as he waited for me. But when I told him, 'This is not a bad place. You should come here, if you can,' he looked horrified and never saw me again. But in the thirty minutes he was with me he gave me all the news. Nalini had cleared out of the town bag and baggage. She had settled down at Madras and was looking after herself quite well. She had given Mani a gift of one thousand rupees on the day that she left. She had a hundred bouquets of garlands presented to her on the railway platform. What a huge crowd had gathered to see her off! Before her departure she had methodically drawn up a list of all our various debts and discharged them fully; she had all the furniture and other possessions at our house turned over to an auctioneer. Mani explained that the only article that she carried out of the house was the book—which she came upon when she broke open the drink cabinet and had all the drink thrown out. She found the book tucked away inside, picked it up, and took it away carefully.

'That was my book. Why should she take it?' I cried childishly. I added, 'She seems to think it a mighty performance, I suppose...! Did it please him? Or did it have any useful effect?' I asked devilishly.

Mani said, 'After the case, she got into the car and went home, and he got into his and went to the railway station: they didn't meet.'

'I'm happy at least about this one thing,' I said. 'She had the self-respect not to try and fall at his feet again.'

Mani added before going away, 'I saw your mother recently. She is keeping well in the village.' At the court-hall my mother had been present. She had come on the last day of the hearing, thanks to our local 'adjournment lawyer', who was my link generally with her, as he continued to handle the tortuous and prolonged affair of half my house being pledged to the Sait. He had been excited beyond words at the arrival of the glamorous lawyer from Madras, whom we put up at the Taj in the best suite.

Our little lawyer seemed to have been running around in excitement. He went to the extent of rushing to the village and fetching my mother—for what purpose he alone knew. For my mother was overcome with my plight as I stood in the dock; when Rosie approached her to say a few words in the corridor, her eyes flashed, 'Now are you satisfied with what you have done to him?' And the girl shrank away from her. This was reported to me by my mother herself, whom I approached during the court recess. My mother was standing in the doorway. She had never seen the inside of a court-hall, and was overwhelmed with a feeling of her own daring. She said to me, 'What a shame you have brought on yourself and on all known to you! I used to think that the worst that could happen to you might be death, as when you had that pneumonia for weeks; but I now wish that rather than survive and go through this...' She could not complete her sentence; she broke down and went along the corridor and out before we assembled again to hear the judgement.

11

Raju's narration concluded with the crowing of the cock. Velan had listened without moving a muscle, supporting his back against the ancient stone railing along the steps. Raju felt his throat smarting with the continuous talk all night. The village had not yet wakened to life. Velan yielded himself to a big yawn, and remained silent. Raju had mentioned without a single omission every detail from his birth to his emergence from the gates of the prison. He imagined that Velan would rise with disgust and swear, 'And we took you for such a noble soul all along! If one like you does penance, it'll drive off even the little rain that we may hope for. Begone, you, before we feel tempted to throw you out. You have fooled us.'

Raju waited for these words as if for words of reprieve. He looked on Velan's silence with anxiety and suspense, as if he waited on a judge's verdict again, a second time. The judge here seemed to be one of sterner cast than the one he had encountered in the court-hall. Velan kept still—so still that Raju feared that he had fallen asleep.

Raju asked, 'Now you have heard me fully?' like a lawyer who has a misgiving that the judge has been wool gathering.

'Yes, Swami.'

Raju was taken aback at still being addressed as 'Swami'. 'What do you think of it?'

Velan looked quite pained at having to answer such a question. 'I don't know why you tell me all this, Swami. It's very kind of you to address at such length your humble servant.'

Every respectful word that this man employed pierced Raju like a shaft. 'He will not leave me alone,' Raju thought with resignation. 'This man will finish me before I know where I am.'

After profound thought, the judge rose in his seat. 'I'll go back to the village to do my morning duties. I will come back later. And I'll never speak a word of what I have heard to anyone.' He dramatically thumped his chest. 'It has gone down there, and there it will remain.' With this, he made a deep obeisance, went down the steps and across the sandy river.

A wandering newspaper correspondent who had come to the village picked up the news. The government had sent a commission to inquire into the drought conditions and suggest remedies, and with it came a press correspondent. While wandering around he heard about the Swamiji, went to the temple across the river, and sent off a wire to his paper at Madras, which circulated in all the towns of India. 'Holy man's penance to end drought', said the heading, and then a brief description followed.

This was the starting point.

Public interest was roused. The newspaper office was besieged for more news. They ordered the reporter to go back. He sent a second telegram to say 'Fifth day of fast'. He described the scene: how the Swami came to the river's edge, faced its source, stood knee-deep in the water from six to eight in the morning, muttering something between his lips, his eyes shut, his palms pressed together in a salute to the gods, presumably. It had been difficult enough to find knee-deep water, but the villagers had made an artificial basin in sand and, when it didn't fill, fetched water from distant wells and filled it, so that the man had always knee-deep water to stand in. The holy man stood there for two hours, then walked up the steps slowly and lay down on a mat in the pillared hall of the temple, while his devotees kept fanning him continuously. He took notice of hardly anyone, though there was a big crowd around. He fasted totally. He lay down and shut his eyes in order that his penance might be successful. For that purpose he conserved all his energy. When he was not standing in the water, he was in deep meditation. The villagers had set aside all their normal avocations in order to be near this great soul all the time. When he slept they remained there, guarding him, and though there was a fair-sized crowd, it remained totally silent.

But each day the crowd increased. In a week there was a permanent hum pervading the place. Children shouted and played about, women came carrying baskets filled with pots, firewood, and foodstuffs, and cooked the food for their men and children. There were small curls of smoke going up all along the river bank, on the opposite slope and on this bank also. It was studded with picnic groups, with the women's bright-coloured sarees shining in the sun; men too had festive dress. Bullocks unyoked from their carts jingled their bells as they ate the straw under the trees. People swarmed around little water-holes.

Raju saw them across his pillared hall whenever he opened his eyes. He knew what that smoke meant; he knew that the they were eating and enjoying themselves. He wondered what they might be eating— rice boiled with a pinch of saffron, melted *ghee*—and what were the vegetables? Probably none in this drought. The sight tormented him.

This was actually the fourth day of his fast. Fortunately on the first day he had concealed a little stale food, left over from the previous day, in an aluminium vessel behind a stone pillar in the innermost sanctum—some rice mixed with buttermilk, and a piece of vegetable thrown in. Fortunately, too, he was able on the first day to snatch a little privacy at the end of the day's prayer and penance, late at night. The crowd had not been so heavy then. Velan had business at home and had gone, leaving two others to attend on the Swami. The Swami had been lying on the mat in the pillared hall, with the two villagers looking on and waving a huge palmyra fan at his face. He had felt weakened by his day's fasting. He had suddenly told them, 'Sleep, if you like; I'll be back,' and he rose in a businesslike manner and passed into his inner sanctum.

'I don't have to tell the fellows where I am going or why or how long I shall be gone out of sight.' He felt indignant. He had lost all privacy. People all the time watching and staring, lynx-eyed, as if he were a thief! In the inner sanctum he briskly thrust his hand into a niche and pulled out his aluminium pot. He sat down behind the pedestal, swallowed his food in three or four large mouthfuls, making as little noise as possible. It was stale rice, dry and stiff and two days old; it tasted awful, but it appeased his hunger. He washed it down with water. He went to the back yard and rinsed his mouth noiselessly—he didn't want to smell of food when he went back to his mat.

Lying on his mat, he brooded. He felt sick of the whole thing. When the assembly was at its thickest, could he not stand up on a high pedestal and cry, 'Get out, all of you, and leave me alone, I am not the man to save you. No power on earth can save you if you are doomed. Why do you bother me with all this fasting and austerity?'

It would not help. They might enjoy it as a joke. He had his back to the wall, there was no further retreat. This realization helped him to get through the trial with a little more resignation on the second day of his penance. Once again he stood up in water, muttering with his face to the hills, and watching the picnic groups enjoying themselves all over the place. At night he left Velan for a while and sneaked in to look for leftover food in his aluminium vessel—it was really an act of desperation. He knew full well that he had finished off the vessel the previous night. Still he hoped, childishly, for a miracle. 'When they want me to perform all sorts of miracles, why not make a start with my own aluminium vessel?' he reflected caustically. He felt weak. He was enraged at the emptiness of his larder. He wondered for a moment if he could make a last desperate appeal to Velan to let him eat—and if only he minded, how he could save him! Velan ought to know, yet the fool would not stop thinking that he was a saviour. He banged down the aluminium vessel in irritation and went back to his mat. What if the vessel did get shattered? It was not going to be of any use. What was the point of pampering an empty vessel? When he was seated, Velan asked respectfully, 'What was that noise, master?'

'An empty vessel. Have you not heard the saying, "An empty vessel makes much noise"?'

Velan permitted himself a polite laugh and declared with admiration, 'How many good sentiments and philosophies you have gathered in that head of yours, sir!'

Raju almost glared at him. This single man was responsible for his present plight. Why would he not go away and leave him alone? What a wise plan it would have been if the crocodile had got him while he crossed the river! But that poor old thing, which had remained almost a myth, had become dehydrated. When its belly was ripped open they found in it ten thousand rupees' worth of jewellery. Did this mean that the crocodile had been in the habit of eating only women? No, a few snuffboxes and earrings of men were also found. The question of the day was: who was entitled to all this treasure? The villagers hushed up the affair. They did not want the government to get scent of it and come round and claim it, as it did all buried treasure. They gave out that only a couple of worthless trinkets had been found inside the crocodile, although in actual fact the man who cut it open acquired a fortune. He had no problems for the rest of his life. Who permitted him to cut open the crocodile? Who could say? People didn't wait for permission under such circumstances. Thus had gone on the talk among the people about the crocodile when it was found dead.

Velan, fanning him, had fallen asleep—he had just doubled up in his seat with the fan in his hand. Raju, who lay awake, had let his mind roam and touch the depths of morbid and fantastic thought. He was now touched by the sight of this man hunched in his seat. The poor fellow was tremendously excited and straining himself in order to make this penance a success, providing the great man concerned with every comfort—except, of course, food. Why not give the poor devil a chance, Raju said to himself, instead of hankering after food which one could not get anyway. He felt enraged at the persistence of food-thoughts. With a sort of vindictive resolution he told himself, 'I'll chase away all thought of food. For the next ten days I shall eradicate all thoughts of tongue and stomach from my mind.'

This resolution gave him a peculiar strength. He developed on those lines: 'If by avoiding food I should help the trees bloom, and the grass grow, why not do it thoroughly?' For the first time in his life he was making an earnest effort; for the first time he was learning the thrill of full application, outside money and love; for the first time he was doing a thing in which he was not personally interested. He felt suddenly so enthusiastic that it gave him a new strength to go through with the ordeal. The fourth day of his fast found him quite sprightly. He went down to the river, stood facing upstream with his eyes shut, and repeated the litany. It was no more than a supplication to the heavens to send down rain and save humanity. It was set in a certain rhythmic chant, which lulled his senses and awareness, so that as he went on saying it over and over again the world around became blank. He nearly lost all sensation, except the numbness at his knees, through constant contact with cold water. Lack of food gave him a peculiar floating feeling, which he rather enjoyed, with the thought in the background, 'This enjoyment is something Velan cannot take away from me.'

The hum of humanity around was increasing. His awareness of his surroundings was gradually lessening in a sort of inverse proportion. He was not aware of it, but the world was beginning to press around. The pen of the wandering journalist had done the trick. Its repercussions were far and wide. The railways were the first to feel the pressure. They had to run special trains for the crowds that were going to Malgudi. People travelled on footboards and on the roofs of coaches. The little Malgudi station was choked with passengers. Outside, the station buses stood, the conductors crying, 'Special for Mangala leaving. Hurry up. Hurry up.' People rushed up from the station into the buses and almost sat on top of one another. Gaffur's taxi drove up and down a dozen times a day. And the crowd congregated around the river at Mangala. People sat in groups along its sandbank, down its stones and steps, all the way up the opposite bank, wherever they could squeeze themselves in. Never had this part of the country seen such a crowd. Shops sprang up overnight, as if by magic, on bamboo poles roofed with thatch, displaying coloured soda bottles and bunches of bananas and coconut-toffees. The Tea Propaganda Board opened a big tea-stall, and its posters, green tea plantations along the slopes of blue mountains, were pasted all around the temple wall. (People drank too much coffee and too little tea in these parts.) It had put up a tea-bar and served free tea in porcelain cups all day. The public swarmed around it like flies, and the flies swarmed on all the cups and sugar-bowls. The presence of the fly brought in the Health Department, which feared an outbreak of some epidemic in that crowded place without water. The khaki-clad health inspectors sprayed every inch of space with DDT and, with needle in hand, coaxed people to inoculate themselves against cholera, malaria, and what not. A few youngsters just for fun bared their biceps, while a big crowd stood about and watched. There was a blank space on the rear wall of the temple where they cleaned up the ground and made a space for people to sit around and watch a film show when it grew dark. They attracted people to it by playing popular hits on the gramophone with its loudspeakers mounted on the withering treetops. Men, women, and children crowded in to watch the film shows, which were all about mosquitoes, malaria, plague and tuberculosis, and BCG vaccination. When a huge close-up of a mosquito was shown as the cause of malaria, a peasant was overheard saying, 'Such huge mosquitoes! No wonder the people get malaria in those countries. Our own mosquitoes are so tiny that they are harmless,' which depressed the lecturer on malaria so much that he remained silent for ten minutes. When he had done with health, he showed a few Government of India films about dams, river valleys, and various projects, with ministers delivering speeches. Far off, outside the periphery, a man had opened a gambling booth with a dartboard on a pole, and he had also erected a crude merry-go-round, which whined all day. Pedlars of various kinds were also threading in and out, selling balloons, reed whistles, and sweets.

A large crowd always stood around and watched the saint with profound awe. They touched the water at his feet and sprinkled it over their heads. They stood indefinitely around, until the master of ceremonies, Velan, begged them to move. 'Please go away. The Swami must have fresh air. If you have had your *darshan*, move on and let others have theirs. Don't be selfish.' And then the people moved on and enjoyed themselves in various ways.

When the Swami went in to lie on his mat in the hall, they came again to look at him and stood about until Velan once again told them to keep moving. A few were specially privileged to sit on the edge of the mat very close to the great man. One of them was the schoolmaster, who took charge of all the telegrams and letters that were pouring in from all over the country wishing the Swami success. The post office at Mangala normally had a visiting postman who came once a week, and when a telegram came it was received at Aruna, a slightly bigger village seven miles down the river course, and was kept there until someone could be found going to Mangala. But now the little telegraph office had no rest—day and night messages poured in, just addressed 'Swamiji', that was all. They were piling up every hour and had to be sent down by special messengers. In addition to the arriving telegrams, there were many going out. The place was swarming with press reporters, who were rushing their hour-to-hour stories to their papers all over the world. They were an aggressive lot and the little telegraph-master was scared of them. They banged on his window and cried, 'Urgent!' They held out packets and packed-up films and photographs, and ordered him to dispatch them at once. They cried, 'Urgent, urgent! If this packet does not reach my office today…' and they threatened terrifying prospects and said all sorts of frightening things.

'Press. Urgent!' 'Press. Urgent!' They went on shouting till they reduced the man to a nervous wreck. He had promised his children that he would take them to see the Swamiji. The children cried, 'They are also showing an Ali Baba film, a friend told me.' But the man was given no time to fulfil his promise to his children. When the pressmen gave him respite, the keys rattled with incoming messages. He had spent a fairly peaceful life until then, and the present strain tore at his nerves. He sent off an SOS to all his official superiors whenever he found breathing space: 'Handling two hundred messages today. Want relief.'

The roads were choked with traffic, country carts, buses and cycles, jeeps and automobiles of all kinds and ages. Pedestrians in files with hampers and baskets crossed the fields like swarms of ants converging on a lump of sugar. The air rang with the music of a few who had chosen to help the Swami by sitting near him, singing devotional songs to the accompaniment of a harmonium and *tabla*.

The busiest man here was an American, wearing a thin bush-shirt over corduroys. He arrived in a jeep with a trailer, dusty, rugged, with a mop of tousled hair, at about one in the afternoon on the tenth day of the fast and set himself to work immediately. He had picked up an interpreter at Madras and had driven straight through, three hundred and seventy-five miles. He pushed everything aside and took charge of the scene. He looked about for only a moment, driving his jeep down to the hibiscus bush behind the temple. He jumped off and strode past everyone to the pillared hall. He went up to the recumbent Swami and brought his palms together, muttering, 'Namaste'—the Indian salute, which he had learned the moment he landed in India. He had briefed himself on all the local manners. Raju looked on him with interest; the large, pink-faced arrival was a novel change in the routine.

The pink visitor stooped low to ask the schoolmaster, sitting beside the Swami, 'Can I speak to him in English?'

'Yes. He knows English.'

The man lowered himself on to the edge of the mat and with difficulty sat down on the floor, Indian fashion, crossing his legs. He bent close to the Swami to say, 'I'm James J. Malone. I'm from California. My business is production of films and TV shows. I have come to shoot this subject, take it back to our country, and show it to our people there. I have in my pocket the sanction from New Delhi for this project. May I have yours?'

Raju thought over it and nodded serenely.

'Okay. Thanks a lot. I won't disturb you—but will you let me shoot pictures of you? I wouldn't disturb you. Will it bother you if I move a few things up and fix the cable and lights?'

'No, you may do your work,' said the sage.

The man became extremely busy. He sprang to his feet, pulled the trailer into position, and started his generator. Its throbbing filled the place, overwhelming all other noises. It brought in a huge crowd of men, women, and children to watch the fun. All the other attractions in the camp became secondary. As Malone drew the cables about, a big crowd followed him. He grinned at them affably and went about his business, Velan and one or two others ran through the crowd, crying, 'Is this a fish market? Get away, all of you who have no work here!' But nobody was affected by his orders. They climbed pillars and pedestals and clung to all sorts of places to reach positions of vantage. Malone went on with his job without noticing anything. Finally, when he had the lights ready, he brought in his camera and took pictures of the people and the temple, and of the Swami from various angles and distances.

'I'm sorry, Swami, if the light is too strong.' When he had finished with the pictures, he brought in a microphone, put it near the Swami's face, and said, 'Let us chat. Okay? Tell me, how do you like it here?'

'I am only doing what I have to do; that's all. My likes and dislikes do not count.'

'How long have you been without food now?'

'Ten days.'

'Do you feel weak?'

'Yes.'

'When will you break your fast?'

'Twelfth day.'

'Do you expect to have the rains by then?'

'Why not?'

'Can fasting abolish all wars and bring world peace?'

'Yes.'

'Do you champion fasting for everyone?'

'Yes.'

'What about the caste system? Is it going?'

'Yes.'

'Will you tell us something about your early life?'

'What do you want me to say?'

'Er—for instance, have you always been a yogi?'

'Yes; more or less.'

It was very hard for the Swami to keep up a continuous flow of talk. He felt exhausted and lay back. Velan and others looked on with concern. The schoolmaster said, 'He is fatigued.'

'Well, I guess we will let him rest for a while. I'm sorry to bother you.'

The Swami lay back with his eyes closed. A couple of doctors, deputed by the government to watch and report, went to the Swami, felt his pulse and heart. They helped him to stretch himself on the mat. A big hush fell upon the crowd. Velan plied his fan more vigorously than ever. He looked distraught and unhappy. In fact, keeping a sympathetic fast, he was now eating on alternate days, confining his diet to saltless boiled greens. He looked worn out. He said to the master, 'One more day. I don't know how he is going to bear it. I dread to think how he can pull through another day.'

Malone resigned himself to waiting. He looked at the doctor and asked, 'How do you find him?'

'Not very satisfactory; blood pressure is two hundred systolic. We suspect one of the kidneys is affected. Uremia is setting in. We are trying to give him small doses of saline and glucose. His life is valuable to the country.'

'Would you say a few words about his health?' Malone asked, thrusting his microphone forward. He was sitting on the head of a carved elephant decorating the steps to the pillared hall.

The doctors looked at each other in panic and said, 'Sorry. We are government servants—we cannot do it without permission. Our reports are released only from headquarters. We cannot give them direct. Sorry.'

'Okay. I wouldn't hurt your customs.' He looked at his watch and said, 'I guess that's all for the day.' He approached the schoolmaster and said, 'Tell me, what time does he step into the river tomorrow?'

'Six a.m.'

'Could you come over and show me the location?' The schoolmaster got up and took him along. The man said, 'Wait, wait. You'll not mind understudying him for a minute. Show me where he starts from, how he gets up, and where he steps and stands.'

The teacher hesitated, feeling too shy to understudy the sage. The man urged him on. 'Come on, be cooperative. I'll take care of it, if there is any trouble.'

The teacher started from the pedestal. 'He starts here. Now follow me.' He showed the whole route down to the river, and the spot where the Swami would stop and pray, standing in water for two hours. The crowd followed keenly every inch of this movement, and someone in the crowd was joking, 'Oh! The master is also going to do penance and starve!' And they all laughed.

Malone threw a smile at them from time to time, although he did not know what they were saying. He surveyed the place from various angles, measured the distance from the generator, shook the schoolmaster's hand, and went back to his jeep. 'See you tomorrow morning.' He drove off amidst a great roar and puffing of the engine as his jeep rattled over the pits and ditches beyond the hibiscus, until he reached the road.

The eleventh day, morning. The crowd, pouring in all night, had nearly trebled itself because it was the last day of the fast. All night one could hear the voices of people and the sound of vehicles rattling over the roads and pathways. Velan and a band of his assistants formed a cordon and kept the crowd out of the pillared hall. They said, 'The Swami must have fresh air to breathe. It's the only thing he takes now. Don't choke the air. Everyone can have his *darshan* at the river, I promise. Go away now. He is resting.' It was an all-night vigil. The numerous lanterns and lamps created a criss-cross of bewildering shadows on all hedges, trees, and walls.

At five-thirty in the morning the doctors examined the Swami. They wrote and signed a bulletin saying: 'Swami's condition grave. Declines glucose and saline. Should break the fast immediately. Advise procedure.' They sent a man running to send off this telegram to their headquarters.

It was a top-priority government telegram, and it fetched a reply within an hour: 'Imperative that Swami should be saved. Persuade best to cooperate. Should not risk life. Try give glucose and saline. Persuade Swami resume fast later.'

They sat beside the Swami and read the message to him. He smiled at it. He beckoned Velan to come nearer.

The doctors appealed, 'Tell him he should save himself. Please, do your best. He is very weak.'

Velan bent close to the Swami and said, 'The doctors say—'

In answer Raju asked the man to bend nearer, and whispered, 'Help me to my feet,' and clung to his arm and lifted himself. He got to his feet. He had to be held by Velan and another on each side.

In the profoundest silence the crowd followed him down. Everyone
followed at a solemn, silent pace. The eastern sky was red. Many in
the camp were still sleeping. Raju could not walk, but he insisted
upon pulling himself along all the same. He panted with the effort.
He went down the steps of the river, halting for breath on each step,
and finally reached his basin of water. He stepped into it, shut his
eyes, and turned towards the mountain, his lips muttering the prayer.
Velan and another held him each by an arm. The morning sun was
out by now; a great shaft of light illuminated the surroundings. It was
difficult to hold Raju on his feet, as he had a tendency to flop down.
They held him as if he were a baby. Raju opened his eyes, looked
about, and said, 'Velan, it's raining in the hills. I can feel it corning
up under my feet, up my legs—' He sagged down.

The Mispaired Anklet

PUHAR WAS a flourishing seacoast town where the River Cauvery joined the sea. This story begins with the marriage of Kovalan, the hero of this tale, and Kannagi being celebrated, with the whole town rejoicing and feasting, every citizen having been invited by an announcer riding on an elephant up and down the streets of the city. Kovalan and Kannagi lived a happy married life in their comfortable home until the day when Madhavi, a young danseuse, gave her first dance recital before the king.

In recognition of her talent the king presented her with a garland of green leaves and one thousand and eight pieces of gold. According to custom, Madhavi could now select a lover for herself. She passed the garland to a hunchbacked woman who stood in the city square, where wealthy citizens passed or congregated, and announced, 'This garland is worth one thousand and eight pieces of gold. Whoever buys it also becomes the husband of the most accomplished dancer honoured by our king.' Kovalan became a ready customer for this garland, and gained admission to Madhavi's bridal chamber and forgot all his problems and responsibilities in life. When he was not making love to her, he spent the time listening to the music of her steps.

The city was celebrating Indra's festival. There were music, dancing, and entertainment everywhere; special prayers were said in the temples; people moved hither and thither in gay dress, and the air throbbed with speech and laughter. Kovalan and Madhavi went about together and enjoyed the festivities. At the end of the day, Madhavi went home, freshened her body with a bath in a cool, scented fountain, put on a new set of ornaments and dress, and in Kovalan's company passed again through the illuminated city to the seashore, which twinkled with lamps hoisted on poles around groups of merrymakers and gaily lighted ships anchored off shore. Madhavi had her own corner on the beach, with canopy and screens set up for privacy, away from the tumult of the waves and the din of the crowds. When they had settled down, Madhavi took her lute out of its silken cover and tuned it. Kovalan took it from her, casually ran his fingers over the strings, and burst into a song in praise of the river and the sea and then addressed to a beauty tormenting a lover with her slender waist and weighty breasts, 'who walks like a swan in the shade of punnai trees, where the waves break on the shore.'

'O foolish swan, do not go near her, your gait cannot rival hers.'

Another song said, 'Your father kills the living things of the sea by catching them in the meshes of his net. You kill living things by catching them in the net of your long eyes.'

'She is a goddess who dwells there in the sweet-smelling groves of flowers' ran another. 'Had I known of the existence of this goddess, I would not have come here at all.'

Madhavi pretended to appreciate the songs, gently took the lute from his hands, and began a song of a lovelorn girl pining for her vanished lover. 'Through the swamps, fenced by the park...someone came and stood before us, saying, "Make me pleased!" and we could not take our eyes off him.'

'Seeing the swan playing with its mate, a godlike one stood looking on all yesterday. He would not leave our minds, even as the gold-tinted moss cannot leave our body.... O crane, come not near our park, for you will not speak of my present lovesickness to my lord of the sea-trace. Do not approach our park...'*

Kovalan muttered, 'I merely sang a good composition, but she has her mind on someone else who inspires her.' He withdrew his hands from Madhavi's, saying, The day has come to a close, let us stir ourselves.' She did not get up. But he hurried home.

After he was gone, Madhavi got into her chariot and went home. She dressed and decorated herself afresh and moved to the upper terrace

---

*The songs are quoted from V.R.R. Dikshitar's translation of *Silappadhikaram—The Epic of the Anklet* published by the Oxford University Press (1939).

and sang more songs, danced, and fell into a languor. Thereafter she wove a garland with several flowers, and, taking the pale inner petal of the screw-pine, etched a message of love on its smooth surface: 'This moon, who has risen with the love-anguish...should kill the poor lonely ones with his sharp darts....Please understand this.' She called one of her maids and sent her off with this message to Kovalan; she was to repeat the message orally, and then give him the garland wherein he would see it written.

The maid came back to say that Kovalan had rejected the message and the garland. Madhavi felt unhappy but sighed, 'If he does not come tonight, he is certain to come tomorrow morning,' and spent a sleepless night.

Meanwhile, Kovalan said to his wife Kannagi, 'We must leave this town.'

Kannagi knew that Kovalan's funds were fast dwindling, through his buying presents and fineries for Madhavi. Kannagi had parted with her ornaments one after another in order that he might find the money for spending. She had been complacent and unquestioning. She replied now, 'I have still a pair of anklets,' leaving unexpressed the thought, 'which you may pawn to buy presents for Madhavi.'

But he said, receiving the anklets, 'This very night we will slip out of this place, go to Madurai, and start a new life in that city with the little money we may get by selling these. I will not be seen by my parents until I have redeemed my integrity. One becomes defiled to the very core through association with low, mercenary women, and by the time one learns the truth of the matter one is too far gone in damnation. This is no occasion for leave-taking. Let us slip away quietly.'

At dead of night they packed their clothes in a small bundle that could be slung over the shoulder, shut their house, and started out. The festive crowd had dissipated out of sight and all the noise of merriment had died down. They passed along the south bank of the river, which was deserted; on the highway they became merged with groups of minstrels and mendicants and wandering scholars and saints, travelling in the same direction, and forgot their own troubles listening to their talk. 'We missed all this staying at home,' Kovalan said.

They reached the ferry and crossed over to the north bank of the river and ultimately came to a town called Uriyur. Kovalan left his wife in a rest house and sought a tank for his ablutions. As he stood waist-deep in water, scrubbing himself, a stranger accosted him and said, 'I want to speak to you.'

'Who are you?' asked Kovalan.

'My friend, don't you recognize me? I am from Puhar. I have worn out the soles of my feet tracking you, inquiring everywhere, "Have you seen such-and-such?"'

'Why did you follow me?' asked Kovalan sharply.

'Madhavi has sent me, she is dying of grief at the separation. She begs a million pardons for any pain she may have caused you. She begs you to return home—begs your forgiveness for her mistakes.'

Kovalan brooded for a moment and said, 'Go back.'

'I saw your parents too, and they are heartbroken.'

Tell them that I'll seek my fortune and return to them as a worthy son some day. I have been living in a sort of fantasy all along; now I see the realities. Tell Madhavi that I have no grudge against her, but I have definitely turned my back on the past.'

When Kovalan returned to his wife, they were ready for the road again. He did not mention his encounter with the messenger from Puhar, for fear of disturbing Kannagi's mind. They trudged along and finally reached the bank of the Vaigai, which skirted the boundary of Madurai, the capital of the Pandyan kingdom. They viewed the soaring temple tower and the mansions of Madurai city and felt happy and relieved that they had reached the end of their quest. Kovalan stood on the edge of the river god, crossed it, and reached the city boundary.

In the city the couple were received into a colony of cattle tenders. They were lodged in a cottage, surrounded by a green hedge, with a cool inner courtyard and walls splashed with red mud, and a kitchen stocked with rice, vegetables, buttermilk, jackfruit, cucumbers, pomegranates, and mangoes. Kannagi felt happy to be running a home again after weeks of tramp-like existence. She washed the floor of the house. When food was ready, Kannagi spread a grass mat for her husband to sit on, and a green plantain leaf for him to dine on. After he was fed, she gave him betel nuts and leaves to chew.

With his lips red with betel juice, Kovalan sat back and said, 'You have been forbearing; how your parents would grieve if they knew of the hardship you have gone through.' He became regretful at the thought of his misdeeds. 'I have wasted my life in the society of an easygoing woman and scandalmongers, wasted my time talking loudly and guffawing at bawdy jokes.'

Kannagi said, 'Why speak of the past again and again? I was unhappy, no doubt, but no one could have guessed how I felt in those days. Your parents were kind and considerate.'

In the end he said, 'I will now take one of your anklets to the city, sell it, and come back with money, and then we will start a new life. Who knows? We may return home soon with riches and re-establish ourselves honourably.' He embraced her before leaving, averting his eyes to conceal his tears; he felt depressed at having to leave her alone in the midst of strangers. As he briskly walked out, he was so preoccupied that he failed to notice a humped bull in front of him, indicating a bad omen.

He passed through various parts of the city. At the bazaar he noticed walking past him an imposing man in a brocade coat, flourishing a pair of pincers to indicate that he was a master goldsmith, followed by a company of minor goldsmiths. At the sight of him Kovalan thought, 'This must be the famous goldsmith of the Pandyan court. I am fortunate to come across him so easily.'

He approached him and said, 'You are the prince of goldsmiths, I presume. Your fame is known even in Puhar.' The goldsmith smiled patronizingly.

Kovalan now asked, 'May I trouble you to appraise for me a piece of jewellery, an anklet fit for the queen's feet?'

The goldsmith said pompously, 'I'm generally concerned with the making of crowns and sceptres for our kings, but I am not totally ignorant of feminine adornments.'

Whereupon Kovalan produced the anklet. The goldsmith examined it with minute care and delight and declared enthusiastically, 'This is not an anklet that an ordinary woman could aspire to, it is fit only for our queen. Let me speak to her and come back. Stay in that hut. Don't go away, I will be back soon.'

The king and the queen had had a lovers' quarrel recently. The queen had left his company on the pretext of a headache. The king transacted some business with his councillors and left for the queen's chambers at the earliest possible moment in order to pacify her.

As he approached the portals of the queen's chamber the goldsmith crossed his path and after formal courtesies of address said, 'Forgive my interrupting Your Majesty, but the matter is urgent. One of the queen's anklets has been missing. I have managed to catch the thief and have shut him in my humble hut. He is a subtle thief who does not operate with daggers and crowbars but with black magic.'

It was a fateful moment, and as the king was in a hurry to meet his wife, he summoned the city watchman and ordered, 'If you find the anklet in the possession of the thief, execute him and fetch the anklet.' He was in a hurry, and the fates were gearing their engines for a tragedy, so the king spoke thoughtlessly, although normally he would have said, 'Bring the thief before me.' He uttered the sentence of death without giving the matter thought, and hurried on to the queen's apartment.

The goldsmith returned with a company of men and said to Kovalan, 'These men have come to examine the anklet at the command of our sovereign.'

Kovalan, pleased that he was coming so near a transaction, messed about with his bag again while the goldsmith explained to the executioners the minute details of the anklet about to be displayed. 'It has workmanship of the highest kind; grooves at the neck; a slight depression with silver garlands entwining, and two leaves. It has a peculiar polish at the stem that has given it the facet of a crystal, reflecting off a diamond-shaped cutting.'

As he described it further, Kovalan's eyes shone with pleasure; he took it as a recommendation from the goldsmith and remarked, 'What an observant eye you have, you great artist in gold!'

'True, true,' said the crafty goldsmith. 'Otherwise how could I have progressed in my profession? I am known for my searching eye, which can find out a lot of things.' He glanced at his companions and smiled wryly.

When the anklet was produced, the chief executioner took it in his hand and examined it in detail. 'Yes, it is the same anklet that you have described,' he said.

'Now let the man pay the price accordingly,' said the goldsmith, and the men stepped forward, encircling Kovalan.

Kovalan looked about in bewilderment. More bewilderment when the chief cried, 'This man does not look like a thief.'

'A thief who has mastered his art will look least like one,' said the goldsmith. 'The science of thieving mentions eight methods that may be employed by an expert thief: drugs, illusion, control of mischievous spirits, and so forth; he can pick up your valuables and walk right into your presence while you watch him helplessly; he can make himself invisible, he can look like a good and saintly one and extract worship from you...' The goldsmith expatiated on this theme.

Kovalan listened to it and said, 'Let us come to a decision; if you noble men approve of this piece of jewellery—'

'Spend no more time,' said the goldsmith. 'Finish your errand and let us go back.'

A young man with a lance said, 'Do you know what once happened when I drew my sword—it jumped into the thief's hand and suddenly I found myself at his mercy. Some are so crafty and deft! Our king's order must be carried out.'

'No more talk,' said a drunken man in their midst, and he hurled his scimitar at Kovalan, practically cutting him in two.

Blood flowed from the fallen man. The goldsmith and executioners withdrew. The goldsmith looked back as if gratified that he had had divine assistance in his crime. He had stolen the queen's anklet earlier in the day and felt it a peculiar good fortune that he should have come across someone to take on that crime with appropriate evidence.

At the cowherd's colony, a matron said to her daughter, 'The milk in the pot has not curdled; tears dim the eyes of our cattle; the butter in the store is all hardened, lambs are dull, cows shudder and bellow, and their bell ropes have snapped. What calamity has befallen whom?'

They thought it over and pronounced the usual remedy for warding off evil and turning the mind to cheerful subjects. 'We shall dance the Kuruvai, for our guest, for our beautiful guest watching us.' An elaborate dance was organized in their midst.

Kannagi felt worried. Why was her husband gone so long? It was diverting to watch her hosts sing and dance as they depicted episodes from the life of the god Krishna, who was the patron god of milkmaids.

After the dance the matron went to bathe in the river, heard rumours about Kovalan, and hurried back home. Kannagi cried at the sight of her, 'Friend, why won't you speak? Where is my husband? Every particle of air in my lungs seems fevered. I can hardly breathe. Where is my husband? I feel restless. Help me, are people saying anything about him? Don't hide anything from me.'

'They said he was a thief who had stolen the royal anklet, and executed him,' said the matron.

Kannagi fell in a faint, recovered, and raved against the fates, the country, and the king. 'The Pandyan king, reputed to hold a righteous sceptre, has committed injustice. My husband a thief!' She shouted at the top of her voice and called up all the women and the girls who had been dancing and addressed them. 'Could my husband be a thief, thieving my own anklet! O sun god, you are witness to all things of this world. Is my husband a thief? Answer!' she cried commandingly.

Kannagi gathered herself, her stature seemed to swell; her eyes blazed with anger. She cried, 'Here is my anklet, the widowed one. They have killed my husband, unable to pay the price for the one he had with him. Now who is the real thief?'

Followed by a sympathizing crowd, Kannagi strode through the streets of the city with authority in her gait and fire in her speech and looks. People trembled at the sight of her. Some persons led her to where her husband's body lay; and the sun (as the poet who composed this tale explains) set behind the hills, in order to draw a curtain over the sad spectacle.

Night came on. Kannagi mourned. 'Is it right that you should be lying there in that bloody pool while I...while I... Are there no women in this city whose purity could prevent such an injustice?

Are there no good people in this country or women of purity and devotion to their husbands? How can such an injustice happen where there are good men and good women? Has god forsaken this town?'

While she lamented thus, hugging the inert body of her husband, strange things seemed to happen. She thought that she saw the body stir and her husband stand up and wipe the tears from her face and mutter, 'Stay here, and go heavenward.'

Kannagi cried, 'What is happening? Is it some mischievous spirit that is deceiving me? Where can I find the truth of all this?' She left the spot and ran towards the palace, saying again and again, 'I must get an explanation from the cruel king himself...'

The king was in the company of his wife. The bell at the gate tolled furiously. Over the sounding of bell Kannagi screamed, 'Go and wake your king who has put his conscience to sleep, whose heart has become granite, and tell him that a wretched woman bearing a widowed anklet is at his gate.'

The gatekeepers were cowed by the appearance of the woman and ran to the king's presence and announced, 'Your Majesty, a woman of frightening aspect seeks audience. Is she Kali, the Goddess of Destruction? Is she...?'

'Let her in,' commanded the king. When she was brought in, he asked, 'Who are you? What do you want here?'

'You have murdered my husband. We came from Puhar only to seek our fortune here.'

'O my most revered sister, is it not my duty to execute a thief?'

'My anklet has been stolen,' added the queen. 'And it was found with your husband, who was trying to sell it.'

'Here is another one, take it also,' said Kannagi. 'All the anklets in the world are yours, O queen, spouse of the embodiment of justice.' She tossed her anklet in the queen's lap.

The queen, looking at it, said, 'This also looks like mine, but how is it there are three anklets now? I had only two.'

'Does a thief take away or add? Do you know?' asked Kannagi with bitter laughter. 'What you are wearing on your left ankle is not yours, it belongs to the thief who lies in bloody dust.'

The king seemed to lose in a moment his regality, and the queen was panic-stricken. 'My evil dream of last night—' she began.

Kannagi asked, 'Do you at least know what it is inside that rattles and tinkles when your anklet is shaken?'

The queen took time to understand the purport of the question and said, 'Pearls, yes... Pearls inside.'

'Break open my anklet, which is on your left foot, and see what is in it.'

The queen handed her the anklet without a word. Kannagi broke it open, and sparkling gems spilled out of it.

The king faltered at the sight. 'What king am I to allow a goldsmith to sway my judgement?' He tottered and fell from his seat, and the queen broke into a loud lamentation.

Kannagi watched the scene coldly and strode out of the palace, loudly shouting the virtue of her town Puhar and all the good things that had happened there since she knew it, in contrast to this city where evil flourished. She walked round the city thrice with unceasing laments, declaring, 'If I am a chaste woman, I shall not let this city flourish.' Then she tore her robes, twisted and tore off her left breast, and flung it over the city. Immediately the god of fire, in the shape of a brahmin of blue complexion, appeared before her and asked, 'I will, of course, destroy this city as you command, but is there anyone you would spare?'

'Spare only the innocent, the good, the learned, the infirm, and the children, and all dumb creatures.'

The city was enveloped in flames immediately. Those who could escape from the city poured out of its gates. The rest perished. The presiding deities of the town left. Kannagi roamed through its streets and alleys restlessly, bewildered and in a state of delirium.

The presiding deity of the city, with her head decorated with a crescent and her matted locks, white radiant face, half of her body dark blue and the other half golden, with a golden lotus in her left hand and a sword in her right, unwilling to face the sorrow-stricken wife, approached her softly from behind and murmured gently, 'Blessed lady, listen to my words. I understand your suffering. I see the havoc that your rage has wrought on our city. Please listen to my words for a moment. The king has never committed any injustice in his life; he comes of a long line of righteous rulers who have observed strictly the laws of justice and humanity. But what has happened to your husband is unparalleled and is a result of fate. Listen, fair lady, to the history of his previous life. Your husband, Kovalan, in his previous birth was called Bharata and in the service of his monarch caught hold of an innocent trader who was selling his merchandise in the streets of Sangama and denounced him as a spy and had him executed. The trader's wife was grief-stricken and wandered as a mad woman for fourteen days, raving and cursing, until she climbed the hill and jumped off a cliff, uttering her curse on the man responsible for her husband's death. As a result of it, now you have to go through this agony. You will have redemption in fourteen days.'

This was consoling, and as Kannagi's heart softened with understanding, the fire in the city abated gradually. She passed the fourteen days wandering and waiting. She walked along the river's edge and reached the northern mountain tracts. A group of country girls while bathing and sporting on the mountain roads saw an extraordinary being who had only one breast appear before them. Her presence was electrifying, and the women worshipped her at first sight. Presently they saw her husband come to her in spirit form and take her heavenward.

The spot became sacred as that of the godly wife. A latter-day king built a temple on the spot and installed the image of Kannagi in it for public worship. The image was carved out of a slab of stone hewn from the Himalayas and bathed in the water of the Ganges, and it came to be known as Pattini Devi—meaning 'the wife who became a goddess'.

SELECTED NON-FICTION

My Days

(An excerpt)

ALL DAY long, I sat half buried in sand piled in a corner of our garden, raising castles and mountain-ranges, unaware of the fierce Madras sun overhead. I had a peacock and a monkey for company. The monkey was chained to a post, on top of which a little cabin was available for his shelter, but he preferred to sit on the roof of his home, hanging down his tail. He responded to the name Rama by baring his teeth, and kept a wary eye on the peacock, which was perpetually engaged in scratching the mud and looking for edible insects. I cannot say exactly when they came into my life, but they seemed to have been always there with me. In an early photo of myself, when I was four years old, I am set on a miniature bamboo chair flanked by the peacock and the monkey. My uncle (Mother's brother), who brought me up, must have been one of the earliest amateur photographers in India. He kept his head, on most bright afternoons, under a black hood enveloping an enormous camera on a tripod. He posed me constantly against the flowers in the garden, in the company of my pets. I had to remain rigid, unblinking, and immobile whenever he photographed us, and it was a feat to keep the monkey and the peacock still. I enjoyed these sessions, although my grandmother declared from time to time that a photograph was likely to shorten the subject's life. I was proud of the group in the picture and hoped that others would see a resemblance between me and Rama. When I sought confirmation on this point, my grandmother was horrified and said, 'What a fool to want to look like a monkey! You are in bad company. You must send away that creature. Wanting to look like a monkey when god has endowed you with such large eyes and all those curls falling down to your cheeks!'

She was so fond of my curls that she never let a barber come near me, which meant that I had constantly to part the veil of hair with my fingers when I wished to look at anyone.

The peacock was not fully grown yet, but he bore his three-foot tail haughtily, and enjoyed the freedom of the house, pecking away every ant that had the ill luck to come within the range of his vision. Most afternoons, when I was tired of the sand dump, I moved to the threshold of the door opening on Purasawalkam High Road and watched the traffic, which consisted of cyclists and horse or bullock-drawn carriages. A caravan of corporation carts passed along, stuffed to the brim with garbage, with the top layer blowing off in the high wind coming from the sea at this hour. The last few carriages forming the rear of the caravan were wagons, tar-painted and sealed, filled with night soil; the entire column moved westward and was soon lost in the dusty glare of the evening sun, but it left an odorous trail which made me jump up and rush in crying, 'Rubbish carts are passing.' This announcement was directed at Grandmother, who would thereby understand that it was time to begin her evening operations, namely, the watering of over fifty flower beds and pots. (She knew a potter who made special giant-size pots for her, a size I have never seen anywhere before or since, each one being capable of bearing a tree.) She reared in her garden over twenty hibiscus families, blue, grey, purple, double-row petals, and several kinds of jasmine, each scattering its special fragrance into the night air—numerous exotic flowers in all shapes and sizes. A corner of her garden was reserved for nurturing certain delicate plants which gasped for breath. She acquired geronia, geranium, lavender, and violet, which could flourish only at an altitude of three thousand feet in Bangalore, and stubbornly tried to cultivate them in the salty air of Madras. When the plants wilted she shed tears and cursed the Madras climate. Even after the plants had perished in their boxes, she tended them hopefully for a few days before throwing them over the wall, to be ultimately gathered into the corporation caravan going westward.

Filling up a bronze water-pot, a bucket, and a watering-can by turns, my grandmother transported water from a tap in the backyard impartially to all her plants, and finally through a brass syringe shot into the air a grand column of water which would descend like a gift from the heavens on the whole garden, dampening down the mud and stirring up an earthy smell (which tempted one to taste the mud), the foliage glittering in the sun like finely cut diamonds as water dripped off their edges. The peacock busily kept pace with us as we moved up and down bearing the water-pots. When a shower of water descended, the peacock fanned out its tail, parading its colours. At this moment, one could hear Rama rattle his chain, since he always felt uneasy when the peacock preened itself thus, and demonstrated his protest by clanking his chain and tumbling around on the roof of his own cabin. As the evening grew dim, I drove the peacock under a bamboo coop in a corner of the living room. Rama would be fed with rice and driven into his cabin. He became purblind and bemused at dusk and one could push him hither and thither as one pleased.

Sometimes, when I sat at the street door, the peacock stood beside me. Every passer-by would stop to admire it; sometimes a youngster would beg for a feather to be plucked out and given to him. The first time I had this request I saw no reason why I should not oblige him; after all, he wanted only a feather while I had a whole bird to myself, and so I allowed him to pluck out a feather of his choice, just one. When he reached for it, the peacock stabbed the back of his hand with its beak and the boy fled screaming. I had not noticed till then how aggressive this bird could be. I began to notice that it possessed the temperament of a watch-dog. Quite a variety of persons had to pass in and out of our home all day, having business with my grandmother—mendicants, vegetable vendors, the tailor and goldsmith—and if anyone stepped in without warning they were viciously chased by the peacock. It generally perched on the wall over the door and directly descended on the visitors, pestering them until it was caught by its tail and dragged away.

My uncle, the only other member of the family, would not be home yet. He had a room upstairs which he used as his study and dark-room combined, where when he was not washing negatives, he pored over his class books. He went out in the mornings to catch the tram for his college and returned late in the evening.

On holiday afternoons, he lugged out his camera on the tripod and fixed me in front of it. Sometimes he sat on the kitchen floor and narrated the day's events at his college; he was a member of the college drama group, and he explained to us Shakespeare's *Tempest* and how they were trying to produce it; he mimicked some of his friends who acted in it and that made us laugh; he was a good raconteur and I knew *The Tempest* long before I knew anything else. My uncle was Prospero and he described how his best chum, who did Caliban, entered his role so heartily that he proved a public menace during the rehearsals. He spoke of his professor, one Dr Skinner, with great admiration, and we all admired him too, although by hearsay.

All sound ceased presently. The streets became silent but for the swear words emanating from the shop across the High Road while the owner berated his habitual debtors seeking further favours. He called his defaulting customers and their mothers names, and if I had picked up choice slang it must have been from the rich verbal arsenal that freely floated in the air.

Over all that hubbub one heard the tramcar grinding the rails at its terminus in the street of shops two furlongs away. Eastward of our home were shops and the tram terminus, where one boarded to get to the wide world and the seacoast beyond, whereas the west side, where the corporation caravans went, seemed full of sinister possibilities. From that direction, one heard bickerings and courses and affrays from an unseen tavern. Corpses were borne in funeral processions in the same direction. I shuddered to look that way, but longed to see the shops and tramway at the other end.

It was exciting, one day, to be asked to go with my uncle to the street of shops. I clung to his arm and marched along. It was the evening hour again. I noticed a man with his hand and shoulder stuck through a bamboo ladder, going from post to post lighting the street lamps. The lamp-posts were few and far between: hexagonal glass shades on top of cast-iron fluted pillars. The lamp-lighter was an old man wearing a khaki coat and a blue turban, equipped with a ladder, a box of matches, rags, and a can of oil. He moved from pillar to pillar, unhurryingly. I was fascinated. I had never suspected that there could be so much to do to light up the dark nights. Clinging to my uncle's fingers, I watched him, my head turned back—a difficult operation, since my uncle dragged me along, never slackening his pace. The lamp-lighter went up his ladder, opened a little ventilator, took out the lamp, cleaned and wiped it with the rag, filled it with oil, lit up the wick and closed the shutter, climbed down, thrust his shoulder through the ladder again, and passed on to the next one. I had numerous questions welling up within me, all sorts of things I wished to know about the man—his name, where he came from, if he slept wearing the ladder, what he ate, and so forth; but before I could phrase them properly, I had to be moving along with my questions unuttered.

Other spectacles presently attracted my attention: the Pankaja Lodge, a sweetmeat shop with edibles heaped up in trays, presided over by a bespectacled man with a gleaming gold chain around his neck. The frying smell generated here reached me every afternoon while I sat at the street door of my home, with the peacock at my back, and made me very hungry. Today, my uncle stopped by to pick up a little packet of eatables for me, wrapped in a crackling brown leaf. I munched it, immediately forgetting the lamp-lighter. My uncle walked me onto the edge of the road in order to protect me from the traffic hazards of those days; one constantly heard reports of persons knocked down by cyclists. Milkmen with milking-cans in hand were driving their cows through the streets. I jumped aside at the sight of the cows, although my uncle tried to convince me they were harmless. When we passed an orange-coloured school building with a green gate, my uncle promised that I would in due course find myself there. I did not welcome the idea. It was a gaunt-looking building with a crucifix on its roof, and I hated it at first sight.

With time my outlook did not change. As far as this school was concerned, my first reaction seemed also to be the final one. In due course I became a pupil there. On the first day I wept in fear. The sight of my classmates shook my nerves. An old man with silvery stubble on his chin, turban crowning his head, clad in a striped coat without buttons and a white *dhoti*, a short cane permanently tucked under his arm, presided over the class of infants. Under his watchful eye we sat on the floor and kneaded small lumps of wet clay and shaped them into vegetables, fruits, and what not; we also cut out coloured sheets of paper and made more vegetables and fruits and also boats and quadrupeds. He brought his cane down violently on the table in order to gain our attention and tell us what to do next. I do not think I ever saw him lay his cane on anyone's back, but he flourished it and used it as a medium of self-expression, like a conductor's baton. My main ambition in life was to remain unnoticed by him. My matter how hard I tried, the clay never assumed proper shape in my hands. It never retained any symmetry or shape; while other boys produced marvellous imitations of all kinds of objects in creation, my own handiwork remained unclassifiable (perhaps I was ahead of my time as a sculptor). I was always afraid of what the teacher might say; luckily for me I was a late admission and was given the last seat, and we were quite a crowd in the class; by the time he reached me, the time would be up, and we would have to run to the water-tap under the tree and clean up the mess on our fingers. Thinking it over, I am unable to explain how this course helped me in becoming literate. If we were not kneading clay, we were only cutting papers and folding them. We were armed each with a pair of scissors; this was a welcome instrument in one's hand, no doubt, but the fingers ached with a dull pain at the joints when one had to cut out angular objects—the scissor points would not easily lend themselves to any maneuvering around the corners. At the next stage I carried a slate, which displayed on its face a single alphabet or number traced over and over again, bloated and distorted by overlapping lines. This again was a mess, the slate having become white with the constant rubbing with the palm of my hand, as if a great quantity of talcum had been spilled on it, and it was always difficult to decipher the writing, which was white on a whiter background. Again my neighbours seemed to excel in this task; their letters were sharper, symmetrical, and they somehow managed to keep their slates shining black, against which the white letters stood out clearly. The teacher did not seem to mind how I wrote or what I produced, so long as I remained within the classroom without making myself a nuisance in any way. All that he objected to, in me or anyone, was sticking out one's tongue while writing, which most children are apt to do. He kept a sharp lookout for tongues-out in the classroom, and tapped his desk violently with the cane and shouted, 'Hey, you brats, pull your tongues back,' and all of us obeyed him with a simultaneous clicking of our tongues— one golden chance, not to be missed, for making a little noise in an otherwise gloomy and silent atmosphere.

We were let off at four-thirty. Emerging from the school gate, we always ran into the rear-guard of the corporation caravan and followed it; there was no way of avoiding it, as its route and time were fixed inviolably like the motion of the stars in their orbits. Boys going in the same direction formed a group, and we chatted and played and giggled on our way home.

My grandmother examined my slate when I returned home, and remarked, 'They don't seem to teach you anything in your school.' Every day she commented this and then ordered, 'Wash your feet and hands under the tap and come into the kitchen.' When I had accomplished these difficult tasks, she would have coffee and tiffin for me in the kitchen. She would have interrupted her gardening to attend to me, and resuming it, go on until late in the evening. From her gardening, after changing into dry clothes, and chewing betel nut and leaf, she came straight for me. She would place an easy chair in the garden for herself and a stool beside it for me, fix up a lamp, and attempt to supplement with her coaching the inadequate education I got in the school. She taught me multiplication; I had to recite the tables up to twelve every day and then all the thirty letters of the Tamil alphabet, followed by Awaiyar's[*] sayings. She also made me repeat a few Sanskrit slokas praising Saraswathi, the Goddess of Learning. And then she softly rendered a few classical melodies, whose ragas were to be quickly identified by me. If I fumbled she scolded me unreservedly but rewarded

*An ancient Tamil poetess.

me with a coin if I proved diligent. She was methodical, noting in a small diary my daily lessons to be gone through. The schedule was inflexible and she would rise to give me my dinner only after I had completed it. I felt sleepy within a few minutes of starting my lessons; but she met the situation by keeping at hand a bowl of water and dabbing my eyes with cold water to keep me awake—very much like torturers reviving and refreshing their victims in order to continue the third degree. Grandmotherhood was the wrong vocation for her; she ought to have been a school inspectress. She had an absolute passion to teach and mould a young mind. In later years, after my uncle was married and had children, as they came of a teachable age, she took charge of them one by one. She became more aggressive, too, as at teaching time she always kept beside her long broomsticks of coconut leaf-ribs, and whacked her pupils during the lesson; she made them sit at a measured distance from her, so that they might not be beyond her reach. Her brightest pupil was my cousin Janaki, now a grandmother, who at ten years of age was commended at all family gatherings for her recitations, songs and prayers, but who had had to learn it all the hard way; she was a conscientious pupil and always picked up a choice of broomsticks along with her books whenever she went up for her lessons (an extension of the non-violence philosophy, by which you not only love your enemy but lend your active cooperation by arming him or her with the right stick).

Ours was a Lutheran Mission School—mostly for boarders who were Christian converts. The teachers were all converts, and, towards the few non-Christian students like me, they displayed a lot of hatred. Most of the Christian students also detested us. The scripture classes were mostly devoted to attacking and lampooning the Hindu gods, and violent abuses were heaped on idol-worshippers as a prelude to glorifying Jesus. Among the non-Christians in our class I was the only Brahmin boy, and received special attention; the whole class would turn in my direction when the teacher said that Brahmins claiming to be vegetarians ate fish and meat in secret, in a sneaky way, and were responsible for the soaring price of those commodities. In spite of the uneasy time during the lessons, the Biblical stories themselves enchanted me. Especially the Old Testament seemed to me full of fascinating characters—I loved the Rebeccas and Ruths one came across. When one or the other filled her pitcher from the well and poured water into the mouth of Lazarus or someone racked with thirst, I became thirsty too and longed for a draught of that crystal-clear, icy water. I stood up to be permitted to go out for a drink of water at the backyard tap. When Jesus said, 'I shall make you fishers of men,' I felt embarrassed lest they should be reminded of fish and Brahmins again. I bowed my head apprehensively at such moments.

What I suffered in the class as a non-Christian was nothing compared to what a Christian missionary suffered when he came to preach at our street corner. If Christian salvation came out of suffering, here was one who must have attained it. A European missionary with a long beard, escorted by a group of Indian converts carrying violins and harmoniums, would station himself modestly at the junction between Vellala Street and Purasawalkam High Road. A gentle concert would begin unobtrusively. A few onlookers stopped by, the priest nodded to everyone in a friendly manner, casting a genial look around, while the musicians rendered a full-throated Biblical hymn over the babble of the street, with its hawkers' cries and the *jutka*-drivers' urging of their lean horses. Urchins sat down in the front row on the ground, and all sorts of men and women assembled. When the preacher was satisfied that he had gathered a good audience, he made a sign to the musicians to stop. His speech, breaking into the abrupt silence that ensued, was delivered in an absolutely literary Tamil, stiff and formal, culled out of a dictionary, as far away from normal speech as it could be. It was obvious that he had taken a lot of trouble to learn the local language so that he could communicate his message to the heathen masses successfully. But Tamil is a tongue-twister and a demanding language even for Indians from other provinces, the difficulty being that the phonetic value and the orthography are different, and it cannot be successfully uttered by mere learning; it has to be inherited by the ear. I am saying this to explain why the preacher was at first listened to with apparent attention, without any mishap to him. This seemed to encourage him to go on with greater fervour, flourishing his arms and raising his tone to a delirious pitch, his phrases punctuated with 'Amen' from his followers.

Suddenly, the audience woke up to the fact that the preacher was addressing them as 'sinners' ('*Pavigal*' in Tamil) and that he was calling our gods names. He was suggesting that they fling all the stone gods into the moss-covered green tanks in our temples, repent their sins, and seek baptism. For god would forgive all sinners and the Son of God would take on the load of their sins. When the public realized what he was saying, pandemonium broke out. People shouted, commanded him to shut up, moved in on his followers—who fled to save their limbs and instruments. The audience now rained mud and stone on the preacher and smothered him under bundles of wet green grass. Actually, every evening a temporary grass market sprang up on this piece of ground for the benefit of *jutka*-drivers, and all through the evening hot exchanges went on over the price of each bundle, the grass-selling women shrieking at their customers and trying to match their ribaldry while transacting business. It was impolitic of the preacher to have chosen this spot, but he had his own reasons, apparently. Now people snatched up handfuls of grass and flung them on him, but his voice went on unceasingly through all the travail; lamps lit up by his assistants earlier were snatched away and smashed. The preacher, bedraggled and almost camouflaged with damp grass and water, went through his programme to the last minute as scheduled. Then he suddenly disappeared into the night. One would have thought that the man would never come again. But he did, exactly on the same day a week hence, at the next street corner.

The preacher was a foolhardy zealot to have chosen this particular area, as this was one place where the second commandment was totally violated. If you drew a large circle with this spot as the centre, the circumference would enclose several temples where people thronged for worship every evening. Vellala Street itself, though a short stretch, had three temples on it—one for Ganesha, the elephant-faced god, next to it Krishna's temple, and farther off one for Ponni Amman, the goddess who was the frontier guardian at a time when this part of Madras was just a village. Where Vellala Street ended, Ponni Amman Street began, with its own row of shops and houses closely packed. If you went up Ponni Amman Street, you reached Lawdor's Gate (who was this Lawdor? What of the Gate? None in sight now), and it led on to Gangadeswarar Street, which again derived its name from the temple of Iswara (the Shiva who bears the River Ganga on his matted locks), a very large and ancient temple with a thirty-foot doorway, spacious corridors for circumambulation, and a tank for holy baths, public washing of clothes, and periodic drownings. (The tank still claims its quota of human life—one a year.) This temple of Iswara is really a focal point for weddings, funeral obsequies (at the tank), and spontaneous social gatherings, not to mention contact with god. The first nationalist agitation in Madras, in 1916, protesting against something named the Rowlatt Act, was organized here. A procession with patriotic songs and slogan-shouting started from the temple and went round the streets. I joined the procession entranced, and when we returned to the starting point, some enthusiast—the Pankaja Lodge, perhaps—provided refreshments for the tired crowd. When I went home after this patriotic endeavour, I was taken to task by my uncle, who was anti-political and did not want me to be misled. He condemned all rulers, governments, and administrative machinery as satanic and saw no logic in seeking a change of rulers.

Beyond the temple at the street corner, there was a little shrine of Ganesha, which was once again a favourite of the school-going public; placed in a position of vantage, this god received a considerable amount of worship, as well as offerings of coconut and coins in the tin money-box fixed to the doorpost. Facing this was the temple of Hanuman, the God of Energy. All these temples attracted the citizens of the area almost every evening. Recently I revisited Purasawalkam and spent a couple of hours viewing the old landmarks, and I found, though multi-storey buildings and new shop fronts and modern villas and the traffic stream have altered the general outlook, that the four or five temples I have mentioned are still solid and unchanged, oil lamps still burning, and the congregations the same as they were half a century or more ago, surviving the street-corner iconoclast as well as the anti-iconoclasts who sought to demolish him with mud and bundles of grass.

Misguided 'Guide'

THE LETTER came by air mail from Los Angeles. 'I am a producer and actor from Bombay,' it read, 'I don't know if my name is familiar to you.'

He was too modest. Millions of young men copied his screen image, walking as he did, slinging a folded coat over the shoulder carelessly, buffing up a lock of hair over the right temple, and assuming that the total effect would make the girls sigh with hopeless longing. My young nephews at home were thrilled at the sight of the handwriting of Dev Anand.

The letter went on to say, 'I was in London and came across your novel *The Guide*. I am anxious to make it into a film. I can promise you that I will keep to the spirit and quality of your writing. My plans are to make both a Hindi and an English film of this story.' He explained how he had arranged with an American film producer for collaboration. He also described how he had flown from London to New York in search of me, since someone had told him I lived there, and then across the whole continent before he could discover my address. He was ready to come to Mysore if I should indicate the slightest willingness to consider his proposal.

I cabled him an invitation, already catching the fever of hurry characteristic of the film world. He flew from Los Angeles to Bombay to Bangalore, and motored down a hundred miles without losing a moment.

A small crowd of autograph-hunters had gathered at the gate of my house in Yadava Giri. He expertly eluded the inquisitive crowd, and we were soon closeted in the dining-room, breakfasting on *idli*, *dosai*, and other South Indian delicacies, my nephews attending on the star in a state of elation. The talk was all about *The Guide* and its cinematic merits. Within an hour we had become so friendly that he could ask without embarrassment, 'What price will you demand for your story?' The cheque-book was out and the pen poised over it. I had the impression that if I had suggested that the entire face of the cheque be covered with closely knit figures, he would have obliged me. But I hemmed and hawed, suggested a slight advance, and told him to go ahead. I was sure that if the picture turned out to be a success he would share with me the glory and the profits. 'Oh, certainly,' he affirmed, 'if the picture, by god's grace, turns out to be a success, we will be on top of the world, and the sky will be the limit!'

The following months were filled with a sense of importance: Long Distance Calls, Urgent Telegrams, Express Letters, sudden arrivals and departures by plane and car. I received constant summonses to be present here or there. 'PLEASE COME TO DELHI. SUITE RESERVED AT IMPERIAL HOTEL. URGENTLY NEED YOUR PRESENCE.'

Locking away my novel-in-progress, I fly to Delhi. There is the press conference, with introductions, speeches and overflowing conviviality. The American director explains the unique nature of their present effort: for the first time in the history of Indian moviemaking, they are going to bring out a hundred-per-cent-Indian story, with a hundred-per-cent-Indian cast, and a hundred-per-cent-Indian setting, for an international audience. And mark this: actually in colour-and-wide-screen-first-time-in-the-history-of-this-country.

A distinguished group of Americans, headed by the Nobel Prize winner, Pearl Buck, would produce the film. Again and again I heard the phrase: 'Sky is the limit', and the repeated assurances: 'We will make the picture just as Narayan has written it, with his cooperation at every stage.' Reporters pressed me for a statement. It was impossible to say anything but the pleasantest things in such an atmosphere of overwhelming optimism and good fellowship.

Soon we were assembled in Mysore. They wanted to see the exact spots which had inspired me to write *The Guide*. Could I show them the locations? A photographer, and some others whose business with us I never quite understood, were in the party. We started out in two cars. The American director, Tad Danielewski, explained that he would direct the English version first. He kept discussing with me the finer points of my novel. 'I guess your hero is a man of impulsive plans? Self-made, given to daydreaming?' he would ask, and add, before I could muster an answer, 'Am I not right?' Of course he had to be right. Once or twice when I attempted to mitigate his impressions, he brushed aside my comments and went on with his own explanation as to what I must have had in mind when I created such-and-such a character.

I began to realize that monologue is the privilege of the film-maker, and that it was futile to try butting in with my own observations. But for some obscure reason, they seemed to need my presence, though not my voice. I must be seen and not heard.

We drove about 300 miles that day, during the course of which I showed them the river steps and a little shrine overshadowed by a banyan on the banks of Kaveri, which was the actual spot around which I wrote *The Guide*. As I had thought, nothing more needed to be done than put the actors there and start the camera. They uttered little cries of joy at finding a 'set' so readily available. In the summer, when the river dried up, they could shoot the drought scenes with equal ease. Then I took them to the tiny town of Nanjangud, with its little streets, its shops selling sweets and toys and ribbons, and a pilgrim crowd bathing in the holy waters of the Kabini, which flowed through the town. The crowd was colourful and lively around the temple, and in a few weeks it would increase a hundred fold when people from the surrounding villages arrived to participate in the annual festival—the sort of crowd described in the last pages of my novel. If the film-makers made a note of the date and sent down a cameraman at that time, they could secure the last scene of my novel in an authentic manner and absolutely free of cost.

The producer at once passed an order to his assistant to arrange for an outdoor unit to arrive here at the right time. Then we all posed at the portals of the ancient temple, with arms encircling each other's necks and smiling. This was but the first of innumerable similar scenes in which I found myself posing with the starry folk, crushed in the friendliest embrace.

From Nanjangud we drove up mountains and the forests and photographed our radiant smiles against every possible background. It was a fatiguing business on the whole, but the American director claimed that it was nothing to what he was used to. He generally went 5,000 miles in search of locations, exposing hundreds of rolls of film on the way.

After inspecting jungles, mountains, village streets, hamlets and huts, we reached the base of Gopalaswami Hill in the afternoon, and drove up the five-mile mud track; the cars had to be pushed up the steep hill after encroaching vegetation had been cleared from the path. This was a part of the forest country where at any bend of the road one could anticipate a tiger or a herd of elephants; but, luckily for us, they were out of view today.

At the summit I showed them the original of the 'Peak House' in my novel, a bungalow built fifty years ago, with glassed-in verandas affording a view of wildlife at night, and a 2,000-foot drop to a valley beyond. A hundred yards off, a foot-track wound through the undergrowth, leading on to an ancient temple whose walls were crumbling and whose immense timber doors moved on rusty hinges with a groan. Once again I felt that here everything was ready-made for the film. They could shoot in the bright sunlight, and for the indoor scenes they assured me that it would be a simple matter to haul up a generator and lights.

Sitting under a banyan tree and consuming sandwiches and lemonade, we discussed and settled the practical aspects of the expedition: where to locate the base camp and where the advance units consisting of engineers, mechanics, and truck drivers, in charge of the generator and lights. All through the journey back the talk involved schedules and arrangements for shooting the scenes in this part of the country. I was impressed with the ease they displayed, in accepting such mighty logistical tasks. Film executives, it seemed to me, could solve mankind's problems on a global scale with the casual confidence of demi-gods, if only they could take time off their illusory pursuits and notice the serious aspects of existence.

Then came total silence, for many weeks. Finally I discovered that they were busy searching for their locations in northern India. This was a shock. I had never visualized my story in that part of India, where costumes, human types and details of daily life are different. They had settled upon Jaipur and Udaipur in Rajaputana, a thousand miles away from my location for the story.

Our next meeting was in Bombay, and I wasted no time in speaking of this problem. 'My story takes place in south India, in Malgudi, an imaginary town known to thousands of my readers all over the world,' I explained. 'It is south India in costume, tone and contents. Although the whole country is one, there are diversities, and one has to be faithful in delineating them. You have to stick to my geography and sociology. Although it is a world of fiction there are certain inner veracities.'

One of them replied: 'We feel it a privilege to be doing your story.' This sounded irrelevant as an answer to my statement.

We were sitting under a gaudy umbrella beside a blue swimming pool on Juhu beach, where the American party was housed in princely suites in a modern hotel. It was hard to believe that we were in India. Most of our discussions took place somewhat amphibiously, on the edge of the swimming pool, in which the director spent a great deal of his time.

This particular discussion was interrupted as a bulky European tourist in swimming briefs fell off the diving plank, hit the bottom and had to be hauled out and rendered first aid. After the atmosphere had cleared, I resumed my speech. They listened with a mixture of respect and condescension, evidently willing to make allowances for an author's whims.

'Please remember,' one of them tried to explain, 'that we are shooting, for the first time in India, in wide screen and Eastman Color, and we must shoot where there is spectacle. Hence Jaipur.'

'In that case,' I had to ask, 'why all that strenuous motoring near my home? Why my story at all, if what you need is a picturesque spectacle?'

I was taken aback when their reply came: 'How do you know that Malgudi is where you think it is?'

Somewhat bewildered, I said, with what I hoped was proper humility, 'I suppose I know because I have imagined it, created it and have been writing novel after novel set in the area for the last thirty years.'

'We are out to expand the notion of Malgudi,' one of them explained. 'Malgudi will be where we place it, in Kashmir, Rajasthan, Bombay, Delhi, even Ceylon.'

I could not share the flexibility of their outlook or the expanse of their vision. It seemed to me that for their purpose a focal point was unnecessary. They appeared to be striving to achieve mere optical effects.

I recalled a talk with Satyajit Ray, the great director, some years earlier, when I had met him in Calcutta. He expressed his admiration for *The Guide* but also his doubts as to whether he could ever capture the tone and atmosphere of its background. He had said, 'Its roots are so deep in the soil of your part of our country that I doubt if I could do justice to your book, being unfamiliar with its milieu...' Such misgivings did not bother the American director. I noticed that though he was visiting India for the first time, he never paused to ask what was what in this bewildering country.

Finally he solved the whole problem by declaring, 'Why should we mention where the story takes place? We will avoid the name "Malgudi". Thereafter the director not only avoided the word Malgudi but fell foul of anyone who uttered that sound.

My brother, an artist who has illustrated my stories for twenty-five years, tried to expound his view. At a dinner in his home in Bombay, he mentioned the forbidden word to the director. Malgudi, he explained, meant a little town, not so picturesque as Jaipur, of a neutral shade, with characters wearing *dhoti* and *jibba* when they were not bare bodied. The Guide himself was a man of charm, creating history and archaeology out of thin air for his clients, and to provide him with solid, concrete monuments to talk about would go against the grain of the tale. The director listened and firmly said, 'There is no Malgudi, and that is all there is to it.'

But my brother persisted. I became concerned that the controversy threatened to spoil our dinner. The director replied, in a sad tone, that they could as well have planned a picture for black and white and narrow screen if all one wanted was what he contemptuously termed a 'Festival Film', while he was planning a million-dollar spectacle to open simultaneously in 2,000 theatres in America. I was getting used to arguments every day over details. My story is about a dancer in a small town, an exponent of the strictly classical tradition of South Indian Bharat Natyam. The film-makers felt this was inadequate. They therefore engaged an expensive, popular dance director with a troupe of a hundred or more dancers, and converted my heroine's performances into an extravaganza in delirious, fruity colours and costumes. Their dancer was constantly travelling hither and thither in an Air India Boeing, no matter how short the distance to be covered. The moviegoer, too, I began to realize, would be whisked all over India. Although he would see none of the countryside in which the novel was set, he would see the latest US Embassy building in New Delhi, Parliament House, the Ashoka Hotel, the Lake Palace, Elephanta Caves and what-not. Unity of place seemed an unknown concept for a film-maker. (Later Mrs Indira Gandhi, whom I met after she had seen a special showing of the film, asked, 'Why should they have dragged the story all over as if it were a travelogue, instead of containing themselves to the simple background of your book?' She added as an afterthought, and in what seemed to me an understatement: 'Perhaps they have other considerations.')

The cooperation of many persons was needed in the course of the film-making, and anyone whose help was requested had to be given a copy of *The Guide*. Thus there occurred a shortage, and an inevitable black market, in copies of the book. A production executive searched the bookshops in Bombay, and cornered all the available copies at any price. He could usually be seen going about like a scholar with a bundle of books under his arm. I was also intrigued by the intense study and pencil-marking that the director was making on his copy of the book; it was as if he were studying it for a doctoral thesis. Not until I had a chance to read his 'treatment' did I understand what all his pencilling meant: he had been marking off passages and portions that were to be avoided in the film.

When the script came, I read through it with mixed feelings. The director answered my complaints with, 'I have only exteriorized what you have expressed. It is all in your book.'

'In which part of my book?' I would ask without any hope of an answer.

Or he would say, 'I could give you two hundred reasons why this change should be so.' I did not feel up to hearing them all. If I still proved truculent he would explain away, 'This is only a first draft. We could make any change you want in the final screenplay.'

The screenplay was finally presented to me with a great flourish and expression of fraternal sentiments at a hotel in Bangalore. But I learned at this time that they had already started shooting and had even completed a number of scenes. Whenever I expressed my views, the answer would be either, 'Oh, it will be rectified in the editing,' or, 'We will deal with it when we decide about the retakes. But please wait until we have a chance to see the rushes.' By now a bewildering number of hands were behind the scenes, at laboratories, workshops, carpentries, editing rooms and so forth. It was impossible to keep track of what was going on, or get hold of anyone with a final say. Soon I trained myself to give up all attempts to connect the film with the book of which I happened to be the author.

But I was not sufficiently braced for the shock that came the day when the director insisted upon the production of two tigers to fight and destroy each other over a spotted deer. He wished to establish the destructive animality of two men clashing over one woman: my heroine's husband and lover fighting over her. The director intended a tiger fight to portray depths of symbolism. It struck me as obvious. Moreover it was not in the story. But he asserted that it was; evidently I had intended the scene without realizing it.

The Indian producer, who was financing the project, groaned at the thought of the tigers. He begged me privately, 'Please do something about it. We have no time for tigers; and it will cost a hell of a lot to hire them, just for a passing fancy.' I spoke to the director again, but he was insistent. No tiger, no film, and two tigers or none. Scouts were sent out through the length and breadth of India to explore the tiger possibilities. They returned to report that only one tiger was available. It belonged to a circus and the circus owner would under no circumstance consent to have the tiger injured or killed. The director decreed, 'I want the beast to die, otherwise the scene will have no meaning.' They finally found a man in Madras, living in the heart of the city with a full-grown Bengal tiger which he occasionally lent for jungle pictures, after sewing its lips and pulling out its claws.

The director examined a photograph of the tiger, in order to satisfy himself that they were not trying to palm off a pi-dog in tiger clothing, and signed it up. Since a second tiger was not available, he had to settle for its fighting a leopard. It was an easier matter to find a deer for the sacrifice. What they termed a 'second unit' was dispatched to Madras to shoot the sequence. Ten days later the unit returned, looking forlorn.

The tiger had shrunk at the sight of the leopard, and the leopard had shown no inclination to maul the deer, whose cries of fright had been so heart-rending that they had paralysed the technicians. By prodding, kicking and irritating the animals, they had succeeded in producing a spectacle gory enough to make them retch. 'The deer was actually lifted and fed into the jaws of the other two,' said an assistant cameraman. (This shot passes on the screen, in the finished film, in the winking of an eye, as a bloody smudge, to the accompaniment of a lot of wild uproar.)

Presently another crisis developed. The director wanted the hero to kiss the heroine, who of course rejected the suggestion as unbecoming an Indian woman. The director was distraught. The hero, for his part, was willing to obey the director, but he was helpless, since kissing is a cooperative effort. The American director realized that it is against Indian custom to kiss in public; but he insisted that the public in his country would boo if they missed the kiss. I am told that the heroine replied: 'There is enough kissing in your country at all times and places, off and on the screen, and your public, I am sure, will flock to a picture where, for a change, no kissing is shown.' She stood firm. Finally, the required situation was apparently faked by tricky editing.

Next: trouble at the governmental level. A representation was made to the Ministry dealing with films, by an influential group, that *The Guide* glorified adultery, and hence was not fit to be presented as a film, since it might degrade Indian womanhood. The dancer in my story, to hear their arguments, has no justification for preferring Raju the Guide to her legally-wedded husband. The Ministry summoned the movie principals to Delhi and asked them to explain how they proposed to meet the situation. They promised to revise the film script to the Ministry's satisfaction.

In my story the dancer's husband is a preoccupied archaeologist who has no time or inclination for marital life and is not interested in her artistic aspirations. Raju the Guide exploits the situation and weans her away from her husband. That is all there is to it—in my story. But now a justification had to be found for adultery.

So the archaeological husband was converted into a drunkard and womanizer who kicks out his wife when he discovers that another man has watched her dance in her room and has spoken encouragingly to her. I knew nothing about this drastic change of my characters until I saw the 'rushes' some months later. This was the point at which I lamented most over my naiveté the contract that I had signed in blind faith, in the intoxication of cheques, bonhomie, and back-slapping, empowered them to do whatever they pleased with my story, and I had no recourse.

Near the end of the project I made another discovery: the extent to which movie producers will go to publicize a film. The excessive affability to pressmen, the entertaining of VIPs, the button-holing of ministers and officials in authority, the extravagant advertising campaigns, seemed to me to drain off money, energy and ingenuity that might be reserved for the creation of an honest and sensible product.

On one occasion Lord Mountbatten was passing through India, and someone was seized with the sudden idea that he could help make a success of the picture. A banquet was held at Raj Bhavan in his honour, and the Governor of Bombay, Mrs Vijayalakshmi Pandit, was kind enough to invite us to it. I was at home in Mysore as Operation Mountbatten was launched, so telegrams and long-distance telephone calls poured in on me to urge me to come to Bombay at once. I flew in just in time to dress and reach Raj Bhavan. It was red-carpeted, crowded and gorgeous. When dinner was over, leaving the guests aside, our hostess managed to isolate his Lordship and the *Guide* makers on a side veranda of this noble building. His Lordship sat on a sofa surrounded by us; close to him sat Pearl Buck, who was one of the producers and who, by virtue of her seniority and standing, was to speak for us. As she opened the theme with a brief explanation of the epoch-making effort that was being made in India in colour and wide-screen, with a hundred-per-cent-Indian cast, story and background, his Lordship displayed no special emotion. Then came the practical demand: in order that this grand, stupendous achievement might bear fruit, would Lord Mountbatten influence Queen Elizabeth to preside at the world premiere of the film in London in due course?

Lord Mountbatten responded promptly, 'I don't think it is possible. Anyway, what is the story?'

There was dead silence for a moment, as each looked at the other wondering who was to begin. I was fully aware that they ruled me out; they feared that I might take 80,000 words to narrate the story, as I had in the book. The obvious alternative was Pearl Buck, who was supposed to have written the screenplay.

Time was running out and his Lordship had others to talk to. Pearl Buck began, 'It is the story of a man called Raju. He was a tourist guide...'

'Where does it take place?'

I wanted to shout, 'Malgudi, of course.' But they were explaining, 'We have taken the story through many interesting locations—Jaipur, Udaipur.'

'Let me hear the story.'

'Raju was a guide,' began Pearl Buck again.

'In Jaipur?' asked His Lordship.

'Well, no. Anyway he did not remain a guide because when Rosie came...'

'Who is Rosie?'

'A dancer...but she changed her name when she became a...a... dancer...'

'But the guide? What happened to him?'

'I am coming to it. Rosie's husband…'

'Rosie is the dancer?'

'Yes, of course…' Pearl Buck struggled on, but I was in no mood to extricate her.

After several minutes Lord Mountbatten said, 'Most interesting.' His deep bass voice was a delight to the ear, but it also had a ring of finality and discouraged further talk. 'Elizabeth's appointments are complicated these days. Anyway her private secretary Lord— must know more about it than I do. I am rather out of touch now. Anyway, perhaps I could ask Philip.' He summoned an aide and said, 'William, please remind me when we get to London…' Our producers went home feeling that a definite step had been taken to establish the film in proper quarters. As for myself, I was not so sure.

Elaborate efforts were made to shoot the last scene of the story, in which the saint fasts on the dry river's edge, in hopes of bringing rain, and a huge crowd turns up to witness the spectacle. For this scene the director selected a site at a village called Okhla, outside Delhi on the bank of the Jamuna River, which was dry and provided enormous stretches of sand. He had, of course, ruled out the spot we had visited near Mysore, explaining that two coconut trees were visible a mile away on the horizon and might spoil the appearance of unrelieved desert which he wanted. Thirty truckloads of property, carpenters, lumber, painters, artisans and art department personnel arrived at Okhla to erect a two-dimensional temple beside a dry river, at a cost of 80,000 rupees. As the director kept demanding, 'I must have 100,000 people for a helicopter shot,' I thought of the cost: five rupees per head for extras, while both the festival crowd at Nanjangud and the little temple on the river would have cost nothing.

The crowd had been mobilized, the sets readied and lights mounted, and all other preparations completed for shooting the scene next morning when, at midnight, news was brought to the chiefs relaxing at the Ashoka Hotel that the Jamuna was rising dangerously as a result of unexpected rains in Simla. All hands were mobilized and they rushed desperately to the location to save the equipment. Wading in knee-deep water, they salvaged a few things. But I believe the two-dimensional temple was carried off in the floods.

Like a colony of ants laboriously building up again, the carpenters and artisans rebuilt the set, this time at a place in western India called Limdi, which was reputed to have an annual rainfall of a few droplets. Within one week the last scene was completed, the hero collapsing in harrowing fashion as a result of his penance. The director and technicians paid off the huge crowd and packed up their cameras and sound equipment, and were just leaving the scene when a storm broke—an unknown phenomenon in that part of the country—uprooting and tearing off everything that stood. Those who had lingered had to make their exit with dispatch.

This seemed to me an appropriate conclusion for my story, which, after all, was concerned with the subject of rain, and in which nature, rather than film-makers, acted in consonance with the subject. I remembered that years ago when I was in New York City on my way to sign the contract, before writing *The Guide*, a sudden downpour caught me on Madison Avenue and I entered the Viking Press offices dripping wet. I still treasure a letter from Keith Jennison, who was then my editor. 'Somehow I will always, from now on,' he wrote, 'associate the rainiest days in New York with you. The afternoon we officially became your publishers was wet enough to have made me feel like a fish ever since.'

The Problem of the Indian Writer

ALL IMAGINATIVE writing in India has had its origin in the *Ramayana* and the *Mahabharata*, the ten-thousand-year-old epics of India. An author picked up an incident or a character out of one or the other and created a new work with it, similar to Shakespeare's transmutation of Holinshed's *Chronicle* or Plutarch's *Lives*. Kalidasa's *Shakuntala* (fifth century AD), one of the world's masterpieces, was developed out of an incident in the *Mahabharata*. Apart from this type of work, many ancient writers dedicated their lives to the rewriting of the *Ramayana* or the *Mahabharata* according to their own genius. Tulasidas wrote the *Ramayana* in Hindi, Kamban in Tamil, and Kumaravyasa wrote the *Mahabharata* in Kannada. Each of these authors devoted his lifetime to the fulfilment of one supreme task, the stylus with which he wrote etching the stanzas on dry palm leaves hour after hour and day after day for thirty, forty or fifty years, before a book came into being. The completion of a literary work was marked by ceremony and social rejoicing. Economic or commercial considerations had no place in a writer's life, the little he needed coming to him through royal patronage or voluntary gifts. The work was read out to the public assembled in a temple hall or under the shade of a tree. Men, women and children listened to the reading with respectful attention for a few hours every evening. A literary work lived not so much through the number of copies scattered over the world as in the mind and memory of readers and their listeners, and passed on by word of mouth from generation to generation.

These traditions were modified by historical changes. Let us skip a great deal of intervening history and come down to British times. The English language brought with it not only a new type of literature but all the world's literature in translation. New forms such as the novel and short story came to be noticed, revealing not only new artistic possibilities for a writer but also stimulating a new social awareness. Our early stories dealt with impossible romance, melodrama and adventure on one side and on the other exposed the evils of certain social customs such as early marriage, the dowry system, suttee, and caste prejudices. Many of the realistic novels of this period are in effect attacks on the orthodoxies of the day. They suffered from didacticism, but there remained in them a residue of artistic quality, and many books of the early Victorian years survive as novels and stories although their social criticism are out of date.

Between then and now we might note a middle period when all that a writer could write about became inescapably political. There came a time when all the nation's energies were directed to the freeing of the country from foreign rule. Under this stress and preoccupation the mood of comedy, the sensitivity to atmosphere, the probing of psychological factors, the crisis in the individual soul and its resolution, and above all the detached observation, which constitute the stuff of growing fiction, went into the background. It seemed to be more a time for polemics and tract-writing than for storytelling.

Since the attainment of Independence in 1947 this preoccupation has gone, and the writer can now pick his material out of the great events that are taking shape before his eyes. Every writer now hopes to express, through his novels and stories, the way of life of the group of people with whose psychology and background he is most familiar, and he hopes it will not only appeal to his own circle but also to a larger audience outside.

The short story rather than the long novel has been the favourite medium of the fiction-writer in India, because, it seems to me: (1) the short story is the best-suited medium for the variegated material available in the country, (2) the writing of a short story takes less time.

A writer who has to complete a novel has to spend at least a year's labour on it. This complete surrender is something that he cannot afford, since most writers write only part-time while they have to be doing something else for a living. Fiction-writing as a full-time occupation has still to be recognized. For that what is primarily needed is a sound publishing organization. Before considering this, however, I have to mention one other factor—that is, the problem of language. The complexity arising from this can be better understood if we remember that there are fifteen languages in India in which writers are doing their jobs today in various regions. Every writer has to keep in mind his own regional language, the national language which is Hindi, the classical language Sanskrit (this is often called a 'dead language' but dead only as a mountain could be dead) and above all the English language which seems nearly inescapable. Some of the regional languages are understood only within limited boundaries and cannot provide more than a few thousand (or even a few hundred) readers for a book. A really livelihood-giving sale for a writer can be obtained only on an all-India basis. That being so, whatever may be the original language of the writing, the urgent need is to have an organization, a sort of literary clearing-house and translation service, which can give a writer a countrywide audience. As conditions are, there is no general publishing in this country. There are several publishing firms but they are only concerned with the manufacture of school-texts, which alone, by diligent manoeuvering, can give a publisher (and incidentally his author) a five-figure public. It must also be admitted that on the other side all is not well with the public either. A certain amount of public apathy for book-buying is depressingly evident everywhere. An American publisher once asked me how many copies of my *Bachelor of Arts* (in the Pocket Book series costing a rupee and eight annas) sold in my own town (Mysore). I suggested two hundred as a possible figure.

'What is the population of your town?' he asked.

'Over two hundred and seventy-five thousand.'

'How many among them can read a novel like yours?'

'At least five thousand,' I ventured.

'How many among them know you personally and like your work in general?'

'Probably all of them and many more.'

'How many among them could afford to pay a rupee odd for your book.'

'Perhaps all of them!'

'In that case what prevents five thousand copies being sold in your own town rather than two hundred?'

I could not answer the question. I am still thinking it over. I think it is for experts in the trade to discover a solution, and when that is done, a major obstacle in the fiction-writer's way in India will have been removed.

In a well-ordered society there should be no problem at all for a writer. It should be possible for a writer to dash off a book in six months and see it automatically reach his reader, thus enabling him to enjoy a few months of rest, holiday and reading so that he may begin a new book at the end of it. How well should a society be ordered before this can happen? What are the things that a dynamic reformer should undertake before he can create congenial conditions in which fiction-writing may flourish?

The writer of a novel is afflicted with peculiar problems. For one thing, the novel is a comparatively recent form in our country and though people have taken to the reading of novels in order to while away their time it never occurs to anyone to ask seriously who writes them. It never occurs to anyone that no novel may be available for entertainment or instruction unless the author is kept in working order. What are the things necessary to keep this man in working condition? All sorts of amenities are devised in order to solve the difficulties of all kinds of workers. Even journalists, hitherto the most neglected of men, have come to state their aims and demand their welfare conditions. But the novelist has as yet no code of social existence. The trouble is the novelist has not attained a vocal status.

The first problem of a novelist is that he must live without too many harassments and distractions. It is necessary that he should arrive at a sort of compromise between his inner life and outer life. A writer's life is a subjective one, and it may not always be feasible for him to discharge his duties competently, as a captain steering the ship of family in the ocean of existence. Though he may be unexcelled as a writer of fiction, the facts, the hard-headed facts of life, may prove beyond his powers. I mean by hard and harsh facts such activities as balancing the budget, looking after dependents, calculating various things and so forth. He is likely to make grave errors of calculation when dealing with numbers, not because he does not know addition and subtraction but (his mind being all the time in the realm of fiction) because his cash in hand may appear exaggerated in value. He is likely to acquire the satisfaction warranted by the possession of 10,000 rupees when all that he has on hand is fifty rupees. This is rather a disproportionate way of dealing with figures but that is how he is and no one can help it. It is not a realistic manner of living and tackling the problems of life but what can he do, he is made that way, it is the only manner in which he can live and work. This creates peculiar difficulties for those who have to live along with him. However realistic a writer he may be he is likely to prove to be the most dreamy of persons on earth, and the demands of practical life may prove bewildering if not actually distressing to him, and against this he always needs something like a cushion between him and crude realities. I don't know what kind of organization could achieve this purpose but if something could be done to relieve him from the necessity of running a family, paying off bills, meeting creditors, and other such odious and devitalizing occupations, he will do his work in peace and the public may ultimately feel gratified that it has more books to read.

To understand this implication fully one must first have an idea of the method of his work. The novelist has to live close to life and keep himself open to its influence if he is to prove successful as a writer. His mind must pick out the material from life, shape it and use it. He is likely to be always busy planning the next chapter. Whether he is the type that sits down methodically to dash off a fixed quota of work each day, or whether he is the one to seize upon his work and go through it in a frenzy without a pause, the actual time of sitting down at one's desk can never be an indication of the quantity of work involved. Whatever may be the actual time spent at his desk, he is always busy. His mind is always at work. There is no such thing as finishing a piece of work for the day and rising from his seat with a free mind. There is no end to the work till the novel is completed, and if one remembers that a novel takes a minimum of 80,000 words, one may understand the labours involved. Many persons ask me whether I have in mind all the details of a novel beforehand, whether I work out an outline, or how a novel comes into being at all. I wish I could answer that question with precision. I know one thing, when I sit down to write I have no more than a vague idea regarding the outcome of the day's work. It would be not far wrong if I said that my fingers on the typewriter probably know more about what is coming on than my head. It is perhaps no compliment to myself, but I do not intend it to be. The details of what I write each day, when I am at work on a novel, work themselves out. This means that one's subconscious self should have a lot of unimpaired freedom. Writing a novel is both a conscious and unconscious occupation; it is something both of the intellect and something superior to the intellect. That means the mind should be left completely free to continue to exercise itself at all levels. The intellect portion of it pertains mostly to technique and expression, and not to the ultimate shape of the thing, though there is always a possibility that the novelist has some idea of the shape of things to come, and to that extent his mind is burdened.

When he sits down on a certain day to begin a new novel, it must be understood that he is undertaking a task which will virtually chain him up for months to come. Even if he is a fast worker, apart from the actual writing it may bind him down for nearly two years. And then he has to spend a few months revising the manuscript, because it always seems to be incomplete and not quite satisfactory. Here revision means watching over 80,000 words and their punctuation, while trying to test the validity and worth of every word. I say nothing of the misgiving that may suddenly assail one about the sense of what one has been writing. It is always there and may involve the scrapping of months of work. Let us grant he has satisfactorily settled all the mechanical details of his work, and has parcelled off the manuscript to his publisher. This is his happiest day. He feels like a schoolboy who has written his last examination of the season, looks back with a shudder on his days of drudgery and looks forward to a happy summer vacation ahead. Now, how far can this author afford to keep away from writing after his two years of labour? If he is to be in a fit condition to give the world his best again, he must rest and recuperate while giving time for the spring of his inspiration to well up again. For that it must be possible for him to afford to rest: the work that he has done must reach the public and must be accepted by the public. When all is said and done it is only public support that can sustain an author. It is important that his work should appear in the bookstalls and that the public must show enthusiasm for it. This alone can help him to live by his best work. This alone can prevent his preoccupation with pot-boiling activities, whereby he pumps himself dry and goes on producing third-rate stuff when he ought to be resting. What exactly can give him this freedom? It is that state of society whereby the publishing activity is organized so well that a good book reaches its readers without delay. From this point of view the novelist in our country suffers greatly. As I've said earlier there is not a general publishing business here as in other countries. There are few publishers who are interested in publishing, advertising and getting the work of a new writer. For this cooperation from all is required, from the press which must make new books known through its literary columns, booksellers who must keep the book in stock, and more than anything else a responsive and appreciative public which buys the book. I use the word 'buy' deliberately. It certainly connotes a different activity from reading, which may be done with borrowed books. It may give an author a vast reading public without any relief or reward. A book-buying campaign must be started on a nationwide scale. Buying books and building a home library must become a citizen's duty, which will have the double advantage of both rewarding the labours of the author and providing a general atmosphere of culture in every home.

My Dateless Diary

(Excerpts)

AN ENCOUNTER*

I LOAFED AROUND San Francisco till 7 p.m. and returned to the Key Station, in order to catch a streetcar for Albany, where I was to dine with Chamu at 8.30.

I paid 45 cents and took a ticket. I asked at the barrier, 'Where do I get the car for Albany?'

'Albany?' said a man standing there. He pulled out a time-table from his pocket, and said, 'There is one leaving in five minutes. Go, go...go straight down those steps.' He hustled me so much that I didn't have the time even to say 'Thanks'. I was in a hurry. I went down and saw ahead, on the road, two coaches with passengers, ready to start. As I hurried on, wondering which of them I should take, two men standing at the foot of the stairs called me to stop, and asked, 'Where are you going?'

'Albany. If that is the bus...'

'Where is your ticket?' I held up my ticket. One of them snatched it, crumpled it into a pellet, and put it into his pocket. These men evidently liked to keep me at the San Francisco station. They were well-dressed, and looked like the presidents of a railroad or a college; one of them looked quite distinguished in his rimless glasses. I demanded an explanation for their arbitrary handling of my ticket, but they strolled away and disappeared into the shadows around a corner of this grim building. Not a soul in sight. It was past eight. I dashed back to the

---

*From the chapter 'Westward Bound'.

ticket office and asked for another ticket of the woman (I purposely avoid the indiscriminate American usage 'girl') at the window. She said, 'You took one now!'

'Yes, but I need another one for a souvenir,' I said. She said, 'You don't get the next bus until nine o' five.'

'Is it a bus or a coach or a train or a streetcar? What is the vehicle one rides in for Albany?' I asked.

'Why?'

'Each time I hear it differently.'

'I don't know, ask there,' she said out of habit and went back to her work.

I went round the station asking for directions. No one was precise. It was surprising how little anyone here cared to know the whereabouts of Albany, only half an hour's ride away. They behaved as if they were being consulted over some hazardous expedition beyond uncharted seas; while the fact remained as any citizen of Berkeley or Albany will confirm, 'F' trains and 'E' trains shuttling between Berkeley and San Francisco wailed and hooted all night, keeping people awake.

The station was getting more and more deserted and I didn't want to miss a possible bus or streetcar that might start from some unsuspected corner of it. So I went round looking for a conveyance. At a particularly deserted corner, I was stopped by the two men who had misappropriated my first ticket. They blocked my way. I tucked away my new ticket securely into an inner pocket. I was not going to give it up again. One of them grabbed the collar of my jacket and said, 'Let us talk.' The other moved off a few yards, craning his neck and keeping a general look-out. The nearer man said, 'Don't start trouble, but listen.' He thrust his fist to my eyes and said, 'I could crack your jaw, and knock you down. You know what I mean?' Certainly, the meaning was crystal clear. I knew at a glance that he could easily achieve his object. It frightened me. In a moment flashed across my mind a versatile, comprehensive news-headline, 'Remnants of Indian novelist found near Key Station. Consulate officials concerned—'. I realized these were men of action.

'What do you want?' I asked simply.

The one on sentry duty muttered something in the local dialect. The collar-gripper took his hand to his hip pocket. I thought he was going to pull out a pistol, but he drew out a gold watch with a gorgeous gold band. He flourished it before me and said, 'How do you like it?'

'Don't hold it so close to my eyes. I can't see what it is. Take it back.' Yes, it was a nice, tiny watch. He read my thoughts and said, 'I'm not a bum, but a respectable member of the merchant marines. I'm on a holiday and have been gambling. I want money. Take this.'

It was of course an extraordinary method of promoting watch sales, but I had to pretend that I saw nothing odd in it. He said in a kind of through-the-teeth hiss, 'I don't like trouble, that's all. See what I mean?' His hand still held the collar of my jacket, and the watch was sunk within his enormous fist. It was very frightening. The lub-dub of my heart could be heard over other city noises. I'm not exactly a cowardly sort, but I am a realist. When I encountered a fist of that size I could calculate its striking force to the nearest poundal. I have always weighed 140 pounds, whatever I did, whether I starved or over-ate or vegetated or travelled hectically. My weight never varied. I felt, in my fevered state, that the man before me must weigh as much between his fist and shoulder. No police in sight. The entire force seemed to have been drawn away to meet a graver emergency elsewhere. I looked casual, as if it were a part of my day's routine, as if someone were always turning up doing this sort of thing to me every two hours. I tried to assume the look of a seasoned receiver of ladies' watches. The whole scene filled me with such a feeling of ludicrous staginess that I suddenly burst out laughing. The man looked puzzled and annoyed. 'You think it funny?' he asked.

'S-u-r-e,' I said in the most approved drawn-out manner, dreading that my tactics might misfire. He gave my jacket a tug. I said curtly, 'I hate to have my jacket pulled. I hate anyone hanging on to my jacket. It shows an infantile mind and mother-fixation.'

'You are a professor, aren't you?' he said sneeringly.

I asked, 'Whose is that watch?'

'My own. I would not be selling it otherwise.'

The other man turned round to say, 'Of course it is of course his. Should you ask?'

'I don't believe it,' I said. 'Maybe you are a guy with a slender-enough wrist to wear that strap. Let me see how you manage to put it on! Seems to me it's a lady's watch.' At this he repeated his threat about my jaw. I had by now got used to hearing it; and almost said that if he broke one jaw, another was sure to grow in its place. I still marvel that he didn't hit me. I took off my spectacles as a defence preparation. I didn't want splinters in my eyes. He ran his hand over the entire surface of my person, trying to locate my purse. Ignoring his action I repeated emphatically, 'It's a lady's watch.'

'It is Pat's,' said his friend.

'Who is Pat?'

'His wife,' he said.

'What does she do now to know the time?' I asked.

'I got her another one,' he said. 'That's why I want to sell it.'

'Does she know about it?' I asked.

'Sure. Peggy will do anything to help me.'

'Peggy?' I asked. 'Who is she and how does she get on with Pat?'

'What are you talking about?' he growled. We had now arrived at a level of conversational ease which must have looked like the meeting of three old school-ties around the corner. The only unsavoury element in it, if one peered closely enough, was that he still had his fingers firmly on my collar. He assumed a menacing tone suddenly, and asked, 'So you don't appreciate our help?'

'Thanks a lot, I don't. You are really mixed up. Your wife, if you have one, must be either Pat or Peggy, not both, unless you are a bigamist who lets two wives manage with a single watch, or am I going to hear about Sally and Jane too? Are you a bigamist or a polygamist? Are such things allowed in this country?'

'Oh, stop that, you talk too much; that's what's wrong with you. Jack made a slip, that's all,' the man said with a touch of sadness.

'What's your time now?' I asked. 'I've a dinner engagement at Albany—' He looked at his own watch. He applied it to his ear and cried, 'The damned thing has stopped.'

'No wonder,' I said. 'All that clenching and flourishing of fist would reduce any watch to pieces,' I said. 'Why don't you look at the cute one in your pocket, Peggy's, is it?' He pulled out the little watch, peered at its face and said, 'Can't see anything in this blasted place.'

'Why don't we all adjourn to a better-lit place?' I suggested.

'And have a drink, eh?' he said.

After Jack had had his laugh at the joke, the other one said, 'Professor, you are a good guy; learn to use an opportunity. You don't appreciate our help. Do you know what this watch actually costs?'

'Do you?'I asked.

He paused to think up a reply. His friend, Jack, turned round to say, 'It cost him one hundred forty dollars,' without taking his eyes off the corner.

'What's your offer?'

'Not even the twenty cents that I am left with now,' I said. 'I would not accept it even as a gift. You know why?'

'Why, Doctor?'

'I've no faith in watches. I never wear one; I've never had a watch in my life. Only recently, for the first time in my life, I bought a two-dollar alarm clock, because every morning I slept till twelve noon, and was in constant danger of missing trains and planes. So now I have a clock, which I strictly look at only once in a day; just to know whether I should get out of bed or continue to sleep.'

'How do you keep your appointments?' he asked.

'I never keep them. I should have been eating a dinner now at Albany. But where am I? What am I doing?'

'Now you know we want to help you.'

'I'll never buy a watch even if I miss all the dinners in the world,' I said emphatically.

'Perhaps you should take this to your girlfriend,' he said.

'No such luck. Never had one in my life,' I said. 'Even if I had one, I'd never inflict a watch on her. It's a misleading instrument. What's a watch-time? Nothing. You don't even know how to look at Sally's or Pat's watch in your pocket. Your watch has stopped; I'm sure Jack's watch is showing some wild time of its own. It's a different hour now at New York; something else in Chicago; morning time in the other hemisphere, Greenwich Time, Summer Time, and god knows what else. What's the use of having an instrument which is always wrong by some other clock?' He looked overwhelmed by this onslaught. His fingers slackened on the collar of my jacket, and I took the opportunity to draw myself up proudly, turn, and briskly walk away, with my heart palpitating lest they should grab me back. I walked off fast.

I don't think I overcame them by my superior wit and escaped. I cannot claim any heroism on that score. I think they let me go because they must have felt that they had caught a bankrupt and a bore. Or it may be Jack espied the police somewhere and they let me go. Although I missed my dinner that night, I was glad to be back at my hotel with my bones intact; and as long as I stayed in Berkeley, I took care not to visit the San Francisco Key Station again.

LYLE BLAIR[*]

Meet Lyle Blair at Bleeker Street, off Washington Square, at an address he has given. It is drizzling, but I manage to find the place and press the bell. A girl comes down the stairs and leads me to a room on the second floor (third according to the American step-counting system), where there is another girl. Lyle is expected. They know my name and I see my books on their shelves; they work in a publishing firm and are Lyle's friends. He comes in presently. He settles down on a sofa and I see him at his best—arguing, contradicting, emphasizing, and overwhelming all through whether the question be publishing, Kashmir, or anything. He has a lot of resemblance to an aggressive uncle of mine, especially when he goes into breathtaking philosophical turns. We repair to an Italian restaurant for dinner. I get an enormous plate of egg-plant fried in cheese and can eat only half of it. During the dinner Lyle declares: I'm terrified for your future, because you are going to be eaten up by the lions of New York; but let me tell

---

*From the chapter 'New York'.

you, in future you may do well or ill, but to have written *The English Teacher* is enough achievement for a lifetime. You won't do it again and can't even if you attempt it.'

'Why are you so arrogant that you will not let people do what they like for you? It pleases them to do something for you; please give them that liberty,' he says later.

'No, but I'd like to be able to do something in return...'

'You write. You've given them *The English Teacher* and that's enough. They like to do something in return. Let them do it.' And so, I had to watch his friend go down two flights and into the rain to fetch me ice cream, for which I had expressed a preference inadvertently at the restaurant.

Our discussions go on until midnight. Lyle constantly swears at a cat, which is a guest here, really belonging to someone involved in a motor accident and now in hospital, the cat alone escaping unhurt; and a parakeet which goes on pecking at its own image in a mirror creating an uproar, the cage kept out of reach of the cat on a shelf high up. Lyle calls the parakeet 'Narcissus'. The cat, like all New York cats, is fat and bloated. It can't go out; it goes to the window and keeps looking out through the glass, at the drunken and the bohemian population of the street below; Lyle who is somehow averse to the parakeet hopes that the cat will go up and make a meal of it, but it is perfectly safe here. The cat is so indolent and demoralized by synthetic cat-food that it can't spring up to the cage on the ledge. When the cat needs exercise, they give it cat's-nip to stir her into action—a small bundle of it flung on the floor makes the cat execute a variety of dances and caperings. Who discovered this? The same civilization which provides tinned food for the cat and saves it the bother of hunting mice and birds, also provides it cat's-nip for exercise—a rather comprehensive civilization. What's happening to the cat is what's happened to human beings since their days of cave-dwelling and food-hunting.

Get up at ten, and do not leave the room till five in the evening. Hear the drums of the St Patrick's Day parade on 5th Avenue, but cannot go down because I feel too lazy to dress. Glimpse a uniformed procession with band on Madison Avenue, from my window—regret that I cannot photograph it although there is such beautiful sunlight outside. I keep revising my book before lunch and after lunch—but have not progressed beyond five pages for the whole day. Every word, on examination, looks doubtful.

At five o'clock, take a subway on Lexington, change to a local somewhere and go up to Bleeker Street, which is full of tottering drunkards today, due to St Patrick's festivities. After my San Francisco experience I've a fear of being held up. Go up to Lyle's friend's house, where a fine dinner is prepared for all of us. Lyle has a terrific cold today, but is still in form.

After dinner I ask, 'When do you plan to visit India?'

'I have been there once, years ago,' he says.

This is rather a surprise for me. Lyle has a tendency to unfold surprises. I ask for details. 'I knew something of the country through my uncle.'

'Who was your uncle?' I ask.

'Robert Flaherty, you know the man who directed *The Elephant Boy*, who brought Sabu to the States, etc. etc.' It is unnecessary to dwell on Flaherty's achievements at this distance, but the sequel to a mention of him is interesting. I say, 'Do you know that he shot *The Elephant Boy* in Mysore, where I live, where there are elephant-jungles all around?' And then I add, 'And I know his daughter who has settled in Mysore. I have met her a few times, and we did a feature together for a radio programme on the trapping of elephants. She was our narrator.' This stings Lyle into unexpected action. 'Do you mean to say that you know Barbara? Wait a minute. I want you to talk to her mother.'

'Where is she?'

'At Vermont, five hundred miles away. You must tell her about Barbara.' I try to excuse myself. 'Well no time for it, let us think of it later, I don't know the lady...' He brushes aside all my objections, and pulls me along to the other room where the telephone is. He dials the operator and cries, 'I want Vermont, Mrs Frances Flaherty.'

'Number?'

'I don't know the number. Don't insist on it.' He adopts a sudden, bullying tone and says, 'I don't know the number but I must talk to the lady immediately. I am giving you her name and address, you will have to find her number somehow...' And he puts down the receiver and waits till the operator calls him again and I hear him shout, 'You have the number? Fine, why do you tell me what it is? I am not interested. Give me the connection.' He turns to me and says, 'We will get the connection now. It is twelve years since we saw Barbara off. You must tell her mother about her.'

'Tell her what?' I ask anxiously. He ignores my question. He gets the connection to Vermont. It is eleven-thirty at night and it is evident that the population of Vermont has retired long ago. They are pulled out of their beds, and feel naturally anxious at being called at that hour. After a few minutes Lyle speaks into the telephone.

'I have a friend here from India who has known Barbara. He is from Mysore.' He hands me the telephone.

It is Mrs Flaherty. She is thrilled to hear about her daughter; she asks numerous questions about her, how she looks now, what radio programme we did together, and what I thought of her voice. She is overwhelmed, as she says, 'How I wish I were going with you to India to see Barbara!' Lyle feels gratified, 'You have made one soul supremely happy.'

Evening went out on a ramble. Never realized till now that I was living so close to the famous Empire State Building, though I have been seeing its tower every day for over a week. This is the worst of working too hard on a novel—you become blind to the tallest building in the world. Proximity makes us indifferent, although, in Laxmipuram I'd have been eloquent about it on hearing about it. Must go up sometime, but I can't bring myself to the point of joining the regular sightseers anywhere, though it ought to be the most sensible, and practical thing to do. But who cares to be sensible and practical? I may probably go back home without ever ascending the Empire State Building but then I shall have done nothing worse than any confirmed citizen of New York. I watch for a while people buying tickets and moving up to the elevator, wondering where they came from. Glance through all the tremendous 'promotion' material around. One would have thought a building like the Empire State was in no need of promotion (my little nephew at home can say exactly how high it is). But there it is. Its statistics are impressive, but I could not accept their own list of eight wonders of the world (which they display at the window—in which the Empire State finds a place but not the Taj Mahal).

FOOD FOR THE GODS

Lyle Blair's party for me at Algonquin to celebrate the publication of the American edition of my *Mr Sampath*. Algonquin party room is so exclusive that only fifty guests are invited. Everyone is there, the Indian Consul General, the Australian Ambassador and his wife, the Breits, the Bowers, Gilpatric, a girl from *Look* looking like Ingrid Bergman, two priests, two publishers of paperbacks, the President of Michigan University and the Vice-President, Professor Blackman, the Viking Press, Balaraman, many men and women from the writing world, whose names I never catch, and above all the Indian delegate at the United Nations Organization, who sits in a chair and says to me when introduced, 'I am dictating my third novel to my secretary, having completed my second in eight weeks. I am surprised where all the ideas come from. In the midst of all my office work, I am able to do it. I'd like to talk to you—what is your address?' I mention my hotel and its whereabouts, which does not interest him. He says, cutting me short, 'Why don't you call up my secretary and leave your telephone number with her, so that I may get in touch with you sometime.' I leave him at that.

After the party a small, compact group stay on for supper. Two New York paperback publishers, whom we shall indicate as Mr A and Mr B, a priest, a girl in a red gown, Lyle, and myself. We have a corner to ourselves at the dining hall of Algonquin. Publisher A, sitting opposite me, leans across to say, 'I like your *Financial Expert*. It is your best book.'

'I like your *Bachelor of Arts* better; it's my favourite,' says publisher

B, sitting to my right.

'William Faulkner, Hemingway, and Narayan are the world's three great living writers,' says A.

I blush to record this, but do it for documentary purposes. After the discussion has continued on these lines for a while, I feel I ought to assert my modesty—I interrupt them to say, 'Thank you, but not yet...' But my own view and judgement are of the least consequence and no one pays any attention to me. They brush me aside and repeat, 'Hemingway, Faulkner and Narayan, the three greatest living...'

'Take out Hemingway and put in Graham Greene. Faulkner, Narayan, and Graham Greene,' says Lyle.

'I don't like Graham Greene,' says one.

'Why not?' asks the priest in a kindly tone.

'His obsession with Catholic theology upsets me.'

'What is wrong in it?'

'I don't like it, that is all.'

'Come, come, you can't dismiss it so easily. You have to explain what upsets you in Catholic theology.'

From this mild beginning a veritable storm soon developed. The waiters came and went. Each whispered his or her choice in their ears. They brought the food and placed it around. The napkins were spread on laps; shining cutlery was picked up, but they were hardly put to their legitimate use; they were being flourished to add punch to arguments. Plates remained untouched. One or the other would draw the plate into position and carve a bit, but before he could stick the fork in, there would occur a theological exasperation, and up would go the knife and fork to emphasize a point or to meet the challenge. Lyle who had ordered a joint done brown, could not proceed beyond pecking at it once every ten minutes. The lady in red was the only one who proceeded smoothly with her dinner, and then of course myself. Out of courtesy I waited for a while to be joined by others, but I found my asparagus soup growing cold. The waiters were bringing in the courses mechanically. I followed the example of the lady in red and ate my food unobtrusively. I quietly worked my way through, and had arrived at the stage of baked apple pie and cream, but found the rest still at the stage of Torment, taking a morsel to the lips and withdrawing it swiftly to rebut an affront. What really stirred them to such a pitch was a thing that I never really understood. It was all too obscure, too much in the realm of higher theology, the minutiae of belief. The only thing that I caught was that publisher A was out to puncture the priest. Mr A was saying, 'Answer my question first. Could a betrayer be an enemy?'

'He has to be a friend. How can an enemy betray?' A sinister laughter followed. When it subsided Mr A said, with a quiet firmness, 'I am a much better priest than you are. Take off that dog collar you are wearing, what is that for?'

'John! John!' pleaded the priest, 'Don't lose yourself so utterly. Pull yourself together.'

'I am all right. I can look after myself quite well. It is you who needs pulling together. You are no better than the drunken, dissolute priests one encounters in Graham Greene's novels.' The priest could do nothing more than cry, 'John! John!' in a tone of tremendous appeal, and then he pointed at me and said, 'We have a distinguished guest with us tonight. Let us not insult him by our unseemly acts.' Which seemed to have the desired effect as Mr A bowed deeply to me from his seat and said, 'I apologize to you, sir, for any inconvenience caused.' The greater inconvenience was to be the centre of attention now, and so I said, 'Not at all, not at all. Don't mind me. Go on with your discussion. Please don't stop on my account.' This was accepted with gusto and publisher B turned to the priest and said, 'You have not really answered John's question.'

'Why should I? Am I bound to answer?' A fresh sinister guffaw followed this. The two publishers seemed pleased at the effect they had produced; they leaned over to each other and spoke under their breath and laughed among themselves. Lyle thought that the time had come for him to assert himself. He held his arms over his head and said, 'All are my guests here; I won't have anyone insulted at this table. Let us have this discussion some other time. Let us eat now.' This was really a sound, practical suggestion. The time was nearly eleven. Three hours had passed since the food had been served. I had noticed through a corner of my eye the progress of the night at the restaurant. All the other guests had left. The linen had been taken off all the tables. The lights had been put out, half the hall was in darkness; on the outer fringe a couple of waiters stood patiently. Cordiality was restored, plates were passed round. One heard not theological remarks but 'Did you order this chicken?' 'Oh, dear, I must abandon this soup... Fish! Lovely!' Everybody settled down cheerfully to eat, drew their chairs closer, rolled up their sleeves, with the exception of the lady in red and myself who were lingering over our desserts in order to let the rest catch up with us. It would have gone on well, but for the arrival of a steward at this moment and a whispered message to Lyle who had just tasted his joint. Lyle immediately cried, 'Listen friends, here is the steward come to say that Mr— the manager of the hotel, wants us to accept a round of drinks in honour of this evening... Please give him our thanks. Surely. Won't he join us?'

'He had to go away, sir, but he requested that you should accept his hospitality. Champagne, sir?'

'Yes, why not? There are,' he counted heads, 'six here.' 'Give him our thanks, won't you?' Conviviality was restored, but the food receded once again into the background. One or two got up to visit the wash. I was relieved to find that religion had gone to the background. When they resumed their seats, they were all smiling. 'We must really get on with the dinner,' Lyle said.

'Of course, of course,' everyone agreed.

The time was nearly eleven-thirty. I noticed less rancour now, the priest as well as the rest were laughing while arguing. I felt relieved. The priest turned to the lady in red and said, 'While all of us are talking you are silent, why don't you say something?' She merely replied between drinks, 'I have nothing to say.' She was the one person who had pursued her food and drink with a steady aim, and now she seemed a little bored. 'What can she say?' said Mr A pugnaciously. 'You are a priest, and it is up to you to talk and save our souls. Here I am asking, what are you a priest for, if you can't answer a simple question?' The priest merely looked at him, pointed at me and said, 'Let us not make fools of ourselves before him. Let us talk it over tomorrow.' 'There he is,' he said pointing at me. 'He is an Indian, he is from the East. He knows these problems inside out. It must all look childish to him. Let us shut up now. He is watching us silently. Remember he is dead sober, while we are drunk. Let us end all this talk.' At this Mr B leaned across to say to me, 'You see sir, we are a young nation, we don't know the answers, we long to have an answer to our questions.' He held his hand to his heart as if there were excruciating pangs there. 'We are a tortured nation, that is why we seek an answer. It is no problem for you really, because you know the answer to all the questions.' I had to say, 'No, I don't think I know the answers, I haven't even understood the questions, you know.' He just brushed aside my protestations. 'No, you know the answers. I know you know because your *Financial Expert* contains in it answers to all our questions.'

'Does it?' I asked, rather surprised. 'Where?'

'The last portions of the book,' he said.

'I didn't know,' I said, completely baffled.

'You wouldn't know, but we know. We can read them,' he said, and left me marvelling at the theological implications of my fiction. He came close to me and said, 'But you must sympathize with us, we are all the time struggling and searching. You must watch us closely. You don't have to do anything except put down all this conversation as you have heard it, and that will be a wonderful conversation piece. I know you can do it, because I admire your *Financial Expert*.' (I have acted on his advice and hence this narrative.)

He pointed to Mr A with a good deal of sympathy, 'His eagerness to know is very real, his enquiry is honest.'

'I must have an answer,' Mr A said, stung by this reminder. He looked straight ahead at the priest and cried, 'I insist upon your answering my question.'

'John, John, you are starting it all over again.'

'Tell him something, why do you spurn his question?' said his friend.

'We have no business to be arrogant, it is arrogance which is at the bottom of all our troubles,' began Lyle. He is ever fond of the word 'arrogance' and brings it up anywhere.

'The priest is the one who is arrogant,' Mr A cried with passion. 'What is he wearing that dog collar for, let him pull it off and throw it away.' Saying this he proceeded to attack his dinner.

At this, the priest looked at him fixedly and said, 'You have provoked me enough. I'll answer your question after you answer mine. Tell me who you are, what you are, and where you come from?' This question stung Mr A unexpectedly. He was livid with rage.

(Later, I understood that Mr A came from a part of the country which was supposed to be known for its display of bigotry.)

'It has nothing to do with my problem.'

'Gentlemen, let us eat our food,' Lyle said. The priest repeated, 'John, who are you? What are you? Where do you come from?' In answer, Mr A pushed his chair back and his plates away. 'I refuse to sit at the same table with this—priest. You are a—priest. No better than a Graham Greene character. I will say it again and again.' He turned to me and said extending his hand, 'I apologize for going, but I can't sit at this table. It has been nice meeting you. Goodbye.' He walked away.